The Reader's Digest Mother and Baby Book

The READER'S DIGEST Mother and Baby Book

PUBLISHED BY THE READER'S DIGEST ASSOCIATION LIMITED
LONDON SYDNEY MONTREAL CAPE TOWN HONG KONG

Consultant Editors

GEOFFREY CHAMBERLAIN MD, FRCS, FRCOG
Professor of the Department of Obstetrics and Gynaecology,
St George's Hospital Medical School, London

DAVID MORRIS FRCP, MRCS, DCH
Honorary Consultant Paediatrician to the
Woolwich Group of Hospitals, London

HARVEY MARCOVITCH MB, MRCP
Consultant Paediatrician, Oxfordshire Health Authority,
and Clinical Lecturer, University of Oxford

Photographer

SANDRA LOUSADA

Editor

URSULA WHYTE

Designer

SANDRA DEON-CARDYN

The Reader's Digest
Mother and Baby Book
was edited and designed by
The Reader's Digest Association
Limited
and includes text and artwork from
The Reader's Digest Mothercare Book
Copyright © 1973 The Reader's Digest
Association Limited, London

First Edition
Copyright © 1986
The Reader's Digest Association
Limited
25 Berkeley Square, London W1X 6AB

Copyright © 1986
The Reader's Digest Association
(Canada) Inc.

Copyright © 1986
The Reader's Digest Association
Far East Limited

Philippines Copyright 1986
Reader's Digest Association
Far East Limited

Typeset by MS Filmsetting Limited
Frome, Somerset
Printed in Hong Kong

Contents

Helping your baby to develop into an individual and independent person is the most exciting reward of parenthood. This book, we hope, will be your guide through the vital first few years.

The five main sections of the book distil the experience of generations of parents to help you to deal with everyday situations that occur from the earliest days of pregnancy. They also provide advice from experts – gynaecologists, paediatricians, nutritionists and teachers.

These sections are followed by a new special feature: a guide to the benefits and care in all the major English-speaking communities around the world. Whether you find yourself bringing up your family at home or abroad, you will now have instant access to all the relevant ante-natal, obstetrical, registration and post-natal procedures, the benefits available (though some of these may be restricted to nationals), the services, and a selection of essential addresses.

Although most of the book is devoted to the day-to-day life of a healthy child, we recognise that at some time every child is bound to suffer from an ailment. There is therefore a Health Guide to help you to recognise symptoms. There is also a First Aid section edged in blue for ease of reference in emergency.

Happily there is still a balance of the sexes among babies, and a welcome increase in the number of women doctors. Our use of "he" for the baby and the doctor is simply for the reader's convenience.

1
PREPARATION

Pregnancy and birth

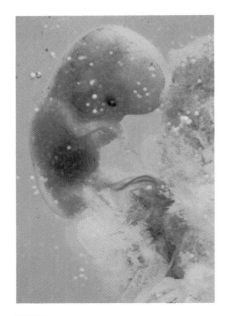 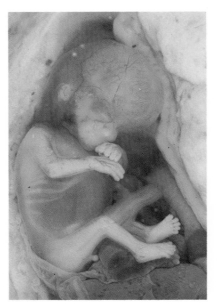 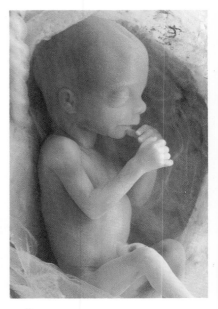

The fetus develops within the uterus (womb) protected and cushioned by liquid known as amniotic fluid. All the nourishment and all the oxygen needed are fed to the fetus through the umbilical cord from the placenta.

By the tenth week of pregnancy, the baby's head and limbs have formed and all the essential organs are present. At this stage the rate of growth is rapid, much more so than at any time in later life.

At 16 weeks, the baby's heartbeat can be heard. The mother may begin to feel the baby's movements – there will have been movement before now but it is not usually felt until about this time. The head and brain grow faster than the rest of the body and look large in relation to the arms and legs.

1 Preparing for your baby

In the months leading up to the birth of your baby you will fluctuate between periods of confident anticipation and nagging doubt, heady moments of excitement and grey hours of boredom, exuberant energy and foot-dragging weariness. These are all part of the momentous experience that will come your way probably no more than two or three times in the course of your life.

The information in the following pages will help you to understand the changes that are going on in your body. You are told how to calculate when your baby is due, and how to prepare for the birth – by making regular visits to your doctor or clinic, by eating sensibly, and by following a routine of simple exercises. You learn to understand how the unborn baby develops, and about problems you may encounter during pregnancy and what to do about them. There are sections on how to stay at your best, and what clothes to wear while you are pregnant. You will find reassurance in the techniques used by doctors to monitor the health of the unborn child and your own health, and an explanation of "low-tech" natural childbirth.

The rest you will discover for yourself – the moments of heightened experience when the doctor confirms that you are pregnant; when you feel your baby's first kick; and when you recognise the first signs of labour. But to go back to the beginning . . .

Are you pregnant?

If you have not had a baby before, you may have difficulty in deciding whether you are pregnant. There are some changes in your body that you may notice yourself, and others that can only be detected by your doctor.

Changes you may notice yourself

Changes in menstruation Once an egg becomes fertilised there is no more menstruation. If you have been having a regular monthly period, its absence may be the first indication of pregnancy.

Try to remember and make a note of the first day of the last normal menstrual period. Your doctor will need to know this to enable him to work out the time the baby is to be expected (see pp. 11 and 12). It will also be helpful to the doctor if there is some record of the dates of the last two or three periods before this, especially if you do not menstruate exactly every 28 days.

A lack of periods is not a certain symptom of pregnancy. Women who very much desire a pregnancy, or, conversely, those who very much fear one, can miss a period for psychological reasons. However, if menstruation is more than two weeks overdue and intercourse without contraception has taken place, it is natural to suspect the possibility of pregnancy.

It is possible to bleed from the vagina and still be pregnant. This is not normal menstruation, but in the first three months of pregnancy there is sometimes a slight blood loss which is usually less than a normal menstrual period. If this does happen a doctor should be consulted.

Changes in the breasts Early in pregnancy the breasts become very sensitive, with a tingling sensation around the nipple area. Soon after this they may become heavier as well. These changes are often noticed within a few weeks of a missed period. The nipples become more prominent and, later, there is a darkening of the pigmented area around the nipple. These are natural changes in the breast due to the increased blood supply.

Nausea and vomiting The early days of pregnancy are commonly associated with nausea. This is often misnamed "morning sickness", but for almost half the number of expectant mothers the sickness does not occur in the morning at all.

Few women escape this problem completely; most suffer nausea and some suffer vomiting as well. However, once the immediate wave of nausea has passed, the expectant mother does not feel ill, as with nausea due to other causes. Most women are not greatly inconvenienced and are able to carry on with their daily tasks. Usually the nausea ends by the 12th or 14th week of pregnancy.

Changes in urination. Many women notice that they pass urine more frequently in the early weeks of pregnancy. This is due to irritation of the bladder produced by an increased blood supply in the pelvis. A little later the growing womb presses on the bladder, and this may also cause increased frequency of urination. By the time the womb grows up into the abdomen (14 to 16 weeks) this symptom usually becomes less marked.

Mucus discharge There is usually an increase in the normal amount of mucus produced at the neck of the womb, and this shows itself as a discharge at the vulva. This is normal, provided it is not irritating or offensive; if it is, you should consult your doctor.

All these symptoms are normal and indicate the body's reaction to pregnancy. In some women they are minimal and pass almost unnoticed; in others symptoms become severe. Consult a doctor whenever you are worried about such symptoms, for he can often bring relief by methods which are quite safe both for you and for the child.

Changes a doctor can detect

In the first few weeks of pregnancy, the growth of the embryo is so minute that it does not enlarge the womb very much. In consequence, a doctor cannot tell a lot by examination of the size of the womb. Only after about eight weeks of pregnancy does this give positive information.

However, the increase in size even at this stage is not such that the womb has grown out of the pelvic bowl into the general abdominal cavity, and so any early examination to confirm pregnancy usually involves a vaginal assessment. The doctor passes one or two gloved fingers into the vagina and gently examines the womb.

Some women are nervous about this, but a properly conducted vaginal examination is not painful and has no effect on the growing baby. After 12 weeks the womb is enlarged sufficiently for the doctor to feel it through the stomach wall. The breast symptoms you have observed (see above) may also be confirmed by the doctor.

Many women like to confirm the presence of pregnancy by doing a pregnancy test themselves. The test

PLACE OF BIRTH

In most parts of the Western world a baby is born in a hospital or a maternity unit. The greater move towards specialisation in all maternity facilities has led to women choosing to be delivered where facilities are at their best, although some women prefer a home delivery.

Everyone realises that hospitals do appear regimented and are very different from the home which a woman has left. On coming in, she leaves her domestic surroundings and the other members of her family at a highly emotional time when she needs the support of those nearest to her. Hospital midwives and doctors try to be sympathetic and help the woman during this short time away from home. The presence of her husband, partner or other relative during labour is of great help.

Hospitals are not all large impersonal places; some are quite small, such as general practitioner units, and whatever their size, there is constant medical midwifery supervision so that the woman can be sure to have her baby in greater safety with the skills available.

See pages 138–148 for further details on the facilities available in different countries.

depends upon the presence of a hormone, chorionic gonadotrophin, in the urine. This hormone is produced early by the clump of embryonic cells. Whilst it can be detected by special tests as early as 9 or 10 days after fertilisation, most of the immunological chemical tests you can buy over the counter do not detect the hormone until about 14–18 days after fertilisation, about the time you may miss your first menstrual period. These tests are available from most chemist shops; they are very simple to do and are very accurate.

If the test is positive you are almost certainly pregnant. The exception to this is a woman in the older age of reproduction (40 years plus) who may make a similar hormone from the pituitary gland which cross-reacts and so produces a falsely positive result.

If the pregnancy test is negative, not enough hormone has been made to make the test work. Either you are not pregnant or, if you are, you are not as far on as you think. Wait a week and check the test again. The test is best done with an early morning specimen of urine, for this is the most concentrated specimen.

Ultrasound (see p. 13) can also be used early on to detect the sac of fluid and embryonic tissue inside. It is fairly precise after seven or eight weeks of pregnancy and a firm diagnosis can be made by nine weeks. Before this time, although the fetal sac can be seen, embryonic tissue often cannot be identified.

X-rays are of no use at this early stage and would be dangerous to the health of the baby.

WHEN IS THE BABY DUE?

About 266 days elapse between the fertilisation of an egg and the birth of a child. Some 90 per cent of pregnancies finish within seven days on either side of this span. There are, however, some variable factors.

To produce an embryo, an egg must meet and be fertilised by a sperm within 36 hours of ovulation, when the egg is released from an ovary. The egg is a small single cell and has only enough food supplies to last 24–36 hours. If not penetrated by a sperm in this time, it dies and is absorbed back into the woman's system. The sperm is an even smaller active cell, and lives for only about a day. In consequence, fertilisation must occur within this short time.

If the egg is not fertilised but dies, the lining of the womb is shed 14 days later in the next menstrual period. If, however, the egg is fertilised, the lining of the womb stays to receive the growing embryo.

The average menstrual cycle of a woman lasts about 28 days, with ovulation occurring in the middle, on about the 14th day.

The expected date of the baby's birth can therefore be calculated as 280 days (266 + 14) from the first day of the last menstrual period – a useful method of calculation since, although few women know when they ovulate, all know when they menstruate.

The formula for 280 days, however, is only accurate for a woman who has a 28-day cycle. If she has a 35-day cycle then the extra seven days must be added to the 14 days. The date the baby may be expected would, therefore, be later: 287 days (266 + 21).

If the menstrual cycle is irregular, no such calculation can be made. This is true also of women who become pregnant within a month or two of ceasing to take the pill. They will not yet have established a regular cycle, so will not be certain on which day they ovulated.

In an average group of women attending an antenatal clinic in early pregnancy, between one-fifth and a quarter either have cycles that are irregular or have just ceased using oral contraception. These women will require their doctor's help to date the pregnancy.

The date of expected delivery of a woman who has a 28-day cycle and has not recently been on the pill can be calculated with a special obstetrical calendar. Obstetricians often do this sum in their heads, by a calculation that is almost as precise as using the calendar. They deduct three months from the date of the last menstrual period and then add on seven days. If, for example, the first day of the last menstrual period was November 4, then the baby is probably due around the following August 11.

If you are not certain of the date of your last menstrual period, or have recently been using oral contraception, you can get help by visiting your doctor early in pregnancy. Examination of the size of the womb by a doctor at this stage makes possible a more precise estimate than does an examination at a later stage of pregnancy.

The doctor may ask for further tests with ultrasound (see p. 13) – harmless high-frequency sound waves that "map out" the size and stage of development reached by the growing baby. It is wise to get the first of these performed early in pregnancy by about 16 weeks to have a baseline on which later readings may be based. Ultrasound allows a very precise measurement of the baby and so a more definite estimate of the expected date of arrival of the baby.

FINDING YOUR ESTIMATED DATE OF DELIVERY

	1	2	3	4	5	6	7	8	9	10	11	12	13	14	15	16	17	18	19	20	21	22	23	24	25	26	27	28	29	30	31	
January	1	2	3	4	5	6	7	8	9	10	11	12	13	14	15	16	17	18	19	20	21	22	23	24	25	26	27	28	29	30	31	**January**
October	8	9	10	11	12	13	14	15	16	17	18	19	20	21	22	23	24	25	26	27	28	29	30	31	1	2	3	4	5	6	7	November
February	1	2	3	4	5	6	7	8	9	10	11	12	13	14	15	16	17	18	19	20	21	22	23	24	25	26	27	28				**February**
November	8	9	10	11	12	13	14	15	16	17	18	19	20	21	22	23	24	25	26	27	28	29	30	1	2	3	4	5				December
March	1	2	3	4	5	6	7	8	9	10	11	12	13	14	15	16	17	18	19	20	21	22	23	24	25	26	27	28	29	30	31	**March**
December	6	7	8	9	10	11	12	13	14	15	16	17	18	19	20	21	22	23	24	25	26	27	28	29	30	31	1	2	3	4	5	January
April	1	2	3	4	5	6	7	8	9	10	11	12	13	14	15	16	17	18	19	20	21	22	23	24	25	26	27	28	29	30		**April**
January	6	7	8	9	10	11	12	13	14	15	16	17	18	19	20	21	22	23	24	25	26	27	28	29	30	31	1	2	3	4		February
May	1	2	3	4	5	6	7	8	9	10	11	12	13	14	15	16	17	18	19	20	21	22	23	24	25	26	27	28	29	30	31	**May**
February	5	6	7	8	9	10	11	12	13	14	15	16	17	18	19	20	21	22	23	24	25	26	27	28	1	2	3	4	5	6	7	March
June	1	2	3	4	5	6	7	8	9	10	11	12	13	14	15	16	17	18	19	20	21	22	23	24	25	26	27	28	29	30		**June**
March	8	9	10	11	12	13	14	15	16	17	18	19	20	21	22	23	24	25	26	27	28	29	30	31	1	2	3	4	5	6		April
July	1	2	3	4	5	6	7	8	9	10	11	12	13	14	15	16	17	18	19	20	21	22	23	24	25	26	27	28	29	30	31	**July**
April	7	8	9	10	11	12	13	14	15	16	17	18	19	20	21	22	23	24	25	26	27	28	29	30	1	2	3	4	5	6	7	May
August	1	2	3	4	5	6	7	8	9	10	11	12	13	14	15	16	17	18	19	20	21	22	23	24	25	26	27	28	29	30	31	**August**
May	8	9	10	11	12	13	14	15	16	17	18	19	20	21	22	23	24	25	26	27	28	29	30	31	1	2	3	4	5	6	7	June
September	1	2	3	4	5	6	7	8	9	10	11	12	13	14	15	16	17	18	19	20	21	22	23	24	25	26	27	28	29	30		**September**
June	8	9	10	11	12	13	14	15	16	17	18	19	20	21	22	23	24	25	26	27	28	29	30	1	2	3	4	5	6	7		July
October	1	2	3	4	5	6	7	8	9	10	11	12	13	14	15	16	17	18	19	20	21	22	23	24	25	26	27	28	29	30	31	**October**
July	8	9	10	11	12	13	14	15	16	17	18	19	20	21	22	23	24	25	26	27	28	29	30	31	1	2	3	4	5	6	7	August
November	1	2	3	4	5	6	7	8	9	10	11	12	13	14	15	16	17	18	19	20	21	22	23	24	25	26	27	28	29	30		**November**
August	8	9	10	11	12	13	14	15	16	17	18	19	20	21	22	23	24	25	26	27	28	29	30	31	1	2	3	4	5	6		September
December	1	2	3	4	5	6	7	8	9	10	11	12	13	14	15	16	17	18	19	20	21	22	23	24	25	26	27	28	29	30	31	**December**
September	7	8	9	10	11	12	13	14	15	16	17	18	19	20	21	22	23	24	25	26	27	28	29	30	1	2	3	4	5	6	7	October

The previous page explains in some detail how the expected date of your baby's birth is calculated. It is easier, however, if you can look up a chart and find out from it when your baby is due. The chart above shows delivery dates 280 days after the first day of your last period. Look up the first day of your last period in one of the top rows set in black type. Your estimated date of delivery (EDD) is given underneath it in blue type. Thus, if the first day of your last period was, say, April 17th, your estimated date of delivery would be January 22nd.

As explained on the previous page, this is only accurate for a woman with a 28-day cycle. If your cycle is longer or shorter than this your EDD can still be easily calculated, but if you have an irregular cycle you will need your doctor's help in order to estimate your date of delivery.

Health of the unborn child

In the last decade much has been learned about how the baby develops in the womb, and there are now several tests that hospitals can make to ensure that the baby is developing normally. Many expectant mothers will encounter one or more of these tests during pregnancy.

Ultrasound Sound waves above the frequency which can be heard by the human ear are passed into the body, and echoes from reflecting surfaces are picked up. By moving the source of the sound waves and the receiver, a composite picture can be built up on a screen like a television screen. This enables the growing baby and his placenta – the spongy structure through which he obtains nutrition – to be seen from several angles.

This is now accepted as a perfectly safe procedure, much research having been conducted to confirm that it does not harm the unborn child. Fears voiced recently about the energy output of ultrasound machines relate mostly to a different type of equipment used in biological laboratories. The low energy output in the small pulses of ultrasound used on the diagnostic machines is very much less than that of the continuous ultrasound used for laboratory work. Many millions of women and their babies have benefited from ultrasound in pregnancy and no cases of abnormality or hazard to the child have been reported attributable to ultrasound.

An advantage of the safety of this non-interventive method is that it can be used several times in any pregnancy, thus checking on the same baby at different stages of gestation. This is very valuable in measuring the dynamic process of the fetal growth.

Measurements can be made of the diameter of the fetal head at different stages of pregnancy and plotted to show that growth of the baby is proceeding along a normal pattern. More sophisticated measurements can be made of the areas of cross-sections of the baby's chest and head, for the two parts of the unborn baby's body grow at different rates. This provides a more sensitive test of variations of growth.

Using ultrasound machines with higher resolution, skilled workers can examine many fetal organs in detail. The heart can be seen working in great detail in the chest and variations of the flow of blood from the normal can be detected. The blood vessels leaving the heart can be examined. The kidneys can be outlined as can the bladder. The brain can be visualised and the fluid filling it can be assessed. Abnormalities, if they are present, can be detected, such as spina bifida and variations to the limbs.

The number of babies present can be counted with ultrasound and women now may know whether they have twins or triplets as early as the 16th or 18th week of pregnancy. The progress and growth of such multiple pregnancies can then be followed readily.

The position and constitution of the placenta can also be spotted precisely. If it is low-lying it may be a hazard to the vaginal birth of the baby and may indicate the need for a Caesarean section.

X-ray X-rays are suited to showing bony parts, and once the developing baby has sufficient calcium in his bones, such pictures can be taken; this usually occurs after 16 or 18 weeks of pregnancy.

Excessive exposure to X-rays may produce harmful changes, but if doctors feel that there is a potential problem they may order a limited number of X-ray photographs. These are usually taken in hospitals, where the problems of excessive exposure to X-rays are well known.

If an expectant mother is recommended to have such a test she should allow it to be carried out; for the risks of not knowing, for example, the size and shape of her pelvis may be much greater than the risks of the irradiation.

Hormone tests The developing baby and his placenta make many hormones which spill over into the mother's bloodstream. From here they may pass to her urine, and therefore tests on the mother's blood and urine can be some guide to the development of the unborn child.

Mention has been made of the hormone human chorionic gonadotrophin (hCG), which is produced by the early clump of fertilised cells before they even implant. The measurement of this hormone in urine is the basis of the pregnancy test; this is just a Yes/No answer. More subtle estimates of the amount of hCG can give rise to quantitative measures of the state of the embryo. This test is being developed in many centres as a measure of the very early embryo and it is of particular use in women who had spontaneous miscarriages in previous pregnancies.

Most pregnant women have their blood tested for a chemical called alpha fetoprotein (afp). This is excreted from the brain and spinal cord of the unborn child; if there is a deficiency in the covers of the cord, higher concentrations of afp appear in the amniotic fluid and then in the mother's blood. This is an indication that spina bifida may be present. This screening test is offered to many women in antenatal clinics at about 16 weeks when their blood is tested. If the level is high, then some fluid is removed from around the baby by amniocentesis (see below) and so the diagnosis of spina bifida may be made at an early stage of pregnancy.

The growing fetus and its placenta make between them a series of oestrogen hormones that flood over into the mother's blood and can be measured there. As pregnancy proceeds, the amounts increase and their levels may be used to estimate the state of fetal well-being. Single readings of oestrogen levels are not very useful, but a series of estimates done on women at higher risk for problems of the fetus may help doctors to know how long it is safe to leave the baby in the uterus without suggesting intervention.

New tests are being evolved all the time, and methods of investigation are being refined to give an increasingly accurate guide about what is happening inside the womb.

Amniocentesis The baby develops inside a pool of amniotic fluid, which is secreted partly by the mother and partly by the baby himself.

In early pregnancy, examination of this fluid can yield much information about possible abnormalities of the brain or spine. One problem that may be encountered is Down's Syndrome, which occurs most frequently in children of mothers aged over 40, and amniocentesis is usual when women of this age become pregnant. It is normally done at about four months; before this, neither cells nor "tell-tale" chemicals are present in sufficient quantities. There is a very slight chance (one per cent or less) that amniocentesis will result in abortion. For this reason it is not normally offered unless the risk of discovering abnormality outweighs the risk from the amniocentesis itself. It is never done against a woman's wishes; you can always choose not to have it if you so wish.

In the middle stages of pregnancy, amniocentesis may be performed on women who have rhesus negative blood (see p. 35) to indicate treatment needed for the baby.

In the later part of pregnancy, tests can give information about the maturity of the baby. Some labours have to be induced for medical reasons, but doctors must be sure that the essential body systems are mature enough to allow the baby to be born. The chemical content of amniotic fluid can be checked as a guide to the maturity of the baby's lungs. Other tests check cells shed from the baby's skin. If such tests as these reveal immaturity, they warn the obstetrician of the need for extra paediatric help at the birth.

WHAT DETERMINES A BABY'S SEX

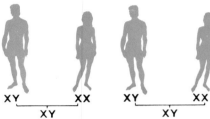

BOY BABY If a sperm carrying a Y-chromosome fertilises the egg, the baby which develops has the chromosome combination XY and is male

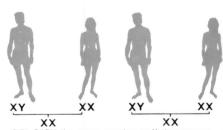

GIRL BABY If a sperm carrying an X-chromosome fertilises the egg, the resultant chromosome combination is XX and is female

Ordinary body cells contain 46 chromosomes, but the reproductive cells – sperms and eggs – have only half that number. All eggs carry a single X-chromosome, although a sperm may carry an X or a Y. During fertilisation, a sperm and an egg unite to give a single cell with the full number of chromosomes. A baby's sex depends on whether the sperm involved carries a Y-chromosome or an X-chromosome. The combination XY results in a boy baby, whereas XX results in a girl.

Antenatal care

During the months you are carrying your baby you will probably feel as healthy and full of energy as at any other time in your life. You may even feel healthier.

The purpose of regular visits to your doctor and midwife, or clinic or hospital, is to keep you that way.

Since you feel so fit, you might wonder why you need to spend time undergoing a series of examinations. The reason is that some problems in pregnancy do not produce symptoms early, and in many cases can only be detected by special tests.

The earlier any problems are detected the easier it is to treat them, and the greater likelihood that there will be a normal baby.

Antenatal visits are usually spaced so that you see your advisers at intervals that vary according to the need at different stages of pregnancy. Monthly visits are sufficient in early pregnancy, but these are increased to weekly attendances near the time of delivery.

Most women make their first visit to a clinic when about 8–12 weeks pregnant. This is the longest visit, and the most thorough examination. You will be asked about any past illnesses or operations that you or your family have undergone. If you have had a baby before, details of the pregnancy and delivery will be recorded, for they may be relevant to what is likely to happen on the next occasion. Such information is entirely confidential.

The doctor will probably give you a full medical examination to detect any diseases, and he will check the size of the uterus (the womb) containing the developing baby. Blood pressure is taken and a sample of blood is drawn to check your blood group, rhesus grouping and level of haemoglobin – the red pigment that carries oxygen from the lungs to the

THE FIRST WEEKS

ACTUAL SIZE
OF EMBRYO

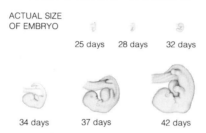

25 days   28 days   32 days

34 days   37 days   42 days

Starting as a minute cluster of cells embedded in the wall of the womb, an embryo takes on a human form during the first 12 weeks of life – the most critical stage of its development. Initially the embryo is an elongated disc which has no external parts, only swellings. Within these swellings the major organs of the body, such as the heart and brain, begin to grow. They start as simple tubes, in which kinks and folds appear. But in a few weeks, some of the systems of the body are sufficiently well formed to start functioning.

Externally, the legs and arms appear in the sixth week of development; the eyes and ears slightly later. By the end of eight weeks, the embryo is an almost fully formed fetus and subsequent development within the womb involves mainly growth and a gain in weight.

tissues of the body. Other tests are often made on the blood sample; for example, if the expectant mother was born overseas she could have unusual haemoglobins in her blood, and these can be estimated in special clinics. The risk to the unborn child can be assessed.

Other blood tests include the estimate of alpha fetoprotein (see p. 14) and a check on whether the mother has been exposed to certain infectious diseases. The commonest is rubella or German measles. If you have plenty of rubella antibodies in your blood at the beginning of pregnancy, you have been exposed to German measles earlier in life; these antibodies will offer protection should you come in contact with German measles in the course of the pregnancy. If there are not enough antibodies, it would be wise to avoid any contact with German measles until the baby is born. Unfortunately you cannot be inoculated during pregnancy for it might be dangerous to the fetus. However, inoculation can be done very soon after pregnancy.

Similarly, tests are made for the hepatitis virus antibodies. These warn your attendants that you might be able to infect others by contamination with blood products and so they would offer you special nursing facilities. Some clinics now check the cytomegalovirus antibodies, which indicate whether any past infection gives you protection against this rare infection during pregnancy. Some clinics may do a routine chest X-ray, but this is becoming less common in early pregnancy. Others perform an ultrasound scan (see p. 13) of the baby to check his size.

Arrangements are often made at this stage for you to attend antenatal classes later.

At each subsequent visit to the clinic or to your doctor, you will undergo a number of precautionary tests. Your blood pressure will be checked and the growth of the baby determined by examining the swelling abdomen. A sample of urine will be examined for protein and sugar, to detect any early signs of kidney problems or of disorder in the body's handling of carbohydrates.

Antenatal classes, in which the father can often participate, are helpful in dealing with the physical problems of pregnancy and also provide opportunities for meeting other women in the same situation. The pattern of these classes varies, but usually they include a series of talks by experienced doctors or midwives about care in pregnancy and labour and about looking after the newborn child, as well as teaching relaxation and breathing techniques, which can be very helpful during labour. It is wise to attend these classes, especially if the baby is your first.

In the last four weeks of pregnancy the doctor or midwife will pay particular attention to the position of the fetus. By gentle examination through the abdominal wall, they can feel your fetus and work out his position in the uterus. Size can be estimated approximately and the way he is lying becomes important. He should be lying longitudinally with his spine parallel to yours. This means he will be presenting ready for delivery when the time comes. The vast majority of babies present head down (cephalic presentation). This allows for an easier delivery. A few however present by the bottom first (breech presentation), and provided this is known about, skilled care can ensure a safe delivery for both you and the baby.

If the baby is presenting by the head in the last weeks of pregnancy, your attendant will be very keen to know whether the head engages, that is, if the maximum diameter of the baby's head passes through the brim or inlet of the pelvis. If it does, there is a very good chance that the baby's head will be able to pass through the outlet of the pelvis into the outside world.

However, when the head is not engaged the attendant will want to ensure that it can be helped to engage by simple manoeuvres or else there could be trouble when labour comes. The pelvis is usually assessed by the doctor at an internal vaginal

THE GROWING BABY

During the first three months of pregnancy, there is little noticeable change in the shape of the mother's abdomen, but at the end of this period the embryo has become a fetus – the unborn baby – with all its major organs and tissues. In the months up to birth, the fetus evolves a fully developed brain, nervous system, muscular apparatus and skeleton.

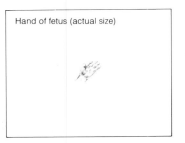

Hand of fetus (actual size)

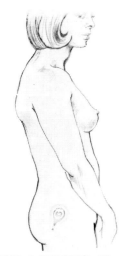

ABOUT 6 WEEKS *The embryo's limbs are forming. The mother's breasts are sensitive and enlarged. Morning sickness may begin.*

ABOUT 8 WEEKS *The mother feels a need to urinate more frequently than usual, because of pressure on the bladder by the womb.*

examination. If he has any doubts he may ask for a special X-ray of the pelvis at this stage. This is wise if there are doubts about the capacity of the canal to let the baby pass.

If you go past your due dates, after 40 weeks of gestation, you need not worry. Many pregnancies are quite normal and go some days after the expected date of delivery, for you will remember that was only a prediction and a probability, not a certainty. Should you go one week over, most obstetricians would not be concerned. However, if you should reach two weeks after the expected date (that is 42 weeks of gestation) many would feel it was time for the pregnancy to finish, and most women would agree with them. The doctor would then assess the neck of the womb (cervix) to see if it was ripe and ready; if it was he would suggest that you should be admitted to hospital for labour to be induced.

During these visits you should take the opportunity of asking your doctor or midwife about any problems that worry you. Often women have worries which they do not like to discuss, for they feel that the questions may appear too foolish. No question is foolish if it causes worry, and you should not hesitate to seek reassurance, however trivial the problem may seem.

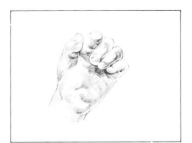

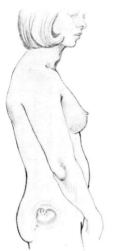

ABOUT 12 WEEKS *There are still few external signs of pregnancy; though the womb is enlarged sufficiently to be felt from outside.*

ABOUT 16 WEEKS *The abdomen has started to enlarge. The fetus is about 20 cm (8 in) long, and the mother begins to feel its movements.*

ABOUT 20 WEEKS *With each increase in womb size, growing pressure on the stomach may force acid into the gullet and lead to indigestion.*

Do's and don'ts

Try to lead as normal a life as possible while you are awaiting the birth of your baby. Generally you may carry on with your favourite sport, such as tennis, golf or swimming, but not riding or ski-ing: the risk of a fall is too great. Swimming is particularly good exercise and can be continued until the end of pregnancy. Your doctor will, if necessary, advise you when to stop. Otherwise, continue until you feel you do not want to go on. Do not start a new sport until after the birth.

Intercourse Sexual intercourse may be continued normally through your pregnancy, within the physical limitations set by the bulge of your growing baby. This becomes more of a problem during the last weeks, but there is no medical reason to stop having intercourse, although it is inadvisable in the early months if you have had more than one miscarriage.

Smoking Any smoking of cigarettes during pregnancy affects the unborn child; lighter smoking affects the child less than does heavier smoking. If you are a heavy smoker (20 cigarettes a day or more), the weight of your baby at term could be reduced by as much as 200 g (7 oz). This may not appear a lot, but in addition

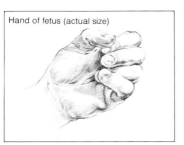

Hand of fetus (actual size)

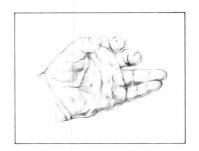

ABOUT 24 WEEKS *The baby may be in the breech, or sitting, position, buttocks down and head up, but may soon turn over in the womb.*

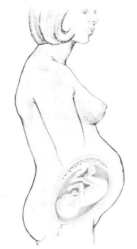

ABOUT 28 WEEKS *The baby turns actively in the womb, for there is still plenty of amniotic fluid. Later he will settle to a head-down position.*

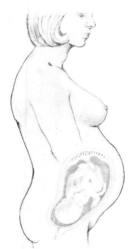

ABOUT 32 WEEKS *The mother is beginning to lean back noticeably, to counteract the baby's weight; and she has to walk with legs slightly apart.*

there can be developmental and physical retardation of the baby. Furthermore, subsequent growth in the early years of childhood can be affected. Most of the effects of smoking are in the last two-thirds of pregnancy, so if you are a heavy smoker, you still have a chance to give up when you know you are pregnant. It is very hard to stop smoking, but if you accept that you are doing good to your unborn child,

it may be the trigger for which you have been waiting. You may be able to throw off the habit that you have wanted to stop for a long time.

Alcohol Alcohol is a tissue poison and undoubtedly does affect the unborn child. Doctors are not so certain of its precise effect as they are with smoking but are sure there must be some influence on the unborn baby. It is probable that if you

are used to an occasional drink with a meal you could continue at that level, but you should avoid drinking to excess; and if you are a non-drinker it would be unwise to start drinking. The combination of smoking and alcohol together is very dangerous for the fetus and should be avoided by all pregnant women.

Travelling You may wear a car safety belt while you are pregnant, but in the later stages you may find it more comfortable to make long journeys by train. You will then be able to stretch your legs occasionally. If you plan to travel by air, remember that some airlines will refuse you after 35 weeks of pregnancy or even less, and a doctor's certificate or letter may be required.

Moving house It is a well-known phenomenon that a high proportion of expectant mothers tend to move house. This may be either because they belong to an age group in which husbands often change their jobs, or else simply because they need more room for the growing family. If you plan to move, take only a supervisory role and leave the heavy work of shifting furniture, cleaning up and redecorating to others.

Medicines and drugs in pregnancy Most women in the pregnancy age group are fit and well. They usually are not taking medicines from their doctor and should pass through pregnancy without having to take any drugs.

It is probably safe when you are pregnant to take extra iron and perhaps zinc tablets, as well as vita-

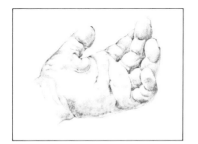

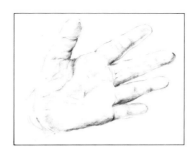

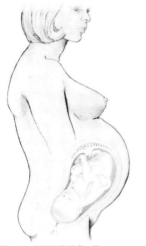

ABOUT 36 WEEKS *By now, the breasts are much enlarged. Pressure on veins of abdomen may lead to varicose veins and piles.*

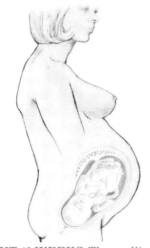

ABOUT 40 WEEKS *The swelling in the mother's abdomen has moved downwards, as the baby's head goes down into the pelvis.*

min supplements, but otherwise any medicines should be prescribed by a doctor who realises that you are pregnant. It is most unwise to take medicines prescribed for another person because you think you have the same symptoms as they do.

Basically a doctor will make sure than any drug or medicine prescribed for a pregnant woman is safe. Generally, doctors try to prescribe only drugs that have been used for many years rather than the more recently introduced ones.

On the whole, most medicinal drugs are perfectly safe in pregnancy and will not affect the woman or her growing baby. However, no pregnant woman should start a new drug without consulting her doctor or midwife. They will usually be able to reassure her, but there are a few drugs which are not good for the unborn child.

Obviously those that are known to produce problems with the unborn child are forbidden. Everyone remembers thalidomide, which caused abnormalities of fetal limbs. This is now never prescribed in pregnancy. Another potentially dangerous group would be those medicines used to treat cancer. Fortunately, very few women in the pregnant age group have cancer, so this does not often arise. It would be unwise to give a pregnant woman any radioactive drug because it could travel across the placenta and affect the fetus.

There are other drugs that should be used with caution. These include the antibiotic tetracycline, which, if given late in pregnancy, can affect the colour of the newborn child's

bone and teeth. The long-acting sulphonamides also are probably best avoided for they cross the placenta and affect the baby, causing jaundice. Certain anti-coagulants which are given to the mother to prevent blood clotting may affect the baby. If an epileptic woman becomes pregnant, she should be careful which of her drugs she takes and her doctor will advise her of this. Similarly women on anti-thyroid or anti-diabetic drugs should consult their doctors in order that the correct dosage and schedule of drugs can be arranged. If the woman has raised blood pressure before pregnancy and is on anti-hypertensive drugs, these may require adjusting. For example, methyl-dopa is probably perfectly safe throughout pregnancy, but there is some doubt about the use of pentolinium. Some pain-relieving drugs like phenacitin are best avoided.

Generally speaking, sex hormones should be avoided during pregnancy. The taking of oestrogens, such as stilboestrol, or progestogens, should not be encouraged unless there is an indication for them which your doctor will discuss with you.

Some women have long-term illnesses such as asthma or large bowel problems and are on cortisone steroids. These are safe in pregnancy provided the dose is adjusted, for they are replacing a deficiency of steroid in the body.

It goes without saying that drugs such as heroin, LSD or cocaine can do incalculable damage to the unborn baby. Marijuana too can cause abnormalities. All such drugs should be avoided for at least several months before conception.

Choosing the right diet

A well-balanced diet is important at any time of life. It is even more important when you are pregnant, since what you eat has to meet your unborn baby's needs, as well as your own requirements.

There is no need to "eat for two", though. That is not only unnecessary – it can even be harmful if it leads to excessive gain in weight.

You do not need to be a nutrition expert to make sure of a properly balanced diet. Just follow two simple rules at mealtimes:

1. Eat as wide a variety of foods as possible. Every food contains a different range of nutrients, and in differing amounts, so no one food can provide a perfect diet. As well as nutrients, you should eat plenty of food containing fibre. This is important as constipation and piles are more common during pregnancy.

2. Eat all things in moderation. Too much of any one food can do more harm than good.

Building up reserves
In addition to the food which is required by the growing baby, a mother lays down stores of food in her body during pregnancy, mainly in the form of fat. This provides reserves to tide her over a period of breast-feeding, which uses up a lot of

YOUR GUIDE TO BALANCED EATING

Here is a guide to balanced eating during pregnancy. Each day, eat something from each food group set out below; the quantities are a rough guide only. Remember that the ideal is to eat all things in moderation, and not to have too much of any one food, which can be harmful. Fresh food is preferable whenever possible.

Foods providing protein and B vitamins	100 g (4 oz) meat or fish; 2 eggs; beans; nuts; 75 g (3 oz) cheese; wholegrain cereals	**Foods providing Vitamin A**	Carrots; apricots; kippers; sardines; mackerel; liver; eggs; margarine
Foods providing Vitamin C	Citrus fruits; strawberries; potatoes; green vegetables	**Foods providing Vitamin D**	Kippers; sardines; mackerel; eggs; margarine
Foods providing iron	Bread; cereals; liver and red meat; dried apricots; figs; peaches; most nuts; beans; leafy green vegetables	**Foods providing calcium**	Milk, yoghurt, cheese; leafy green vegetables; fish bones (e.g. in tinned sardines); almonds; sesame spread (tahini); beans; cereals
Foods providing fibre	Wholemeal bread (4 slices) and cereals; pulses; nuts; fruit and vegetables	**What you crave**	Food cravings may be due to increased hormone levels. Indulge them a little. When you are pregnant, *"a little of what you fancy does you good"* is especially true

nutrients. Because of the increasing body fat, it is normal for a woman to gain 9–12.5 kg (20–28 lb) during pregnancy, and there is often a natural increase in her appetite.

Do not try to prevent this gain in weight by dieting, since doing so may impair the growth of your baby. If you are overweight, ask your obstetrician for advice.

To meet your increasing needs, you will need more calories. These are needed for all bodily processes, and particularly during growth. We get most of our calories from cereals (including bread), root vegetables, dairy products and cakes and sweets of various kinds. The cakes and sweets tend to be short of additional nutrients, and are sometimes called "empty calories". These are best kept to a minimum. Instead of cakes or sweets, fill up with foodstuffs which have other value as well as calories – wholemeal bread, for example, is also a useful source of protein, B vitamins and iron.

The developing baby needs a great deal of protein, particularly towards the end of pregnancy. We get about half our protein from animal products (meat, fish, eggs, milk) and the rest from vegetable sources, mainly in bread and other cereals, nuts, peas and beans.

Vegetarian mothers should make sure they get plenty of these high-protein vegetable foods. Otherwise nutrition is not on the whole a problem for vegetarian mothers, except for vegans, who eat no dairy produce, and should realise that they may be dangerously short of Vitamin B_{12} (cyanocobalamin), which is found almost exclusively in animal produce, especially milk and eggs. Commercial supplements are available; special nutritional yeast and fortified soya milk are also good sources of Vitamin B_{12} for vegans.

Vitamins and minerals
Vitamins are also necessary for your baby's growth and development. The main vitamins are Vitamin A, the Vitamin B group (containing several different vitamins) and Vitamins C, D and E. On a good diet, you are unlikely to lack any of these, but

demand may increase during pregnancy, so you need to take care to guard against deficiency.

Probably the most common vitamin shortage in a pregnant woman is lack of folic acid, a B-group vitamin which is needed for, among other processes, the making of blood. Folic acid is found particularly in leafy green vegetables – "folic" comes from the same root as "foliage".

Folic acid, or folate, and iron tablets are given to many expectant mothers throughout pregnancy. Both folic acid and iron are important in preventing anaemia, and help to build up the iron stores in your baby's liver – stores which must last until he is ready to start mixed feeding, at the age of four or five months. Folic acid is easily lost in cooking, so salads of leafy greens like watercress, endive or raw spinach are valuable. Wheatgerm and bran are also good sources of folic acid. It is most important to take adequate amounts: the body cannot store it, and there is evidence that folic acid deficiency is associated with neural tube defects such as as spina bifida.

If iron tablets are taken, it is recommended that you also take extra Vitamin C, which helps greatly in the absorption of iron. Remember that iron tablets can be poisonous to children and must be kept out of their reach.

Another important mineral is zinc, found in cheese, meat, most nuts and shellfish.

B vitamins are found in most protein foods, including cereals, and in vegetables (except for Vitamin B_{12}). Several, especially Vitamins B_1 (thiamin) and B_6 (pyridoxine), are much reduced by cooking, so try to eat plenty of raw salads.

Some women become short of Vitamin D, the "bone vitamin". This is most abundant in eggs, oily fish and skim milk powder. It is also produced in your skin by the action of sunlight, and has by law to be added to margarine.

Vitamin C, needed by all body cells, is found particularly in potatoes, green vegetables and citrus fruits, such as oranges, grapefruit and lemons. Vitamin A – found, like Vitamin D, in eggs, fish and milk products – is necessary for good eyesight. About 25–35 g (1–$1\frac{1}{2}$ oz) polyunsaturated oil or 50 g (2 oz) nuts or seeds a day will ensure a supply of essential fatty acids and Vitamin E.

Calcium is another special need in pregnancy. It is vital for healthy bones and teeth. As long as you take in enough calcium for your own needs and those of your baby, calcium will not be drained from your body to supply the baby.

The best sources of calcium are milk and foods made from it, such as cheese and yoghurt. If you normally drink about 0.25 litre ($\frac{1}{2}$ pint) of milk a day, double the quantity while you are an expectant mother. Lower fat milk has just as much calcium as full fat milk. If you are not keen on milk, eat more leafy green vegetables and other calcium foods (see chart on previous page). Ensure you are getting enough Vitamin D as without it calcium cannot be absorbed.

Obviously, your greatest concern during pregnancy is for your unborn baby's well-being. Sensible eating will benefit both of you.

NORMAL GAIN IN WEIGHT

Most women gain 9–12.5 kg (20–28 lb) during pregnancy. Your doctor or clinic will keep a close watch on your weight, and you should not be alarmed if the gain is slightly more or less than average.

You may wonder how you will gain so much weight when the baby will probably weigh 3–3.6 kg (7–8 lb) at birth. The reason is that there are also weight increases of the placenta and amniotic fluid surrounding the baby (see p.14) and of your womb, breasts, volume of blood and extra body fat. Your body lays down this fat as a food reserve to supplement your diet during the demanding period of breast-feeding.

This is a typical example of how your weight gain is distributed; the conversions are approximate:

Baby	3 kg (7 lb)
Placenta	1 kg (2 lb)
Amniotic fluid	1 kg (2 lb)
Womb	1 kg (2 lb)
Breasts	1 kg (2 lb)
Blood	2 kg (4 lb)
Mother's body fat	2 kg (4 lb)
Total	11 kg (23 lb)

The gain in weight is not constant. In the first ten weeks of pregnancy there is no noticeable gain. In the following ten weeks or so there is a gain of about 0.22 kg ($\frac{1}{2}$ lb) a week, and in the final 20 weeks about 0.45 kg (1 lb) a week.

If you allow yourself to gain excessive fat, you may be heavily overweight even after your baby is born; several months of breast-feeding may not remove all your surplus.

If you feel that you are putting on too much weight do not start a slimming diet: consult your doctor or clinic. (Problems during pregnancy, pp. 32–35.)

Staying at your best

While you are awaiting your baby, set some time aside every day to carry out a few simple exercises and to practise controlled breathing and relaxation.

The physical exercises prevent muscles overstretching, as the weight of your growing baby puts unaccustomed strains on you. The breathing and relaxation exercises (see p. 25) will not only relieve tensions during pregnancy but will also be of great value and assistance to you during all the stages of labour and the birth of your baby.

Avoid over-exertion and violent exercise. Simply follow the gentle exercises described on the following page and use your muscles in the day-to-day routine of living. The specific exercises shown here are excellent, but if you cannot do them, general exercise is still good for your growing baby. You should ensure you get some walking or swimming on most days. It can be shown that a woman who keeps herself in good physical shape by gentle, general exercise does much good to her baby and to her figure for later life. This can be augmented by the special exercises outlined.

What the muscles do
The design of the abdominal muscles may be compared with that of many man-made foundation garments.

There is a thin but strong panel of non-elastic material at the back and front, to which are attached layers of elastic fibres that contract and stretch in different directions. As your baby increases in size he takes up more space in the abdominal cavity, and the strain on these muscles increases. The elastic fibres become stretched and bowed forward.

If, when standing, you allow these muscles to sag, the baby will tilt forward and your front abdominal wall will be stretched more than necessary. With good posture and daily exercise, the abdominal muscles will retain their elasticity and will recover after your baby is born. If, however, you allow the muscles to drop into disuse, they may recover sluggishly and be unable to give you proper support.

EVERYDAY HINTS ON HOW TO EASE THE STRAIN ON YOUR BODY

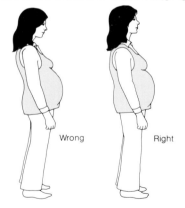

Wrong Right

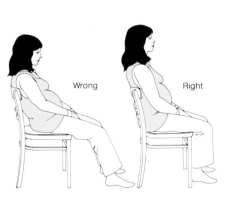

Wrong Right

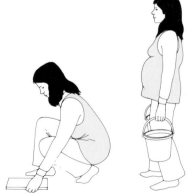

Standing *Avoid dropping your pelvis forward and making your back hollow. Stand with your feet apart, distributing your weight evenly on your heels and the balls of your feet. Hold up your head.*

Sitting *Do not sit on the edge of a chair. Push yourself right back so that the whole length of your thighs is supported by the seat. In some armchairs with deep seats you may need to place a cushion at your back.*

Lifting and carrying *To pick up an object, keep your back upright and bend from the knees and hips – never from the waist. Use your thigh muscles to straighten up. Walk with your head up.*

As well as giving support, the muscles are essential for expulsive actions. They assist, for example, in evacuating the bowels. During labour, they exercise the pressures that help a baby to be born.

Pelvic floor exercises

The pelvic floor muscles form a springy hammock to support the womb, bladder and rectum (the lower part of the bowel). During labour they direct the baby downwards and forwards. At a later stage they must then relax so that their edges are drawn up over the baby's head to allow it to emerge.

If, therefore, you learn to control your pelvic floor muscles you will be able to relax them during the various stages of labour (see pp. 36–38) and make the birth easier. Your muscles will also become more elastic so that they spring back to normal after the birth.

To practise this control, either sit on a hard chair, fully supported, or lie in bed on your back or side, with knees drawn up. The control action is similar to sucking the lips into the mouth: draw up inside the vagina. Feel yourself tightening inside, then let go gently and feel the area around the birth canal slackening. Let go as much as possible and try to relax still more. Be aware of the different sensations: drawn up, resistant, relaxed, yielding. Repeat four times a day.

You can also try the exercise in other positions: lying on your back with your knees drawn up, or sitting on the floor with your back supported against a wall. Keep the sides of your feet together and raise your knees, keeping them apart.

EXERCISES TO LIGHTEN YOUR BURDEN

As your baby rapidly gains in weight from about the sixth month of pregnancy, you will probably get periods of weariness. When you feel tired, drop household chores and take a short rest, with the feet up. If you get backache, you may find that you will get more value from this spell if, instead of lying down, you kneel, thereby taking the baby's pressure off your spine. If, however, you must carry on working, try to keep changing the position of your legs and body.

EXERCISE 1 (do A or B)

A. Kneel with forearms on low table. Rest forehead on hands. Round your back and draw up hips – then relax.

B. Kneel as before, without table: arms and thighs vertical. Rock pelvis gently: repeat six times.

EXERCISE 2

To help to tone up your stomach muscles, kneel with your knees apart and your arms stretched upwards. Reach as high as you can so that you feel the waist lifting, to relieve pressure under ribs.

Swing your arms to the right like a windmill, then turn to touch your heels with both hands. Swing back to first position, then stretch up. Do movement to left; repeat each way six times.

LEARNING REST AND RELAXATION

Pregnancy is a time when your body has to work extra hard. This can lead to fatigue and tension, so it is essential to learn how to relax, in body and mind.

You should always make sure to take a complete rest during the day. If you cannot do this at home in the middle of the day, take your rest as soon as you return, *before* tackling household chores.

Relaxation of your body is closely linked with your breathing: learning to breathe easily and rhythmically will also help you in the first stage of labour.

Lie down or sit, comfortably supported, and breathe in and out at a pace that comes naturally. Sigh gently each time you breathe *out*. Notice the gentle rise and fall in chest and waist; let go the muscles of the shoulders, chest, stomach and back. To check that you really have let go completely, think of a different area of your body with each successive sigh: thighs, pelvic floor, stomach, back, shoulders and chest.

To rehearse for labour, imagine the contractions of your womb coming like waves, lasting half a minute, then three-quarters of a minute, and finally a full minute. As each wave begins, switch off all tension: concentrate on your gentle sighs and keep thinking about the areas to relax, one after the other, until the wave has gone.

As you become used to doing these exercises regularly, you will learn to recognise muscular tension anywhere in your body, and can train yourself to "switch off" that tension, at will.

During the stages of labour, your medical attendants may ask you to bear down strongly, gently or not at all.

To practise bearing down, breathe in and hold your breath: then bear down steadily, with chin on chest. Finally, let go, with mouth open and chin relaxed. In case you are told not to bear down at all, practise for this by breathing in and out through the mouth – fairly quickly, but still easily and rhythmically, stressing the sighs as if out of breath.

RELIEVING TENSION

Sit well back in a comfortable chair, with feet, thighs, back, neck and head fully supported; rest hands in lap. Press knees and inside thighs together and feel muscles tensing. Let them fall apart: inside thighs are no longer tense. Press waist, back, neck and head into chair: feel the pressure. Then let go. Stomach muscles are no longer tense.

THREE WAYS TO REST

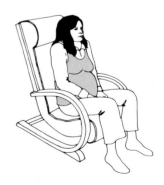

One way to rest (left) is to lie on your back on a bed, supported by three pillows. Another very restful position in pregnancy (centre) is lying on one side, with two pillows under the head and one under the upper knee. Sometimes it can be even more restful to kneel on hands and knees (right), for a couple of minutes. This relieves backache, as the baby drops forward, away from the spine.

Hunch the shoulders and draw your upper arms inwards, then let them dangle. As your arms hang limply away from your sides, your chest relaxes, and your breathing is easier. Repeat all exercises daily.

Caring for your body

Apart from keeping yourself in condition for your baby's sake during pregnancy, you must also take care of your body for your own sake. In the months before the baby is born you should pay special attention to your teeth, weight, bowels, skin, breasts and blood circulation, not forgetting your hair.

Your teeth

An expectant mother can get so involved in her coming baby's welfare that she forgets to look after her own teeth. During pregnancy, it is very important to do this, and to have a dental check.

Sensible eating not only aids good health, but also helps to prevent tooth decay by lessening any desire for sweet biscuits, cakes and sugary drinks. Make sure you get enough calcium. (Diet in pregnancy, p. 20.)

Inflammation and bleeding in the gums – gingivitis – may occur. This is caused by a sticky film called plaque, formed from food debris and bacteria, which irritates the gums. Efficient brushing can remove the plaque, but hormonal changes in pregnancy may aggravate any inflammation. If this happens, consult your dentist.

Your weight

You must be careful not to put on too much weight in pregnancy. The myth of eating for two is still perpetuated in some country areas and is not only useless but can be harmful to the woman. Many women's weight excess starts in pregnancy and is difficult to remove afterwards. Follow the advice given in the section on diet (pp. 20–22) and you will provide quite enough nutrients for your growing child without putting on excess fat yourself. In essence you should avoid excess carbohydrate and fat while concentrating on protein and vitamins, particularly the B group and Vitamin C, as well as the minerals iron and zinc.

Your bowels

Women in pregnancy often get constipated. This is due to a relative diminution of moisture in the stools, which become harder and more difficult to pass. During pregnancy make sure that you drink plenty of clear fluids in order that the last priority in the body, the large bowel, gets its supply of water too; this will help keep your bowels moving. In addition, do ensure you have roughage each day from the group of foods that contain fibre. Include some bran in your diet but do not rely on it solely for fibre, since bran affects the absorption of some other foods.

Your skin

Many expectant mothers worry about being left with permanent stretch marks on the skin after childbirth. Unfortunately creams cannot help, whatever claims may be made for them.

However, it can be comforting and soothing to use an oil-and-massage technique, starting in the fourth or fifth month of pregnancy, as soon as your shape begins to change. Take a fairly hot bath, dry the skin, then work a small amount of olive oil (or almond oil) into the abdomen, buttocks, hips and thighs. Then massage sections of your skin between the thumb and finger of each hand, moving each pinch of skin in all directions. This may help to keep the skin soft and elastic.

Your breasts

To keep your breasts in condition throughout pregnancy, you will need a well-fitted bra (Bras for pregnancy, p. 28) and a routine of care for breasts and nipples.

Your nipples need no more than the wash they normally get at bathtime, but do not use too much soap, because it is a drying agent which may increase the risk of cracked nipples later on. Avoid toilet water – another drying agent. Keep the nipples supple by massaging with a little pure lanolin or baby oil.

Before your baby is born, your breasts will make "early milk" colostrum. (Breast-feeding, p. 52.) This can be expressed, using your hands. In any case, get used to handling your breasts and nipples before you have a baby to feed.

Your circulation

When you stand still, the downward pressure of your baby may interfere with the flow of blood in the pelvis, and all the way back through the thighs and legs to the feet. This can increase the risk of varicose veins and haemorrhoids (piles). You can reduce the effects of this pressure by moving about.

Walking is also a good way to prevent cramp in the legs. If you do get cramp, you can ease it by stretching and massaging whichever muscle is affected. If the cramp is in your calf, keep the leg straight and try to get someone else to hold the foot and pull it upwards.

Circulation in the legs can be improved generally by lying down once a day and working the feet in circles, and flexing toes and ankles.

Your hair

Some expectant mothers find that hair problems such as dryness or greasiness are aggravated. The best care for any type of hair is regular washing, using a suitable shampoo and, if needed, conditioner.

Dry hair, in particular, can be caused by permanent waving, which is best avoided during the last four months of pregnancy and in the two or three months after your baby is born. You may also find that hair dyes and tints do not "take" as well as usual. Many women find during pregnancy and breast feeding that hair falls out very readily. It is a reflection of the weakness of the hair follicles in pregnancy and happens to many women. This does not mean you are going bald; it is a temporary phenomenon that is reversed once breast-feeding has stopped.

The condition of your hair reflects your general health, so one of the rewards of taking proper diet, exercise and rest will be healthy hair.

You will want to look your best once labour is over, but motherhood will not leave a great deal of time for attending to complicated hair-styles. It is therefore worth spending money on a good, easy-to-handle style by an expert cutter before the baby is due.

MULTIPLE PREGNANCY

Twins occur in about 1 in 100 pregnancies in the United Kingdom but much more frequently in other parts of the world (in West Africa they could be as often as 1 in 30 pregnancies). Triplets are much rarer at about 1 in 6000 pregnancies and other multiples are rarer still. Most twins are non-identical for they are made from two eggs which have been produced by the mother at one menstrual cycle and fertilised by two separate sperm from the father. A few twins are identical and come from a single egg which has been fertilised by one sperm and has split into two separate individuals at the beginning of development.

Twin and other multiple pregnancies are often diagnosed by an ultrasound examination at 16 weeks. If that has not been performed, they may be detected at antenatal checks from about the 28th week of pregnancy, when the uterus is much bigger than it should be and the parts of individual babies can be felt. Multiple pregnancies cause more stretch in the abdomen so the mother with twins is more likely to have varicose veins or piles, urinary problems or stretch sensations. In addition, she is more likely to have pre-eclampsia (see p. 34) and will probably go into labour earlier, some weeks before the expected date of delivery of a single child.

The birth weight of each twin is between 2 kg and 2.5 kg (4½ lb and 5½ lb) compared with an average of 3.5 kg (7½ lb) for a single baby. Twins may therefore need to be kept for some time after birth in an intensive-care unit.

Delivery of twins under expert care usually has no complications but things at this time can change swiftly. A senior doctor should be present and twin deliveries should always take place in a consultant obstetric unit with a good medical cover.

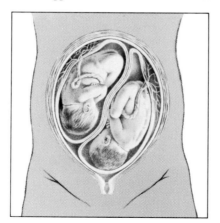

Fraternal twins *Of all the twins born, three-quarters are fraternal, or non-identical. They develop when two eggs are fertilised by two different sperm. The twins may or may not be of the same sex.*

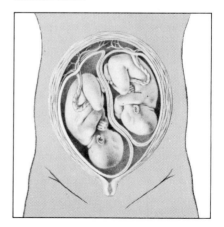

Identical twins *These twins come from the same fertilised egg, which divides into two. The twins grow up to resemble each other closely. They are of the same sex, and they have the same hair colour.*

The right support

During pregnancy, your underwear and foundation garments should give support to your breasts and to the muscles in your abdomen and back. In fact you will need this support both while you are pregnant and in early motherhood.

Easing the abdomen
The most noticeable change during pregnancy takes place in your abdomen, between the third and ninth months. Your growing baby is supported in the womb by a criss-cross network of muscles. Unless you are very fit, these muscles may grow tired with the constant burden of carrying the baby.

If this happens, the doctor or midwife may recommend a special maternity pantie-girdle, to relieve the feeling of strain and backache. If a pantie-girdle is worn, it must be of a type specially designed for pregnancy. An ordinary garment is useless, and may even be dangerous for an expectant mother.

Legwear and footwear
After the first few months, ordinary tights cannot be worn. Maternity tights have an expanding front panel to pull up well over the "bump", without pressing on it. Cotton or wool socks are also suitable, but avoid anything that feels tight or

BRAS FOR PREGNANCY AND AFTERWARDS

One of the early changes in pregnancy is that the breasts feel full and begin to enlarge. Even a very slender bust becomes rounder and heavier. Each breast may increase in weight by as much as ½ kg (1 lb), and grow two whole bra-cup sizes larger. Even if you do not normally wear a bra, you should do so from the start of pregnancy. This is far more than

just a matter of comfort. Without proper support, the breasts will sag with the increasing weight and will permanently stretch the tissue that holds them up.

Wide shoulder-straps are very important. As the breasts grow heavier, the narrow straps of an ordinary bra can cut into the flesh and cause permanent damage to the shallow tissue over the collar-

bone. Modern bras have straps that stretch for comfort in wear, but the stretch is limited, so that proper support is always there.

The maternity bra should also allow for ample adjustment, so that an expectant mother can let it out from time to time. The size is often the same as that normally worn, because a good manufac-

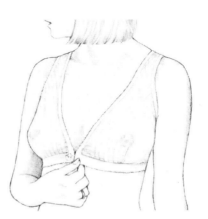

Sleep-bra *Ideal for nightwear, gives gentle support. Also useful for relaxation classes and at resting times.*

Feeding bra (fold-back) *Each cup folds away from the breasts for feeding, and prevents soiling by dribbles.*

Support-bra *Shoulder straps stretch enough for comfort, while not losing their support. Straps must be wide.*

that is strongly elasticated.

The extra weight of pregnancy can lead to tiredness and aching in the legs, and a risk of varicose veins. Maternity support tights are available, designed to give comfort and support without causing any constriction. Put them on in bed first thing in the morning, before your legs have a chance to swell. Make sure that the tights allow plenty of room for your toes.

Your feet and legs will swell during pregnancy, so shoes that you have been used to wearing may now be uncomfortable. Be sure to wear shoes that are comfortable, and do avoid high heels. They will cause bad posture and discomfort while you are pregnant and may lead to chronic backache later on.

Nighties and slips

These need plenty of room for your stomach to expand, and, later, to allow you to breast-feed easily. Some models button down the front: others have concealed front openings, or a ruched neckline which can be opened wide. A big choice of attractive nighties is available.

Hygiene

For some time after the baby is born, you will need sanitary protection. Ordinary press-on pads can be used, or maternity pads which are specially absorbent. Briefs are available that have a plastic pocket to hold the pad in place, or you may prefer to use disposable pants during this period. Do not use internal tampons.

PANTIE-GIRDLES

turer will have allowed in the design for normal expansion. But it is important to have your measurements taken first.

Apart from the support-bra, there are a sleep-bra and two types of special feeding bra (drop-down or fold-back). You can use disposable, absorbent bra pads inside the cups, to prevent leakage soiling clothes.

If you are having your first baby and you are reasonably fit, a lightweight maternity pantie-girdle will probably give all the help your muscles need.

The waistband should come high on the stomach, well over the "bump", to avoid any pressure.

If you have already had one or more children you may need a firmer support.

You can get this by asking at your shop for a girdle in a fabric that gives firmer control.

An adjustable back support continues the "cradle" round from the front so that it fits correctly.

A hook-and-eye adjustment allows you to arrange exactly the right degree of support for yourself.

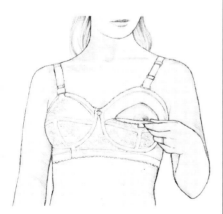

Feeding bra (drop-down) *Another kind of bra, in which the cups fold down, instead of folding sideways.*

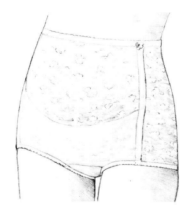

Light, firm support *The special maternity pantie-girdle gives the help that muscles need in pregnancy.*

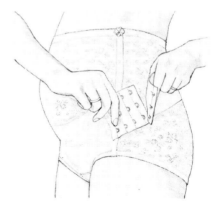

Back-sling *The hook-and-eye adjustment enables the mother to obtain just the right amount of support she needs.*

Clothing your baby

When you go shopping for your baby, do not choose clothes that are all in the first size; these may be outgrown before they are even worn, and will only last three months at the most.

It is worth remembering that a baby may get through four stretch suits and vests a day, so make sure you have an adequate number.

Choose clothes that are machine washable, preferably on the same wash cycle to save time and effort. Avoid pale and pretty baby clothes that need hand washing and ironing because you will be washing the baby's clothes constantly.

Try not to choose clothes which pull off over the baby's head: this will prove messy if the clothes are soiled. Also avoid small head holes (look for poppers or buttons on the shoulder) and clothes with ribbon or tapes to tie on that could get caught as these can be dangerous.

You should remember above all that a baby cannot regulate its own body temperature, so be careful that you neither underdress nor overdress your baby for the climate.

Vests

A vest goes next to your baby's skin, so it must be of soft, non-irritant material. Some babies are uncomfortable in thick wool vests, especially if they are prone to eczema (in which case wool should never be worn), but since your child will be wearing several layers of clothes, the vest need not be thick, or made of all wool. Vest can be made of cotton or wool mixed with man-made fibres.

There are several kinds of vest to choose from. For the first weeks, you may find it easier to use a wrap-over style: make sure that the ribbons are well sewn on.

Another type of vest is the envelope neck. You can easily stretch the neck wide to pop over the baby's head without frightening him, but once the vest is on, it fits snugly. The envelope-neck vest has no buttons to come loose and no ribbons to get tied up in knots.

SUGGESTED BASIC WARDROBE

- 6 vests
- 6 all-in-one babystretch suits
- 4 cardigans
- 1 knitted bonnet
- 1 pair outdoor mittens
- 1 quilted outdoor "ski suit" or pram suit

optional:
- 3 nightgowns
- 2 pairs anti-scratch mittens
- 3 pairs knitted bootees

FOR THE COT
- 4–6 sheets
- 2 blankets
- 1 waterproof undersheet
- Cot duvet and 2 covers (if preferred)

NAPPIES
- 24 terry nappies
- 6 pairs waterproof pants
- 6 nappy pins
- 1 pack nappy liners
- 1 pack nappy sanitising powder
- Bucket for soaking

or Large pack of newborn size all-in-one disposable nappies with resealable tapes. (You will use about 6 per day).
or Large pack of disposable nappies and 1 pack of tie-on or 12 pop-on plastic pants.

Stretch suits

The all-in-one babystretch suit is invaluable. It has front popper fastenings to facilitate dressing and undressing; it covers the feet, and the smaller sizes often have mittens that can be folded over the hands to prevent the baby from scratching himself. They are suitable for boys or girls and come in sizes right up to the toddler age.

Babystretch suits of this type are easily washed and dried and, as they can be worn both day and night, make other night garments unnecessary.

You should always make sure that the feet of the suit are really loose around the baby's toes. The garment must never pull on the toes, as this can deform them and cause ingrowing toenails. If the feet of the suit become too small, while the suit itself is still serviceable, cut the feet off and use socks instead.

Nightwear

Unless, for the younger baby, you use a "cosy-gown", which closes a drawstring or poppers at the hem, it is better to use an all-in-one babystretch suit at night so that the baby's feet are always covered even if the bedclothes get kicked off. In colder weather a cardigan can be worn as well.

Knitted jackets

For safety, check that there are no

large holes in the knitted pattern which could catch and injure your baby's fingers.

If the garments are well made, they can be washed over and over again, without shrinking or fading.

When your baby reaches the age of about six months, and is able to sit up in his pram, he will need a warm pram suit. This consists of a jacket (preferably with hood) and pants. The two halves should overlap well at the waist, and the hood should fit snugly around the ears and neck. Make sure that the pants leave plenty of room for nappies and waterproof pants underneath, or your baby's movements and circulation will be restricted, and he will become chilled.

Nappies

Nappies have to be changed often, so you will need to have a good supply. The choice is between terry towelling, disposable, and all-in-one disposable nappies.

The best solution may be to combine the different types, using towelling nappies at night and disposables during the day or when travelling. (Putting on a nappy, pp. 58–59.)

Towelling nappies, square or shaped (easy fit), are probably marginally cheaper overall. They do involve a lot of soaking and washing, but this can be made easier by using disposable nappy liners, which are laid on the folded towelling nappy like a lining, filtering the urine through to the outer nappy without getting soaked themselves. The baby's skin thus stays drier and nappy rash is less likely. The liners can be flushed away.

Disposable nappies do not need washing: just tear them in half and flush them away. However, they are expensive to use continually, may absorb less well than towelling, and are not so warm. Also, they must be used with waterproof pants. Disposables are most useful on special occasions, such as when travelling.

All-in-one disposable nappies come with or without elasticated legs and

WHAT YOU WILL NEED IN HOSPITAL

- Sanitary towels and pants
- 2 front-opening nightdresses (for breast-feeding)
- Dressing gown (lightweight as hospitals tend to be well heated)
- Slippers
- Nursing bra and nursing breast pads
- Brush, comb, shampoo
- Soap, flannel, toothbrush etc.
- Make-up and small mirror
- Child's rubber ring for sitting on if you have a episiotomy
- Soft toilet paper
- Nipple spray or cream
- Bran, to add to the hospital food and prevent constipation
- Money for the telephone
- Money for purchasing magazines, newspapers etc.
- Clothes to take your baby home in
- Vitamins (especially C and E)
- Arnica (for bruising)
- Scent and/or eau de cologne

WHAT YOU WILL NEED FOR LABOUR
- Flannel or sponge
- Glucose or dextrose tablets for energy
- Something for your partner to eat or drink (there may not be a canteen or shop open)

in various sizes, and most have re-sealable tapes to extend their useful life. They can be bought in quantities of about 10 to 100 per pack. Some manufacturers operate a home delivery service at no extra charge which avoids your having to carry heavy packs of nappies while shopping. All-in-one disposables must be wrapped and disposed of in the dustbin; you cannot flush them away.

Waterproof pants

These are needed when travelling and at other times when it is inconvenient to change nappies. The pants should not however be worn all the time, because they prevent air from reaching the skin. There are three popular styles: pull-on pants with elastic at waist and legs, pants which fasten at the waist with popper studs, and the tie-on type, one size of which fits all babies.

Blankets

Cotton cellular blankets are ideal not only for use in the cot but also for wrapping your baby when he is being carried about. The air-holes in the material act as insulation to keep in warmth, and still allow perspiration to evaporate. Cotton blankets can be boiled.

Buying for twins

If you are expecting twins, roughly double up on all clothes, as well as cots, bedding, nappies, accessories and bottles. If possible, provide yourself with more than you strictly need.

Twins usually arrive between the 36th and 38th weeks of pregnancy, so do not leave your shopping until the last minute.

Problems during pregnancy

For most women, pregnancy is a happy event with no major problems. Sometimes, however, there are troubles. Some of these pass away of their own accord as the pregnancy progresses, and others can be cleared up by your doctor or clinic.

Sleeplessness You may have difficulty in sleeping during pregnancy. In the beginning this is due to the unusual sensation of the growing womb. Later it is caused by the stretching of the whole stomach. There may be backache, and discomfort in the pubic region.

People turn in their sleep as often as 30 times during a single night. When you have a large swelling in your stomach, each turn may wake you. There is no need, however, for you to go without sleep. Your doctor can give you safe tablets that will not affect your unborn baby.

Breathlessness As the pregnancy advances you will find that you become increasingly breathless after even slight exertion. This may first be due to minor emotional problems, but, later, it is caused by a greater movement of blood away from the heart and lungs into the growing womb. The womb is growing bigger under the diaphragm, and pushing up on to the lower lungs. To avoid discomfort, cut down physical effort as much as possible.

Heartburn and indigestion You are likely to feel some soreness in the pit of the stomach, below the breastbone. This indigestion-like sensation is due to the acid contents of the stomach being forced into the gullet. Bending forward or lying flat makes the feeling worse. This is a normal physiological change, and is best treated by mild antacids obtained from the chemist. At night, prop yourself up with several pillows.

Piles and constipation Piles are enlarged veins at the lower end of the bowel. During pregnancy extra blood pumped to the pelvis passes through the rectal veins, which are also under pressure from the bulk of the growing womb. There may be a little bleeding when the bowels are open, or the piles may protrude.

Constipation makes this condition worse, so it is necessary to keep the motions soft by drinking more than usual and eating roughage, such as bran, salads and vegetables. A doctor may recommend a mild laxative. Smear piles which have protruded with anaesthetic ointment, obtained from your doctor, and push them back. After the baby is born, most piles disappear completely and do not need further treatment.

Ligament pains The womb is held in place in the pelvis by a series of ligaments that tether it to the side walls. Two of these, the round ligaments, have to stretch as the womb grows. Occasionally the pull is a little too much, and a small amount of bleeding occurs on to the ligaments, producing a sharp pain. To reassure yourself, consult your doctor. Ligament stretch usually settles down without major treatment.

Varicose veins Two sorts of varicose veins occur in pregnancy. The first are small, spidery groups of thin, blue lines on the thighs and are often accompanied by a discoloration of the skin of the lower legs. These varicose veins are due to hormone changes and usually disappear after the baby is born.

The larger varicose veins are knots of the blood vessels under the skin. In the later stages of pregnancy these occur inside the thighs, behind the knees and along both sides of the calves. The wearing of elastic tights or stockings will collapse the veins and remove some of the discomfort, but they will not stop the veins forming. Put on the tights before getting up in the morning and do not remove them until going to bed.

After the birth most of the large varicose veins reduce considerably. However, the veins may not disappear entirely.

Urinary infections Whilst many women pass urine more frequently during pregnancy, it should not be painful. If stinging or burning occurs on passing water, it may mean an infection has started. You should consult your doctor as soon as possible; in the meanwhile drink plenty of water. Although it may hurt it is better to dilute the urine and wash out the urinary tract.

If an infection is confirmed on

examination of a clean specimen of urine, the doctor will start you on an antibiotic agent to try to kill the bacteria.

It is important to treat urinary infection as soon as possible in pregnancy. The high temperatures that are often associated with urinary infection can affect the growing baby. Further, if an infection is allowed to take hold, it can affect your kidneys in later life.

Bleeding Once pregnancy has started, no more vaginal bleeding should occur.

In early pregnancy a little vaginal blood loss may be the warning of a threatened miscarriage. Consult your doctor, who will help you sort out the more serious causes of this. If the neck of the womb stays closed, bed-rest may be enough to allow the pregnancy to continue without any further effect. Occasionally, however, the neck of the womb opens and an inevitable miscarriage occurs which may need hospital treatment. The commonest cause of a miscarriage is that something is wrong with the embryo. This is expelled in due course as nature's way of preventing you from giving birth to an abnormal child.

In the later weeks of pregnancy, if you should have any bleeding from the vagina you should contact your doctor immediately. It does not matter if that bleeding is not painful; it still is a symptom the doctor should know about. Do not wait for your next antenatal appointment to report this symptom. Most bleeding does not come from a serious cause but from some local problem such as

NATURAL CHILDBIRTH

Modern technology has led to a dramatic drop in the risks of childbirth and therefore a much greater sense of security and confidence for the mother-to-be, far removed from the apprehension and even terror that would accompany childbirth in the Middle Ages. Nevertheless, many women dislike the "high-tech" approach and feel that as childbirth is a natural process and not an illness it should happen "naturally".

WHAT IS IT?

Natural childbirth means giving birth with the minimum of medical intervention.

Over the last fifty years, doctors such as Grantly Dick-Read, Fernand Lamaze, Frederick Leboyer and Michel Odent have pioneered a variety of low-tech approaches to childbirth ranging from antenatal preparation by means of mental and physical exercises, to delivery in comfort and privacy, sometimes in subdued lighting with music playing, sometimes in a warm bath. Michel Odent, for instance, favours the supported squatting position, a position which many women adopt instinctively; others may prefer to stand or kneel on all fours, or use a birthing stool.

Supporters of natural childbirth point out that it avoids many of the situations which themselves call for medical intervention. For example, lying on your back (the position required for fetal heart monitoring) may reduce your blood pressure and therefore the flow of blood and oxygen to the baby, and the force of gravity will be opposing the birth process rather than helping it. This in turn increases the need for episiotomy, forceps delivery and anaesthetics. (That is why in many labour wards you are offered a thick rubber wedge to prop you up at an angle – see also p. 39.)

In April 1985, a report from the World Health Organisation and the Pan American Health Organisation included the following recommendations:
● Moving around should be encouraged during labour.
● Each woman should decide for herself what position to adopt during delivery.
● Routine use of electronic fetal monitoring, anaesthetics and episiotomy should be avoided, as should the artificial, early rupture of membranes.
● Shaving pubic hair and use of enemas before delivery should not be necessary.
● The dorsal lithotomy position (on the back with feet in stirrups) should not be used.
● Induction of labour should be reserved for specific medical indications.
● Immediate breast-feeding should be encouraged.

WHAT YOU CAN DO ABOUT IT

Obviously not all these recommendations could be implemented immediately in every hospital throughout the world, nor indeed can any single approach to childbirth suit everyone. What is vital is that you should decide what you would prefer, whether it is classed as high-tech or low-tech, and discuss it with your doctor or clinic at the earliest opportunity.

Natural childbirth is possible in many births – perhaps the vast majority. However, a birth aided by the latest technology may be necessary for the safety of the mother and/or baby. If you would prefer a natural birth but find that for some reason other procedures are needed, remember the paramount concern of the doctors is for the health and safety of you and your baby and it is to this end that all the medical technology is directed, even if it seems to be at the cost of your own feelings and comfort.

an erosion of the neck of the womb, but you cannot tell this without professional help. Very occasionally, the placenta is lying low and this would give rise to serious bleeding when the neck of the womb is taken up or dilates (placenta praevia). It could obstruct an attempted vaginal delivery and lead to a severe haemorrhage. Vaginal delivery may therefore not be possible and a Caesarean section will be necessary.

Sometimes the placenta, even though it is sited in the right place in the upper part of the uterus, separates early and is associated with vaginal bleeding and sometimes severe abdominal pain (abruptio placentae). This is a serious symptom for the fetus and sometimes for the mother also. If this should happen, you will need to go to hospital and it may require a Caesarean section to save your baby.

Anaemia With the increased demand for iron in pregnancy to cope with the growing baby and the increase of mother's blood volume, you may become anaemic. A woman whose diet is usually on the borderline of obtaining enough iron might find it too sparse during pregnancy. The best way to prevent anaemia is to ensure that your diet is adequate (see pp. 20–22) and to take iron supplement pills which your antenatal clinic or doctor will prescribe. These are useful in pregnancy for they make up for any deficiency in your iron intake. Vitamin C should be taken to help absorption of the iron, and folic acid supplements are also important in preventing anaemia (see p. 22).

A HERBAL REMEDY

Many women find infusions of raspberry leaves are helpful during the latter half of pregnancy and in labour. They are said to tone the muscles, help prevent miscarriage, ease delivery and aid return to normal after the birth. Tablets are available for those who dislike the tea.

In the Western world, anaemia is very rarely severe enough to cause a woman to become ill, but if anaemia is allowed to proceed in pregnancy it may affect the iron stores of the fetus and the woman's health after her baby is born.

Blood pressure One of the major problems of pregnancy is raised blood pressure. In the past this sometimes led to the serious condition of pre-eclampsia, or toxaemia, that claimed many lives. Today this is no longer such a big problem because of regular checks at antenatal clinics, where rises in blood pressure can be detected early; but 10 per cent of mothers still suffer from them.

If in later pregnancy you have mildly raised blood pressure you will probably be advised to take extra rest in bed. Often no other treatment is necessary, but if the blood pressure rises or protein is found in the urine, you would be advised to enter hospital for tests on the unborn baby to ensure that he is well. This often is enough to carry you through for the rest of pregnancy. Should however the blood pressure rise further or the amount of urinary protein increase, doctors may think it wise to induce the birth in order to remove the baby from the hostile intrauterine environment.

Raised blood pressure can, to some extent, be prevented by taking proper rest throughout pregnancy. This is one of the valuable things you can do to help your unborn child. It means resting during the day for at least an extra hour on your bed or on a couch. In the last weeks, it is preferable to lie on your left side so helping the flow of blood to the placental bed.

Poor fetal growth With the better methods of diagnosis provided by ultrasound, doctors can now diagnose that the unborn baby is not growing as fast as he should. Probably this is due to a diminution of the blood supply to the placental bed or a defect in the transfer of nutrients across the placenta itself.

In either case, it would be wise to stay under closer observation at the antenatal clinic or even to become an in-patient in the hospital. Your doctors and midwives will want to watch the baby very carefully and try to help him grow. One way of doing this is for you to rest a lot to allow a better blood supply to the uterus and placental bed, as less then goes to the muscles of your body. If normal fetal growth is resumed, you will be allowed up to move around for the rest of pregnancy. If however growth is still retarded, your doctor will advise you on the optimal time for delivery to get the best result for your baby.

German measles The symptoms of rubella, or German measles, are a transient rash and swelling of the lymph glands at the back of the neck, accompanied by a fever. An attack in early pregnancy can bring a high risk of permanent damage to the baby's heart, eyes or ears. The risk may be avoided by immunisation against German measles before pregnancy occurs.

Rhesus problem Most humans are rhesus positive, that is, they possess a substance known as the rhesus (or Rh) factor, but a small proportion do not possess this and are known as rhesus negative.

If a rhesus negative woman conceives a baby who has inherited rhesus positive blood from his father, some of the fetal rhesus positive red cells may escape into the mother's blood, either across the placenta during pregnancy or, more usually, when the baby is born, and cause antibodies to form. This does not harm the mother and seldom harms her first baby. If however, she conceives another rhesus positive child, these antibodies may leak back into the baby's bloodstream and destroy its red cells, leading to anaemia, brain damage and in a few cases to the death of the fetus.

Tests can be done on the amniotic fluid to see if the fetus is affected and if so to what extent. The baby can be given a blood transfusion, if necessary while still in the womb, to prevent anaemia or other damage.

The mother can be treated by an injection of a blocking serum (anti-D-gammaglobulin). This prevents antibodies forming and is now given to a rhesus negative mother who has had a rhesus positive child, within a day or two of delivery. Its use has to a large extent overcome the rhesus problem.

The birth of your baby

The onset of labour, leading to the birth of your baby, will be determined by the baby himself. After months of development in the womb, hormones produced by his adrenal and pituitary glands will trigger off your labour contractions.

In the last months of pregnancy your uterine muscle has been gently limbering up, and you will have felt contractions of the womb. These are technically known as Braxton Hicks contractions, and are usually not painful, but they can be sharp enough to make you stop what you are doing. True labour contractions are more painful than the limbering-up spasms, and they occur at regular intervals.

Labour starts in one of three ways. Usually it is signalled by contractions starting in the small of the back and moving round to the front of the stomach to just above the pubic bone. When you have had several contractions at regular 20- to 30-minute intervals, you can feel sure that you are in labour and should go to the hospital or obstetrical unit where you are to have your baby.

Less often, labour can start by a show of blood or by "the breaking of the waters", the release of amniotic fluid that usually occurs at the end of the first stage of labour. In either event, it is advisable to lose no time in getting to hospital.

There is a big difference in the form of labour between a woman who is having a first baby and a mother who has had a baby before. A first-time mother may in many cases have

HOW A BABY MAKES HIS WAY ...

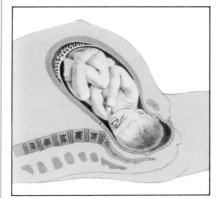

1 Towards the end of pregnancy, the baby is usually lying head down in the womb.

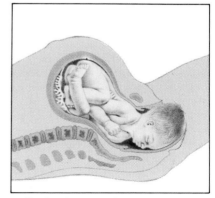

2 In the first stage of labour, which lasts many hours, the muscular walls of the womb contract.

uncomfortable contractions of the womb for several days before she feels sure that their frequency and regularity indicate that she is in labour. On the other hand, a mother who is expecting a second or subsequent baby will nearly always give birth more speedily than she did the first time. She should, therefore, go to hospital without delay as soon as the contractions occur at regular 20- to 30-minute intervals.

Labour is divided into three stages. In the first stage, the contractions stretch open the cervix, the neck of the womb, to allow the baby to pass. During the second stage, the baby is pushed from the womb and delivered out of the birth canal. The third stage involves the expulsion of the placenta, the "exchange station" through which the unborn baby obtained nourishment and discharged waste products.

The length of these stages varies. The first stage is by far the longest, lasting many hours; the second stage lasts usually about an hour and rarely more than two hours. The third stage lasts only a few minutes.

If you have not had a baby before, you will probably wonder why the muscular contractions should go on for so long. It will undoubtedly help you through labour if you understand what is going on in your body.

Care in labour

During labour, most women are advised not to eat or drink too much. Sips of water may of course be taken to relieve thirst but it is not wise to drink large amounts of fluid. The stomach does not pass food and fluid on to the intestines during labour and so everything just sits there and may lead to vomiting later on. If labour is to be long, often fluids can be given intravenously to the mother as they will then pass straight into the circulation, avoiding any blockage in the intestines.

The first stage of labour

The uterus, or womb, is a large muscular bag. When the muscles start to contract in labour, they pull on the cervix to widen it. If you are having your first baby, the cervix takes some hours to open to the width of 10 cm (4 in) necessary to allow a baby's head to pass. In many women who have had a baby before, the cervix begins to dilate in the last weeks of pregnancy. This leaves them less work to do in labour.

During labour, avoid heavy meals and keep to a light fluid diet. Sleep if you can in the early part, to conserve your energy for the hours just before your baby is born. Start the relaxation exercises that you practised in pregnancy (see p. 23). Between contractions go as limp as possible. When the contractions start, take deep breaths. If your husband or partner is going to be present at the birth, he will be able to help you to relax at this time.

...INTO THE WORLD

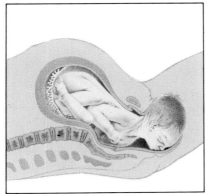

3 As contractions continue, the pressure of the baby's head slowly opens the cervix.

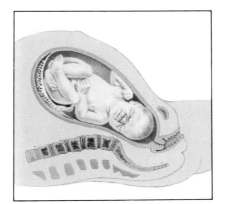

4 At the end of the first stage, the cervix is open so that the head can pass down the dilated vagina.

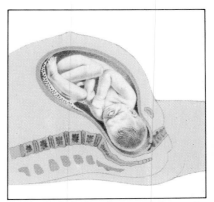

5 The baby's head passes down the vagina. The mother usually helps to push the baby outwards.

As the first stage ends, several possible sensations may make you uneasy. They are, however, perfectly normal. You may feel, for example, hot and cold shivers. You may feel that you need to open your bowels or empty your bladder, but both feelings are caused, in fact, by the pressure of your baby's head. At this time there is often a great desire to push the baby down. Avoid doing this on your own initiative. The midwife will advise you when your cervix is fully open, and when the time has come for you to push.

The second stage of labour

Most mothers find it a great relief when the doctor or midwife tells them that they can start pushing and, by doing this, take an active role in the delivery of the baby.

This is the way in which you can help:

At each contraction, take two quick breaths in, out and in again.

With the lungs full, hold the breath and push steadily down into the lower pelvis, keeping up the pressure for about 10 to 15 seconds.

With the midwife's co-operation, you can repeat the push in the same contraction by letting the breath out quickly, sucking in another deep breath and pushing again. You should be able to get three or four pushes to each contraction. Between contractions, go limp and take a rest.

When your baby is nearly ready to emerge, you may feel discomfort as the muscles at the bottom of the vagina are stretched. Let the muscles go limp, as you did in relaxation exercises during pregnancy.

Sometimes when the baby's head comes down into the lower vagina the tissues are over-stretched and liable to tear. If this seems likely to happen, the doctor or midwife will perform a small cut, known as an episiotomy, to reduce the damage

that the baby's head would do. It is done under local anaesthetic (unless an epidural has already been given) and is generally painless. Episiotomy is carried out in some parts of the world as a routine: however, in other parts of the world, including Britain, it is now not normally done unless the doctor or midwife considers it necessary to avoid tearing the perineal tissues at the bottom of the vagina. A tear in these tissues would be more difficult to repair and would heal less well than a cut.

An episiotomy is repaired in the same way as a tear and is no more painful in the healing process, but it can give rise to discomfort and sometimes pain (see p. 51 for the best ways of dealing with this). If you wish to avoid having an episiotomy, do discuss it beforehand and make sure your wishes are known.

When the midwife tells you to, push from the stomach muscles and

THE LAST STAGES OF BIRTH

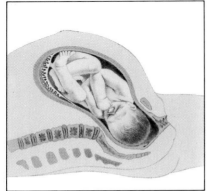

6 At the end of the second stage of labour, which usually lasts half an hour to two hours, the baby is born.

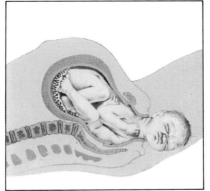

7 After the baby's head has emerged, the shoulders slip out easily. The rest of the body quickly follows.

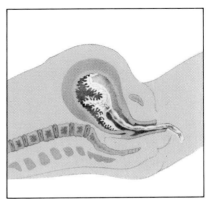

8 In the final stage of labour, the womb discharges the placenta, the umbilical cord and the membranes.

relax the pelvic floor muscles. While the baby's head is being delivered, you may be asked to stop pushing. The easiest way to do this is to pant in and out.

If your head and shoulders are raised on pillows you will experience one of the most moving moments of your life – the sight of your baby being born. After the baby's head emerges, the doctor or midwife helps the shoulders out and the rest of the body quickly follows. The umbilical cord is then cut to separate the baby from his mother. There are no nerves in the cord, and the baby therefore feels no pain.

When the baby is separated, it is essential that he should begin to breathe. Usually the light and temperature of the room and the handling he receives provide enough stimulus to start respiration. If this does not happen spontaneously, the doctor or midwife will help breathing to start.

Warmth is essential to your baby at this stage, so he will be wrapped in a blanket for you to hold in your arms for the first time.

The third stage of labour
Although your baby is born, there remains a final stage of labour in which the placenta and its membranes are expelled. In this stage you may feel mild contractions, but you will not have to work as hard as in the first two stages.

The midwife helps to expel the placenta, usually by putting one hand over the top of the womb and, with her other hand, gently pulling the umbilical cord.

This is the end of long hours of

BREECH POSITION

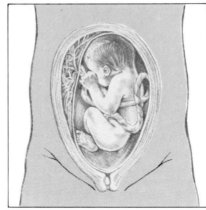

Normally, a baby lies head down in the womb, but in a few pregnancies he lies head up, and delivery will be more difficult. The baby may turn over, but if he does not do so the doctor at the clinic may try to turn him.

labour. Now you can relax, admire your baby and look back with pride on your achievement.

Pain relief in labour
Labour is a painful business and most women ask for some help, particularly to cover the contractions at the later part of the first stage of labour. It is sensible for you to consider all this before labour starts and discuss it with whoever is going to be looking after you. The pros and cons of various methods can be considered objectively and you can learn about their advantages and disadvantages in detail.

When you decide that the pain is going to be sufficient to make you want some help, ask for it but remember that from the time you request it to the time the pain relief actually

works may be 20 to 30 minutes, whichever method is used.

The most commonly used method of pain relief in Britain is injection of pethidine given by your midwife. This is a very good drug and can be used throughout the first stage of labour. Most doctors and midwives try to avoid the giving of pethidine too close to birth for it can affect the baby's breathing after birth.

In the second stage of labour, a mixture of nitrous oxide and oxygen may be inhaled. This gives excellent pain relief. It cannot be used over long periods, however, for you could over-breathe and depress your respiration.

A very common method of pain relief is an epidural anaesthetic. A local anaesthetic agent is injected into the tissues outside the spinal cord where the nerve roots emerge from it. This is done by a skilled anaesthetist who introduces a fine, soft plastic tube into the epidural space. All injections are given subsequently through this tube and so it is much more convenient for the mother. Each injection lasts for three or four hours and repeated doses can be given if labour goes on.

An epidural is probably the most effective form of pain relief; it leaves you completely conscious with an unclouded mind so that you can take part in childbirth. Further, there is a minimum effect on the fetus. However, it does require a skilled anaesthetist and so is rarely available in small obstetrical units. Occasionally it removes the sensation of pushing and so some of the satisfaction for the mother in the second stage of labour may be lost.

Monitoring

During labour the state of the baby will be watched carefully. A midwife may listen to your baby's heart at intervals through your abdominal wall to check this. In many units you will be offered a continuous check of the fetal heart by a monitor strapped on your abdomen. This should not be uncomfortable but if it is, ask the midwife to adjust it, for the belt is made of elastic and has a big buckle on it. For most women, occasional short runs of monitoring are sufficient, but for others monitoring is continuous if the obstetrician or midwife is concerned about the baby.

If monitoring shows the fetus to be coping well in labour then all proceeds normally. If, however, there are signs that the baby is beginning to stand into danger your doctors will learn of this sooner with a monitor. The early stages of such distress are not dramatic and the baby is quite safe for the moment; if he is showing signs of lack of oxygen in the earlier part of labour, it may mean the doctor has to act in order to help your baby while he is still in a good state. If you are still in early labour, this may lead to Caesarean section; in the second stage of labour, a forceps delivery may be required.

Induction of labour

Three out of four women go into labour spontaneously. With the remainder, a doctor induces labour by introducing hormones that stimulate labour contractions, or by breaking the waters that surround the baby, or by a combination of both methods. A mother's raised blood pressure or a long-overdue pregnancy are the two most common reasons for inductions.

An induced labour is usually no more painful than a spontaneous one, and it can greatly reduce the risk to a baby.

Position in labour

In the early part of labour, many women are restless and like to move around. This is not harmful for your baby so long as the membranes are intact; once they have burst, it may be wise to settle into your delivery room. Even if you do not walk around you need not lie down but can sit in a chair or sit up on your bed.

When it comes to delivery, most women prefer to be on a bed, propped up to about 45° by a rubber wedge or a lot of pillows. This allows you to see what is happening and to help your contractions by pulling up on your legs. Some women prefer to adopt other positions. A bean bag is very similar to the 45° rubber wedge; such a delivery often takes place on the floor, the bean bag adapting itself well to the curves of the body and to changes of posture.

A birth chair is available in many units and if you have been trained in its use, it is a good aid for some women having a normal delivery. Others like to squat or deliver on all fours, and these methods are performed in units that are used to them. They are probably best done on special gymnastic mats on the floor to prevent you harming yourself should you tilt sideways during delivery. Midwives used to these ways of delivering are present in most units. It is wise to discuss your posture in labour beforehand with the individuals who will be looking after you.

Assisted deliveries

You will probably have a normal delivery. On some occasions, however, problems do arise and these may need medical assistance. It is wise to know about these even though they may not happen to you.

Forceps delivery After the neck of the womb is fully dilated and the mother is in the second stage of labour, the baby might start to show signs of distress and the delivery should be accelerated. Under local anaesthesia, a pair of carefully constructed guards are placed on either side of the baby's head and linked together. These form the forceps which cradle the baby's head so that it can be eased from the vagina; delivery of the rest of the child takes place with assistance.

Forceps seem large instruments but you must remember only a very small part of them enters the body, where they are positioned on either side of the baby's head. They have been used for 300 years in the Western world and have saved millions of babies from death or spasticity.

Vacuum extraction or ventouse Some doctors speed delivery when the baby is showing signs of distress by placing a small metal hollow cap over the baby's scalp. Air is evacuated from it so that a rim of tissue is built up; this allows light traction to be applied to the head. The baby then follows the normal line down the pelvis and is delivered. There is no negative pressure inside the skull (i.e. on the brain) but only on the outside tissues.

Babies born with vacuum extraction may have a small raised ring on their head but this fades after 48 hours. This method is less formidable than a forceps delivery and is used in many units to speed delivery once the second stage of labour has arrived. Vacuum extraction can also be used at the very end of the first stage of labour, before the cervix is quite dilated, by those who are experienced in its use.

Caesarean section About one woman in nine in the United Kingdom is now delivered by Caesarean section. This may be as a planned procedure before labour even starts in order to avoid the risks of uterine contractions to the fetus, if there is disproportion between the size of the pelvic bones and that of the baby's head, or if the placenta is low-lying so that the baby would be in danger if labour were allowed. A Caesarean section is also sometimes done as an emergency once labour has started but the cervix is not yet fully dilated.

An anaesthetic is given; this may be a general anaesthetic by inhalation or an epidural anaesthetic just to numb the lower part of the body. The latter is becoming more popular with the non-emergency Caesarean sections, for the mother is awake, her partner can be there and they can both take part in the delivery, seeing and holding their baby within seconds of birth. If however there is urgency then a general anaesthetic is used for it is swifter. Babies are born through a small incision in the lower abdomen; this is done by a surgeon and the operation takes between 30 and 45 minutes. In the days after Caesarean section you may feel sore but this passes rapidly. Remember that the operation is done on a fit, young person, unlike most operations, which are done on ill people who take a considerably longer time to recover.

Pre-term labour

Whilst most women deliver their babies at around 40 weeks of pregnancy, a few start uterine contractions before this. If this happens at about 36 weeks, it is not a serious problem. These babies are born weighing about $5\frac{1}{2}$ lb and usually do as well as their heavier brothers or sisters.

Below 36 weeks, the problem becomes increasingly more complex the earlier labour starts. Generally speaking, labours before 24 weeks do not have good results and so most doctors would try to postpone labour by the use of drugs to cause the uterus to stop contracting. After this time babies are born very small, often only a pound or so in weight, and require expert delivery and neonatal care. If your obstetrician can help you gain a few weeks at this stage, it greatly improves the chances for your baby. The nearer to 28 weeks you can get, the better.

If a woman does go into pre-term labour, she should be delivered at the hospital with the best neonatal facilities available in the area. This may mean moving the mother in early labour and although this sounds hard, it is better for the baby to travel to the place where the expert neonatal unit is in her uterus, rather than in an incubator after delivery, for very small babies do not travel very well. In consequence, the mother may be surprised to be told she is going in an ambulance to a hospital which is strange to her and where she had not planned to have her baby, but this is in the interests of her child.

During a pre-term labour, the obstetricians and midwives will pay extra attention to the baby. They may recommend a Caesarean section to deliver a very small child in order that he or she will arrive in the best shape. Once the baby is delivered, the first aim is to ensure that breathing starts and is maintained. The baby may need to be in an incubator to provide warmth and a barrier from the outside world. Extra oxygen is often needed for a few days for very small children. Such babies are usually cared for in special care baby units and after the first few days usually have an excellent chance of survival.

If delivery should take place in a smaller unit where there are no expert care facilities, the baby may be moved in a special travelling incubator to the larger centre. Usually when that happens the mother goes with the child to that hospital and stays near her baby.

The very small baby usually catches up with his brothers and sisters and there is no evidence that babies born at very low birthweights are in any way disadvantaged later on in life. Remember Winston Churchill was born long before there were expert neonatologists. He was a very small baby at birth and survived to become a great leader.

2
FIRST DAYS

Settling to a routine

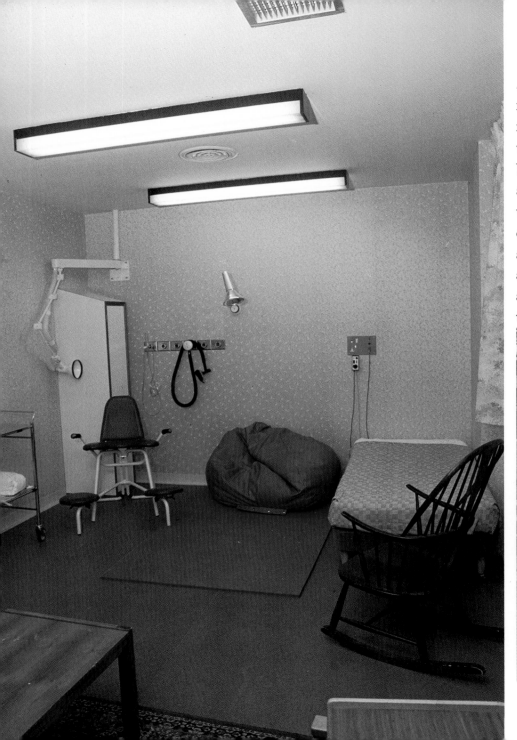

A delivery room (left) may offer a choice of methods, including a bed on which the mother can lie or be propped up at an angle; a bean-bag, which many women find more comfortable as it will accommodate them in almost any position they adopt; and a modern version of the traditional birthing stool or

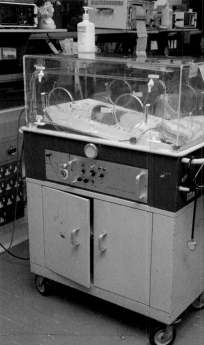

birth chair. The movement of a rocking chair can be very soothing for women in labour. An incubator (opposite, below) is on hand for babies who are born prematurely. During labour the state of the baby will be watched carefully. A midwife may listen to the baby's heartbeat at intervals through the abdominal wall,

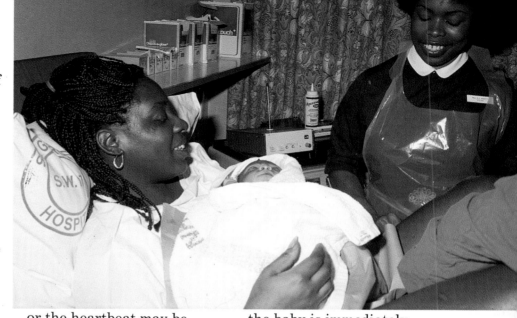

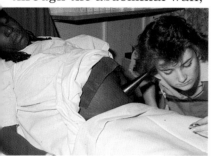

or the heartbeat may be checked by a monitor strapped to the abdomen. After the baby's head emerges, the doctor or midwife helps the shoulders out and the rest of the body follows. In some hospitals

the baby is immediately placed on his mother's stomach while delivery of the placenta is completed. He will then be weighed, washed and wrapped up warmly before being handed back to his mother.

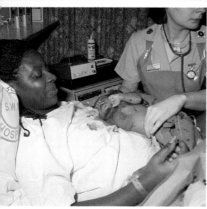

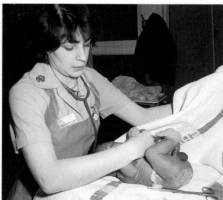

In the first two weeks of his life, a baby will put one foot in front of the other in a stepping action if you hold him upright on a firm surface. This reflex action, like the "grasp" reflex illustrated on the opposite page, is an instinctive reaction.

At birth a baby has a "grasp" reflex – an automatic, involuntary action that makes him clench his fist round an object placed in his palm. This is thought to be a relic of the primitive need of man's early ancestors to cling to the mother or to the branch of a tree for survival. It seems to disappear in about the third month. Another automatic reflex present at birth is the sucking reflex: a newborn baby placed against his mother's breasts will seek her nipple and begin to suck, and research has shown that even in the womb a baby may suck his thumb.

Bottle-feeding offers a chance for the baby's father to become involved with his child, and can be a source of great satisfaction to him. The baby's head must be kept up to reduce any risk of choking, and the bottle must be tilted to prevent air getting into the teat.

As early as his first days, a baby is capable of focusing his eyes and concentrating with great interest on what he sees. His mother is usually the first part of his world to be studied. He sees her from different angles while at her breast or being bathed and dressed.

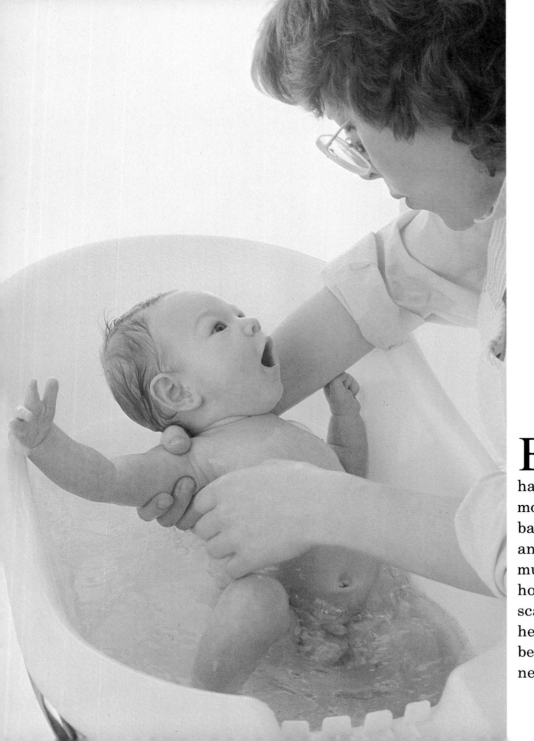

Bathtime should be a happy time for both mother and baby. Most babies will enjoy kicking and splashing. The water must be warm rather than hot, to avoid any danger of scalding the baby. His head and shoulders must be supported and he must never be left unattended.

2 | First hours with your baby

During the first few hours after birth babies are remarkably awake and alert, fixing their eyes upon your face if you hold them close and seemingly aware of every sight, sound and smell. Of course, this may not be true if a baby has been born after a difficult delivery or if he is ill or premature, but for nine out of ten babies the description is accurate.

How their mothers feel is more variable. You may be equally exhilarated and alert, but you might also be exhausted, wanting only to sleep; you might be thrilled and excited with your new baby or you might feel confusingly flat. After an anaesthetic or a lot of pain-killers you might feel light-headed and confused. However you feel, these first few hours offer a wonderful chance to get to know your baby.

In most hospitals nowadays, and in many home births, the baby is handed to you to hold, or placed on your stomach, while delivery of the placenta is completed, and you are encouraged to put the baby to the breast as soon as possible. This helps to establish breast-feeding and form a mother-baby bond. Also when the nipple is stimulated the womb contracts, thereby aiding delivery of the placenta and helping to prevent loss of blood.

There is however no need to feel cheated if for any reason you cannot, or do not wish to, put the baby to the breast straight away. There is no milk yet available so the experience is for comfort rather than nutrition. Indeed the only thing you yourself may want to do is sleep for several hours: it does not matter if the baby has no feeds during this time.

Immediately after birth the midwife removes mucus from the baby's nose and mouth, dries him and weighs him, attaches a clamp to the cord and checks quickly that all is well. In some maternity units this ritual is gone through before the baby is handed to his mother. If you want to hold your baby as soon as he is born, make sure your wishes are known beforehand. Many husbands and partners now attend deliveries. They, too, should have a chance to cuddle the baby.

Popular myth suggests that the first thing a mother asks is whether she has a boy or girl. Experience in labour wards does not bear this out. Whether or not the baby is normal and how much he weighs are generally the first questions.

Wonderful as these first few hours can be, the importance of this time should not be too much exaggerated. Many mothers cannot experience it because they or their babies are ill or have to be separated for medical treatment. Others do not feel instantly consumed with love and tenderness for their babies: this is in no way abnormal and you should not feel surprised or disturbed if it happens to you. It does not mean that you will not come to love and enjoy your baby wholeheartedly.

The first few days

In the first days after your baby is born, there may be times when you feel anxious about his feeding, crying or wakefulness. These worries can be eased if you know something about the wide range of feeding, sleeping and crying patterns that normal babies can follow, and what a parent can do to smooth out difficulties.

Babies, like adults, have great temperamental differences. Some are more easily irritated and upset than others; some are easier to soothe than others. Do not expect all babies to react in the same way.

Scientific studies have shown that differences of temperament in babies remain fairly steady over the first months – and even years – of childhood. This demonstrates how a baby's personality and individuality are marked and definite from his earliest days.

Because of these personality differences, your baby will begin to show his own style and pattern of feeding. If he regularly wakes up in the middle of the night, it is because he needs comfort or food or both.

By observing your baby's patterns of waking, crying and feeding, you can make a great difference to his happiness.

Feeding

Some babies gulp down their feed eagerly; others dawdle and fall asleep over their milk. Some scream impatiently as soon as they wake; others fit more placidly into a feeding routine.

In one study of babies, a large number were fed whenever they felt like feeding: it was found that some wanted as many as 12 feeds a day, others no more than five or six.

During the first two or three days after they are born, most babies seem fairly sleepy and do not need frequent feeds. From around the fourth to the ninth day, they may wake every two hours or so; after about the first two weeks, most babies settle into a pattern of waking every three or four hours.

However, the pattern can vary even within the same 24-hour period, especially at night time. After the first feed of the day, your baby may be content for five or six hours, but needs to be fed much more often in the late afternoon. If your baby does not seem to be conforming to a routine of feeding every three or four hours during the first weeks, this is perfectly normal. There are many babies like him.

If you are breast-feeding, it is essential to be very flexible about feeding times in the first two or three weeks, and to feed your baby as often as he wants to be fed. This is often described as "demand feeding", but the term is an unfortunate one, as some mothers then fear quite needlessly that they will be unable to meet all their babies' "demands".

Bottle-fed babies can also be demand fed. Most hospitals have ready-mixed feeds to hand out and the midwives will advise on the amount to be offered.

After this early period, your baby will probably settle quite quickly into feeding every four hours or so.

Sleeping

From birth onwards, babies also vary greatly in their sleeping habits – how often they wake, and how long they stay awake each time. Because of this variation, it is not very helpful to suggest an "average" figure for sleeping and waking times.

If your baby seems wakeful, becomes restless and perhaps cries only two hours or so after being fed, do not automatically assume that there is something wrong with the way you are feeding and caring for him. Some babies sleep for much shorter spells than others during the first year. Many of these "short-sleepers" may continue to need little sleep all through early childhood.

If you are breast-feeding, and your baby wakes often, do not assume that this is necessarily because he is hungry. Many babies thrive on a series of short sleeps, and as long as your child is steadily gaining weight, he is being adequately fed.

Babies also vary in the *way* they doze off and wake up: some always cry for a few minutes before going to sleep, while others slip off to sleep easily, especially if they are allowed to do so in their mothers' arms.

Crying

Perhaps the greatest worry to new parents is hearing a baby crying often and – apparently – inconsolably. This can be deeply upsetting, especially when you know that your child has been fed, has had his nappy changed and is not obviously cold or ill. But it does help a bit to realise that all babies are different and some simply do cry more than others.

You can try carrying the baby about with you: if you carry him in a sling it will leave both your hands free to get on with other jobs. You can also try the age-old method of swaddling, or wrapping him securely in a small shawl or blanket. This sometimes helps the baby to go off to sleep, and to stay asleep longer.

Be prepared, also, for babies to change their habits: a baby that has contentedly napped for much of the time may, after the first few weeks, become more wakeful, and when you put him down, hoping for an hour or two of peace, he may begin to scream from sheer boredom.

As the weeks go by, most babies – even the least predictable – become easier to cope with, and to fit into a routine. Many problems which loomed large at first become less important. Your baby will probably digest his food better, and cry less after meals.

Apart from the lessening of your difficulties with time, there will be positive benefits to the baby: his power of attention and interest in the world about him will increase, and he will amuse himself more and more. Most important, he will become increasingly able to communicate with his parents, for instance by giving them meaning looks and happy smiles.

Possible problems

Many women suffer some degree of discomfort or pain after an episiotomy (see p. 37). You will probably have been told that it is routine procedure and nothing at all to worry about, so that it may come as an unpleasant surprise to find that it does hurt after all. The degree of discomfort depends partly on how skilfully the repair was carried out and partly on how long and hard you pushed and therefore how swollen the tissues had become. The stitches may feel very tight, so that sitting down to feed your baby may be unexpectedly painful. Try sitting on a rubber ring or on cushions, or feed your baby lying down.

The best treatment is to soak in a salt bath for as long as possible. In between, keep the stitches dry and, if you can, exposed to air. Pain relievers are sometimes necessary and your midwife may advise mild laxatives since passing a hard motion may be very painful – bran with your food helps greatly. She will also remove your stitches if necessary as they do not always dissolve as expected, prolonging the discomfort, which, however, normally passes in a couple of weeks.

If you are not breast-feeding your milk should dry up over about three or four days but it may take longer. Your breasts may be very engorged and painful for some of this time. Wear a good firm bra to give them support all the time, day and night, and take pain-killers if necessary. Other measures include hormone injections, and cutting down on fluids.

Post-natal depression

Sometimes known as the "three-day blues", a feeling of depression often occurs around the third day after the birth (although it may well not start until the fourth or even fifth day). It is caused by the sudden hormonal and physical changes after childbirth. You may feel weepy and irritable and full of unfounded fears and worries about your new baby. However you should not worry about the feeling of depression itself: it is unfortunately not uncommon and can persist after you return home, particularly if you become very tired by the baby's sleeping and feeding habits. It usually soon passes, and true depression in the weeks and months after delivery happens to only about 5 per cent of women. If after two weeks you still feel weepy and unable to cope, you should seek help. Apart from medical advice, the support of a self-help group can be invaluable (see p. 138–148 for addresses), as often it helps enormously simply to be able to talk to someone sympathetic.

Resuming intercourse

A combination of vaginal discomfort (if you have suffered bruising and if you have been unskilfully stitched up), sheer exhaustion and your natural preoccupation with the baby may make you feel less than enthusiastic about sex. It is common to feel so wrapped up in the baby that you resent anyone else making what you see as demands. It may take several weeks, even months, before your interest returns. Some women find that having had an anaesthetic, particularly an epidural, also seems to have a depressing effect on their sex drive. There is no need to worry about it, but if you feel your lack of interest is continuing for rather too long or if intercourse is painful, you should seek medical advice.

Breast-fed babies

Breast-feeding is being increasingly encouraged as its advantages are becoming better known. Some of these have, of course, been known for a long time. For example, there is the obvious pleasure it can give to mother and baby, also the fact that it does away with the cost and fuss of the powdered milk and the equipment needed for bottle-feeding.

Benefits of breast-feeding

In addition, however, much more is now understood about the way in which the composition of breast milk is precisely suited to the human baby. It contains a highly complex range of substances which give defence against infection. It also has a slightly acid property, and a particular content of sugars which help the growth of harmless bacteria in the baby's intestines; these in turn discourage harmful germs which produce diarrhoea. Gastro-enteritis is rare in breast-fed babies.

Obviously it is not easy for human milk to be contaminated, while with bottle milk a mother must pay constant attention to sterilisation. Other advantages of breast-feeding are that the milk supply automatically adjusts to the baby's needs, it is never made up in the wrong strength, it is always ready, and it may reduce the risk of allergic disorders, such as eczema and asthma, in childhood, as well as protecting against infection. Also, breast-fed babies are rarely obese.

Although the mother has to eat more herself during breast-feeding, it is still cheaper than bottle-feeding. Furthermore, and very important, breast-feeding encourages the bond between a mother and her new baby.

Nutrients in breast-milk

Some mothers breast-feeding for the first time feel anxious or inadequate, or are worried that their milk looks thin. Such worries are groundless. A mother's milk contains all the nutrients necessary for normal growth of the infant until about six months old, provided that enough milk is being produced – and most mothers can manage that. There is really no need for supplementary vitamins, so long as the mother eats a good diet. The vitamin most likely to run low in breast milk is Vitamin C, so a nursing mother should be sure to take plenty of foods that contain it, such as fresh fruit and vegetables. If any supplement is to be recommended it is fluoride, which is available from chemists in a form suitable for babies, and protects teeth from decay in later life.

How to breast-feed

The main stimulus to milk production is suckling, so the sooner the baby is put to your breast, the better. Try putting the baby to the breast the first time you hold him, and then at least every four hours after that.

It is important to get yourself and your baby into the right positions. Make yourself comfortable and support his head with one arm. Make sure his nose is not obstructed. Hold the breast so that the nipple stands out and touch his cheek with it, near his mouth. He will usually respond by turning towards the nipple and taking it into his mouth. Do not squeeze his cheeks to open his mouth; this will usually upset him. If your baby seems unwilling to take the nipple, he may simply not be awake enough. Wait a little while before trying again.

Once your baby has taken the nipple, make sure it is directed towards the roof of his mouth, and that he takes in as much as possible of the dark areola around the nipple. The nurse or midwife will show you how to do this. The first few sucks are very tentative, but he will soon settle down to strong, regular sucking.

There is only a very little amount of milk until about the third day. During this time your breasts give "early milk" (colostrum). Although there is little of it, what there is is very valuable to the baby, being rich in proteins and antibodies which will increase the baby's immunity to disease and help fight off infection in infancy. Frequent suckling for up to five minutes helps your baby get used to the breast. On the third or fourth day the full milk comes in.

Unless there is a medical reason to the contrary, such as the baby having inadequate stores of his own (such babies are called "small-for-dates"), there is no need for any feeds of milk or dextrose while waiting for your milk to come in. By the third day you can feed on demand, sitting up in a chair or lying in bed with the baby beside you.

Babies, like adults, vary widely in the amount of food they need, but your milk supply will automatically adjust itself to suit your baby's needs. Once breast-feeding is established, you will be providing 500 to 600 calories' worth of milk, or about 0.75 litre (1½ pints), every day, and even more as the baby grows.

Possible problems

The most common problem is impatience. Some babies take four or five days before they feed properly. They will come to no harm from this temporary starvation and patience will usually correct the situation. Some mothers develop engorged and painful breasts if the baby's hunger and their own hormones do not synchronise exactly. The solution is to continue frequent small feeds, use a breast pump to relieve congestion, and take mild pain-relieving drugs if necessary.

If a baby pulls for a long time on a nipple it may become cracked and sore. Expressing the milk by pump and treating the nipple with antiseptic cream or spray will generally allow healing to take place.

Most babies lose a little weight during the first week of life: this is caused not by lack of food, but by normal loss of water from the body, in urine. Do not worry if your baby does not seem to be getting much milk at first. The flow will soon be under way, and the first week should become a matter of matching your supply with his needs.

However tired you may feel, as you begin to take up the household chores again, your baby should always be able to stimulate your breasts to produce the right amount of milk.

CARING FOR YOUR BREASTS

Breast-feeding usually improves the figure: it stimulates the contraction of tissues which have changed during your pregnancy. It is important, however, to make sure that while the breasts are heavier than usual (this of course happens whether you plan to breast-feed or not) they are properly supported, and never allowed to drag down.

To keep your breasts in good condition while breast-feeding, you must sit properly. Choose a comfortable low seat which supports your back. If your baby cannot reach the nipple, *do not* stoop forward: put a pillow on your lap to raise him to the correct height, without having to round your shoulders.

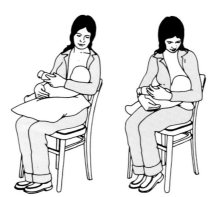

FEEDING *The correct posture (left) is to bring the baby up to your breast. The wrong way (right) is to stoop.*

Because there are no muscles in the breasts themselves, it is often thought that their shape cannot be helped or improved by any form of exercise. This is not so: the proper exercise can help a good deal to keep

your breasts in firm shape.

This is because the breasts are very firmly attached to the chest muscles (feel them in front of your armpits), and when those muscles contract, the breasts are drawn up with them. The connecting fibres can be shortened, with beneficial results to the shape and firmness of your figure, if you do the Top Lift exercise when your baby is weaned.

The Top Lift can also be used while you are breast-feeding, but if the breasts are temporarily overfull, while supply is adjusting to demand, put off the exercise.

TOP LIFT EXERCISE

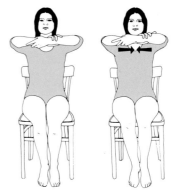

Sit or stand and raise both arms to shoulder level. Cross them, so that the right hand clasps the left forearm. With successive jerks, push across your chest, so that the skin on both arms is pressed towards the elbows. Keep up this exercise until at least six weeks after your baby is born – and even longer, unless your figure is in as good a condition as you feel you can possibly achieve.

In the early days, especially, one or both breasts may leak milk, particularly around the time when a feed is due. This does not mean that there is anything wrong, and the problem should lessen as your milk supply adjusts to your baby's requirements.

However, even after that, some leakage may continue. This inconvenience may be reduced by wearing nursing breast pads inside your nursing bra. (Bras for pregnancy and afterwards, p. 28.) To keep your nipples healthy, do not leave wet padding inside your bra for long.

When your breasts begin to make milk, they will become suddenly larger, and feel tender; before long, they will become smaller again, even though you will be producing much more milk for a growing baby. It is important that your breasts do not become too congested: any extreme swelling or tenderness should be reported to your doctor or midwife. Any acute pain, tender spot or bleeding from the nipple should also be mentioned.

If the dark area around the nipple (areola) is too swollen for your baby to grasp the nipple easily, remove a little milk from the breast by expressing it – lightly massaging the breast with both hands, working inwards to the nipple. Do not try to squeeze out the milk: the massage will stimulate it to move towards the nipple ducts. Next, squeeze the base of the nipple several times between your finger and thumb, gently but steadily and firmly, until the milk starts to flow. It should not hurt at all.

This should make your breast less swollen and allow your baby to take the nipple in his mouth.

Feeding by bottle

A baby who is not being breast-fed will need one of the specially prepared milk mixtures, which have been made as much like human milk as possible.

Never give ordinary cow's milk to a baby under nine months old. Cow's milk has more protein, less sugar, different fats and more salts, particularly sodium, calcium and phosphorus. It puts a strain on a new baby, whose body cannot cope with the large amounts of protein and salts in cow's milk.

Most present infant-milk products consist of cow's milk altered to some extent – usually by reducing the protein, sodium and phosphate, increasing the sugar and adding iron and vitamin D. These preparations have greatly reduced the incidence of two ailments which used to be prevalent when babies were fed on cow's milk: convulsions caused by low blood calcium and a kind of dehydration linked with a high level of salt in the blood.

You may find that your baby is allergic to cow's milk. Goat's milk can be given instead, or a special soya milk formula, but you should check with your doctor or midwife to see what they recommend. You can also give expressed breast milk.

Before you begin bottle-feeding your baby, you will need to decide whether you are going to prepare each feed as it becomes due, or make a whole day's batch at once, and keep it in the refrigerator until it is needed. If you decide to prepare all the feeds at once, you will need half-a-dozen bottles and teats, at least. Even if you prepare one at a time, it is wise to have a spare bottle and teat, because the first bottle (if it is glass) might break and a rubber teat can perish.

There are different kinds and shapes of bottle: which one you choose will not matter to your baby. You may, for example, prefer one kind of bottle for the ordinary feed, a smaller size for fruit juice or water, and a special type for travel. The travelling bottle is wide-necked, and has a teat which can be pushed down into the neck and covered with a cap to keep it clean and airtight. It is also convenient for storage.

Modern bottles, usually made of boilable polycarbonate plastic, are light and unbreakable. Make sure that the bottles you buy are completely clear, so that you can check that they are really clean and see how much milk they contain.

In choosing a teat, pay attention to the size of the hole. When you turn the bottle upside down, the hole should be big enough to let the milk out in a series of quick drips, but not in a steady stream.

A hole that is too big will allow an excessive flow of milk which could choke the baby, or make him sick. If it is too small, he may swallow as much air as milk. After being used for a time, the hole may gradually grow bigger; before each feed, check that the milk is still coming out in a succession of rapid drops, rather than in a constant stream.

Teats are sold with holes graded small, medium and large. If you find that the size you have chosen is not quite big enough for your baby's needs – or if it gets blocked and you have not got another one sterile – you can easily enlarge or clear the hole. Take a needle and push the eye end into a cork. Make the other end red hot. Then gently push the teat-hole onto the needle-point. Do not do this quickly, or you may make the hole too big.

There are two possible health risks in bottle-feeding. Both can be avoided by following simple rules.

Sterilising

The first risk is infection; everything connected with feeding the baby must be kept scrupulously clean. This can be achieved by washing all empty bottles and teats and then putting them in a solution of liquid steriliser. Tablets for making steriliser solution are also available, and can be more convenient. Make a fresh batch of solution every day.

The milk itself must also of course be kept clean and sterile. Always put the lid back on the tin of milk as soon as you have used it, and make sure that the milk-scoop is absolutely clean.

After each feed, rinse the milk residue from the bottle and teat. To rinse the teat, turn it inside out with a spoon-handle. When convenient, scrub the bottle out with a special bottle-brush (kept only for that purpose), using hot water and detergent. Clean the teat thoroughly with the brush, under running water; a little salt on the brush, as an abrasive, will help to remove milk and grease,

which can harbour bacteria.

When bottles and teats have been thoroughly cleaned, immerse them in the sterilising solution. They must be completely submerged. Remember also to put in the measuring jug and any other utensils used, after washing them. Do not put metal articles in the sterilising solution, and use a plastic, not a metal, container.

Make sure that no air bubbles are trapped in the liquid, because they interfere with the sterilising process. The bottles are most likely to trap air bubbles; it will be easier to prevent this happening if you make sure that the bottles are standing upright in the sterilising solution.

Put the lid on the container to keep out dust and dirt, and to maintain the strength of the sterilising solution. Leave for 30 minutes to one hour, to ensure full sterilisation. Next time you use the bottles and other items, there is no need to rinse first: just shake off any excess liquid.

After 24 hours, the old mixture can be used for soaking nappies in.

If you are in a hurry, you can sterilise bottle and teat by simply boiling them in water for ten minutes.

Mixing the feed correctly

The second risk in bottle-feeding is that the feed may not be made up correctly. If the mixture is too weak, the baby will be under-nourished. If it is too strong, it could make him overweight – and, even more important, introduce some of the undesirable qualities of ordinary cow's milk, such as high salt level.

This can be potentially harmful in circumstances when the baby's body

is already losing more water than usual – for example, if the weather is hot, or if the baby has diarrhoea or fever. In any of these conditions, the blood tends to become more concentrated; a feed which is too strong will add to the difficulty and may lead to dehydration.

Feeds may become too strong for several reasons. The obvious one is the use of too many scoops of powder. But a too-strong mixture can also be caused by "heaping" and "packing" scoops, as well as simply by using the wrong scoop. Always use the scoop supplied with the milk, follow exactly the directions for the number of scoops to be used, and level off each scoop with a mixing stick.

Bottle-feeding parents can see how much milk the baby is getting, where a breast-feeding mother can only guess. This is not necessarily an advantage; one of the biggest causes of misunderstanding in child care is about the question of just what

MIXING THE FEED

When making a bottle-feed, use only the correct number of scoops, and level off with a mixing stick.

quantity of food a baby should have.

Every baby needs a different amount of food. The best guide to what your own baby needs is what he is happy to take. If he finishes one bottle and wants more, let him have more – and next time, be prepared for his appetite by making up extra. If he stops feeding, and there is still milk in the bottle, do not worry: he knows when he has had enough.

Most mothers will feel they should give their babies warm milk, as from the breast. But cold milk does no harm, and most babies will take it, although some brought up on warm feeds may refuse. It is obviously convenient to give cold milk in the night, or while travelling: certainly there is no need to worry about getting the milk to the "right" temperature, as long as it is not too hot.

When you are bottle-feeding your baby, never leave him propped up with the bottle, to feed by himself. Not only is there the risk of choking, but also he will be deprived of the comfort of being held and cuddled, as he would be if he was breast-fed. Hold him as if he were going to feed at your breast, but a little lower down, so that you can hold the bottle to his mouth in comfort. The baby's head should be kept up to reduce any risk that he will choke. The bottle should be kept tilted, so that the teat is always filled with milk and not air.

One advantage of bottle-feeding is that the baby's father can take over some of it, and often derives great satisfaction from doing so.

If your baby suddenly goes off his bottle-feed, do not try a different brand – consult a doctor, because this may be a warning of some ailment.

Bathing your baby

Whether or not your baby has very sensitive skin, it is not necessary to bath him every day. Indeed, too much bathing can do more harm than good to a baby's skin. In between bath days you need only "top and tail" a baby using cotton wool and warm water to clean him.

Topping and tailing

The "top and tail" routine is also followed for washing your baby prior to putting him in the bath. Undress him and wrap him firmly in a towel. Using cotton wool dipped in warm water and squeezed out until it is just moist, carefully clean your baby's face (cheeks, forehead and chin). Using a separate piece of moist cotton wool for each eye, to avoid spreading any infection, very gently wipe over the eyes. With another fresh piece of moist cotton wool wipe over and behind the ears, being careful never to poke inside them. (Never use cotton buds on sticks for eyes, ears or nose.) In some countries oil is considered better than water for cleaning a baby's skin. Ordinary baby oil can be used. Almond oil is wonderfully soothing to irritated skin, but is very expensive.

Cradling the baby under one arm and supporting the back of his head with your hand, wash the hair and scalp gently, using a circular movement. If you want to use a baby shampoo, or have to use a special cradle-cap baby shampoo, rinse thoroughly afterwards with clean water. Dry the hair by stroking gently with a towel, but avoid covering your baby's face with the towel as this might frighten him.

Next, clean the baby's bottom from front to back, again using cotton wool and warm water or oil.

Now your baby can go into the bath water (remember to check the temperature before putting him in. Never run hot water into a bath while the baby is in it). Support him firmly by cradling him in the crook of your arm. With baby bathcare liquid already in the water, all you need do is wash his hands, feet, underarms and body with your hand. Then let him kick about and enjoy the sensation of the water, knowing that he is securely and safely supported by your arm.

Lift him out, using both hands, and wrap him in a large warm bath sheet. Carefully pat him dry, paying attention to the folds of skin around his neck, armpits and legs which can easily become sore if not dried thoroughly.

Baby powder, often associated with being part of a baby's special "smell" is unnecessary. It can make skin sore, especially in the nappy area, and is easily inhaled by a small baby. It is better not to use it at all.

Use a good simple barrier cream such as petroleum jelly to protect the baby's bottom from nappy rash.

Bath your baby at a time when you can both enjoy the experience uninterrupted and at leisure. For this reason, early evening may not be the best time if you have to prepare a meal for the rest of your family. Try to choose a time in between feeds. A hungry baby will object to having a bath when he really wants to eat, and a baby that has just been fed may regurgitate some of his feed while he is being bathed.

To ensure that you both enjoy bath time, preparation is the key. As long as you have to hand all the items you will need during and after bathing, you can both relax and enjoy bath-time as a recreation rather than a necessary chore.

There are two vital rules to remember when bathing your baby. Never

WHAT YOU WILL NEED

- A warm room
- Bath (rigid plastic or folding)
- Bath stand (for rigid bath)
- Chair
- Baby bathcare liquid/soap/emollient
- Rubber slip mat
- Cotton wool balls
- Large towel
- Shampoo (if used)
- Barrier cream
- Clean nappy
- Clean clothes

1. Test the water temperature with your elbow. It should feel just warm.

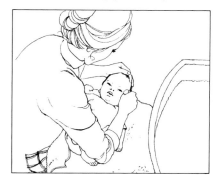

2. Use cotton wool and water only to wash the baby's face.

3. Wash his hair with a little soap or special shampoo.

4. Clean the baby's bottom, hands and feet, and under his arms.

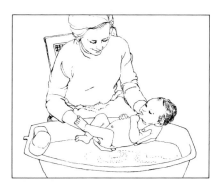

5. Lower him into the bath, with his head supported on your arm.

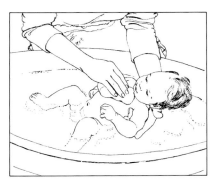

6. Keeping his head supported, wash his body gently.

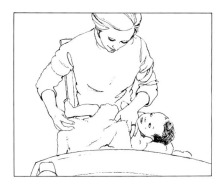

7. Put him on a towel on your lap and dry him thoroughly.

leave a baby unattended in the bath, even for a second (if the telephone or doorbell rings, ignore it). And never put a baby into the water without testing the temperature with your elbow first (it should feel warm to the submerged elbow, never hot). A baby has very delicate skin and can be scalded by water that feels the right temperature to the adult hand.

Bathing a baby need not be a complicated operation involving special equipment. If you have not got a rigid plastic or a folding baby bath, a small baby can be bathed in a clean hand basin, sink or washing-up bowl. But if you do use a sink or basin remember to cover the taps with a towel so that the baby cannot get scalded by touching the hot tap. Also, make sure that whichever room you are using has been well warmed before you start or your baby will quickly lose body heat and get chilled. (Never, though, have an electric heater switched on near water.)

Bathing a baby has been greatly simplified by the arrival of baby bathcare liquids which have done away with the need for separate baby soap and baby shampoo, as these bath care liquids can be used for both body and hair.

However, not all babies, and especially not young babies or those prone to eczema, can tolerate baby bathcare liquids or baby soap on their skins. Should this be the case, special emollient liquid or emulsifying ointment for the bath, which will not irritate the baby's skin or interfere with his natural protective skin oils, is available either from the chemist or on prescription.

Changing nappies

After bathing and drying your baby, put on his nappy (see p. 31 for different types of nappy). Small babies can easily get upset if they miss the feeling of security and warmth that

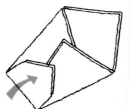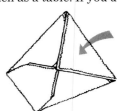

THE KITE *1. Take a corner and fold it to the middle, unevenly – from about halfway along one side and three-*

2. Lay the baby on the wide end of the nappy with the fold crossing his back, at the level of his waistline.

4. Bring the other side corner over the stomach, tuck it under the rest of the nappy, and pin together.

clothing next to their skin gives them.

You will change your baby's nappies a number of times a day, but there is no need to give him a wash with soap every time. If he is dirty, clean him with a swab of cotton wool moistened in warm water: a baby's skin can be made sore by excessive washing with soap and water.

You can put on your baby's nappy by placing him on your lap or on a flat surface such as a table. If you do

quarters along the other. Do the same to the opposite corner. Fold the narrow end up, and the wide end down to meet it.

3. Bring a side corner over to his stomach. Bring the bottom flap up between his legs and pin to the corner.

5. See that the fitted nappy is tight enough not to slip about, without being too tight for comfort.

it on your lap, use an apron of towelling or plastic. Cover a table top with a towel or changing mat to stop your baby from slipping or rolling. You can change a baby's nappy in his pram or cot, provided that the bedding is protected and you can get at the baby easily.

Putting on a towelling nappy
Three main ways of folding a nappy are known as the KITE, the RECTANGLE and the TRIANGLE. The method you choose depends largely upon your baby's size, for the nappy must not bunch so much between the legs that it keeps them widely apart. Nor should the nappy fit too tightly – just tightly enough to keep it comfortably in position. Always slip your fingers between the baby and the nappy for protection before fixing a nappy-pin.

However often you change a nappy, it is still possible for your baby to get nappy rash. You can try to avoid it by making sure the nappies are thoroughly rinsed (and preferably washed in mild soap flakes); by using water only, not soap, to clean the baby; and by not using talcum powder but drying very carefully with a soft towel. Don't use plastic pants, and leave the baby out of nappies whenever possible.

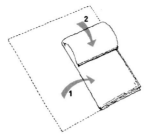

THE RECTANGLE *1. Fold the nappy in two to form an oblong. Then fold over the upper third of the oblong.*

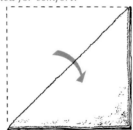

3. Bring the thinner length of nappy up between the legs. Make sure it is not too bunched for comfort.

THE TRIANGLE *1. Fold the nappy, corner to corner, to make a triangle shape of double thickness.*

3. Fold the side corners of the triangle inwards, so that they overlap neatly across the baby's stomach.

2. Lay the baby on the nappy, with the double-folded part as the top edge, about level with the waistline.

4. Spread the thinner part over the stomach, slip a hand beneath the nappy and fix each side with a safety-pin.

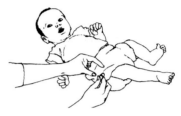

2. Lay the baby on the nappy, with legs towards the point of the triangle and the longest edge under his waist.

4. Bring the bottom corner up between the legs, so that it meets the other two overlapping corners.

5. Fix all three corners to each other with one safety-pin. Be careful not to prick the baby with the pin.

Returning to normal

After the months of pregnancy and hours of hard work in labour, your body will naturally need time to recover. Muscles must return to their previous condition while you adapt to the feeding of your baby and gradually return to normal, everyday activities.

In former days, the first stage of this return to normal was spent entirely in bed, but this is unnecessary. Many women today get up the day the baby is born. However, extra rest is required at this time, so that your body can recover.

If your baby was born in hospital, you are likely to stay in hospital for anything from two days to a week, but the exact time can vary depending on circumstances.

How you recover

In the first few days, the main return to normal is happening in your womb and other pelvic organs. To accommodate the growing baby, the womb will have been stretched to about ten times its normal length, and its muscle fibres also to about ten times their usual length.

This may sound a tremendous expansion, but in the first days after your baby is born, the womb contracts very quickly, at the same time expelling a certain amount of blood, with some clots. Although it does not return to precisely its former size, within two weeks the womb goes back to being just a pelvic organ, instead of filling the whole abdomen.

In the first six weeks, the muscles of the vagina and pelvic floor, also stretched by childbirth, recover, although they may not return to the condition they were in before pregnancy. However, post-natal exercise can help a great deal in reconditioning these muscles (see pp. 80–82).

For a few weeks after your baby is born, you will experience a vaginal discharge, bright red at first, but later becoming brown, and finally yellow. This discharge is normal: your body is merely getting rid of blood which has been in the cavity of the womb since the baby's birth. However, if the discharge increases, smells offensive or changes back from brown or yellow to bright red, you should tell your doctor.

As your womb contracts, in the first week or so, you may feel sharp pains resembling menstruation pains, especially when your baby is put to the breast. You can safely relieve these pains by taking an analgesic prescribed by your doctor. The pains are a normal part of the contraction of the womb, and usually stop about a week or ten days after the baby is born.

Some mothers have difficulty in passing urine at this time. The baby, travelling through the pelvis, may have caused a swelling of bladder tissues. It is sometimes necessary to relieve this trouble with a fine tube called a catheter, but it usually passes away on its own accord.

For personal hygiene, which is very important, you can take a salt-water bath, which is comforting as well as cleansing. Fill the bath with warm water to a depth of 15–20 cm (6–8 in), and add a fistful of ordinary kitchen salt. The vulva should be kept covered for a week or two with sterile sanitary pads, which the midwife will want to inspect before they are thrown away.

You must take care not to overstrain your back. During pregnancy, it will have been subjected to stress, and minor problems caused in the first few weeks after childbirth can stay with you. When bending over to attend to your baby or pick anything up from the floor, bend knees and hips – not your back. If you have backache immediately after childbirth, it should not last more than a few days; if it does, tell your doctor.

A mother's diet

After your baby has been delivered, it is unlikely that your thoughts will turn immediately to food, but you will probably feel thirsty. Labour is hard work, and you will have lost a considerable amount of fluid in various forms, so that first drink will be welcome. In the next few days, you will probably want to drink a lot.

At this time, your body is undergoing enormous hormonal changes, in adjusting to *not* being pregnant and in starting to produce breast milk. A diet of high nutritional value is therefore essential.

Appetites vary, but if you carry on with the principles of a balanced diet which you followed while you were pregnant (see p. 20), you will be getting an adequate, balanced diet. Some loss of blood is inevitable during and after your baby's birth, and to help to make up for this loss it is important to have plenty of foods that contain iron, folic acid and Vitamin B_{12}, such as meat (particularly liver) and leafy vegetables such as cabbage and spinach.

If you breast-feed

To supply the amount of milk needed for breast-feeding (see p. 52), you need to have extra food and fluid. Some of your extra needs will be met by the stores of fat laid down during pregnancy, and most women find that their appetite increases anyway. The best guide to how much extra to eat is to become aware of your appetite: eat sensibly (see Choosing the Right Diet, p. 20) and stick to plain food. Increased thirst will also help to ensure that the extra fluid which is lost in your milk is replaced. Do not drink excessive amounts of water: it will simply make more urine, not more milk. Drink only enough to satisfy your natural thirst.

Since cow's milk is a good source of calcium and phosphorus salts, which your baby will need from you, it is reasonable for you to drink some milk every day. However, if you do not like milk as a drink, do not worry: the same salts are present in many other kinds of food.

The quality of breast milk is less affected than its quantity by what a mother eats and drinks. Only when a mother has been living near starvation level before the birth of her baby will variations in diet make much difference to her milk. Some people believe that if a mother has a certain type of food – for example, curry – it may alter her milk and make the baby unwell. In fact, it is most unusual for anything a mother eats to upset her baby in this way. Just occasionally, some particular

A DIET FOR REDUCING WEIGHT

For each day's diet, choose one breakfast, one lunch and one dinner from the list of suggestions. You are also allowed:
- 300 ml (½ pint) milk or 500 ml (scant pint) skimmed milk
- 15 g (½ oz) butter or margarine or 25 g (1 oz) low-fat spread
- 2 slices bread or 4 slices slimmer's bread
- 1 apple and 1 orange (or other fruit e.g. peach, pear, melon, but not banana)

BREAKFAST
(Each breakfast may also include a half grapefruit or other fresh fruit, or 1 carton low-fat, unsweetened fruit yoghurt)

2 eggs, boiled, poached or scrambled;
or
2 rashers lean bacon, grilled, with mushrooms;
or
25 g (1 oz) unsugared breakfast cereal or porridge with 150 ml (¼ pint) milk (extra to daily allowance);
or
Baked beans, bread or toast with minimum spread, and tomatoes if liked

LUNCH
170 g (6 oz) fish, grilled, 4 tablespoons peas, 1 grilled tomato;
or
Home-made vegetable soup (e.g. leek, celery, cauliflower), large mixed salad, 2 teaspoons salad dressing;
or
Cheese omelette (2 eggs, 1 tablespoon grated cheese), green beans or corn on the cob;
or
100 g (4 oz) liver or liver pâté on 2 crispbreads or 1 slice of toast, salad as above, 2 teaspoons salad dressing;
or
2 slices lean meat or 1 sliced hard-boiled egg in sandwiches (using bread allowance), 1 tablespoon coleslaw

DINNER
1 chicken joint in casserole with mixed vegetables and 100 g (4 oz) boiled rice or potatoes;
or
100 g (4 oz) pasta with tomato sauce, medium-sized grilled chop or steak, spinach or broccoli;
or
100 g (4 oz) lean roast meat, 1 roast potato, vegetables and gravy;
or
225 g (8 oz) shepherd's pie, cabbage (or sprouts) and carrots;
or
170 g (6 oz) fish, grilled or steamed, with 2 tablespoons cheese sauce, cauliflower or courgettes

TIPS TO HELP YOU TO SLIM SENSIBLY
- Drink as much liquid as you like, as long as you do not use more than your daily allowance of milk. Try to take your drinks unsweetened; avoid alcohol and large amounts of strong coffee or tea.
- Give yourself generous helpings of vegetables, if no amount is specified.
- Do not have more than the suggested amount of any food.
- Do not try to eat less than the recommended diet, which has been designed to make sure that you get adequate food value while you slim.

food may seem to react badly on the baby. If this happens often, it is best to avoid that food. Tea or coffee in small amounts will not however affect your baby while you are breast-feeding.

Slimming sensibly

Once you have your baby, you will want to regain your figure as quickly as possible. But if you are breast-feeding, do not attempt any sort of slimming diet; this will result in half-starving your baby. In any case, all women lose weight while they are breast-feeding.

Even if you are not breast-feeding, you cannot afford to neglect your diet. Coping with a new baby is tiring, physically and emotionally, and your body is still getting over the strains of pregnancy and labour. If, however, you are still overweight a month or two after your baby is born, it is sensible to try to get back to normal weight.

To lose weight safely and sensibly, follow a diet such as the one recommended on page 61. You may lose 1.35–2.75 kg (3–6 lb) in the first week, 0.5–1 kg (1–2 lb) a week after that. A mother who is heavily overweight will lose more quickly than one with only a little excess weight. More physical activity can also speed up the weight loss. Even an ordinary activity like walking can help.

However eager you may be to slim, do not keep weighing yourself every day. Normal ups and downs can mask the real weight-loss you have achieved, and this can be rather discouraging. It is enough to check your progress once a week.

Caring for the needs of twins

Going home with twins presents more problems than going home with just one baby. There is more work for the mother who, during the first few weeks, will have little time or energy for anything except looking after the babies' needs. It is essential that you should have some sort of help in the home. If there is nobody in the family who can lend a hand, try to arrange some assistance before you take your babies home.

Once you have your twins home, try not to worry too much just because they are twins. Be as relaxed as possible: if you are coping with two babies at once, and have to turn a deaf ear to the cries of one of them for a few moments while you attend to the other, it will do no harm.

Twins need not cause unreasonable expense. If you do have any money to spare, it may be wise to spend it on help in the home or on a nappy laundry service. A washing-machine and tumble-dryer are well worth investing in.

If you have decided to breast-feed your twins, you should find that you can satisfy them easily without having to use bottles as well. Your own milk supply will automatically adjust to their demands.

However, coping with two new babies at once will mean that you need plenty of help and encouragement during the early days, and also plenty of rest.

You will probably feel more hungry and thirsty: satisfying these needs will go a long way towards ensuring an adequate milk supply for the twins. But do not fill up with low-nutrition foods, such as cakes or biscuits. A wholemeal sandwich, some fruit or a yoghurt will provide far more nourishment.

How to feed twins

If you breast-feed your twins, you can feed them both at the same time, or one after the other. Lay one baby on each side of you, with the heads towards you and the legs tucked under your arm. Twins may be different sizes, and if your milk flows very strongly, it may be too much for the smaller baby; this can result in surprise for the baby and messiness for you. It may prove more practical for you to feed each twin in turn, although this means taking up much more of your day.

If you decide to bottle-feed your twins, you can still feed them both at the same time by propping them up and holding the bottles between them. Never leave your babies with their bottles to feed unattended.

The big advantage of bottle-feeding is that someone else can take over the task from you for perhaps one feed a day, and this becomes an even greater benefit when you have twins. If you have other children and cannot get enough rest to produce sufficient breast milk, you may need to give your twins bottle-feeds to supplement your own milk. At this stage, it is usually best to stop breast-feeding, because mixed feeding means considerable extra work.

Establishing a routine

Whether you decide to breast-feed or bottle-feed, aim for a basic daily routine, so that both babies are fed more or less the same time. Otherwise you will begin to feel you are spending almost 24 hours a day just feeding the babies and changing their nappies.

As the months pass, life will become slightly less hectic, and you will have more time to enjoy your twins, watching as they develop into individual personalities. Even identical twins can have distinctly different characters, so it is sensible to treat them as individuals from the beginning.

Non-identical, or fraternal, twins are more like ordinary brothers and sisters than twins. As they grow older they become distinguishable from each other, and they may not share the same tastes and inclinations. It is therefore essential that they should be allowed to develop their individualities.

As part of the process of treating your twins as individuals, it is a good idea to make sure that each twin has one or two toys which can be regarded as his or her own. Larger playthings, such as a train set or garden swing, can of course be shared satisfactorily.

One outstanding advantage of twins is that they make ideal company for each other. They mean a lot of hard work for you, especially in the first year, but the compensations of bringing up a pair of babies together can be enormous.

Babies with special problems

About one in five babies will have some special problem from the time of birth. Half of these are premature (doctors prefer the term "born early") – that is, delivered before 37 weeks – but about 1 in 10 mature pregnancies are not straightforward because of some medical problem with mother or baby.

The most obvious problem is that of the baby who does not begin to breathe when he is born. In most cases the midwives will have anticipated the likelihood of trouble and a member of the hospital's paediatric team will be at the delivery. Resuscitating a newborn baby is usually simple though it does demand certain technical skills not possessed by all midwives. All labour wards have a special resuscitation trolley on which such babies are placed. If this happens to your baby, do not be frightened if nobody answers your anxious questions. The doctor cannot hear you if he has a stethoscope in his ears and the midwife is probably concentrating on delivering the placenta.

Premature babies

In most hospitals these babies will be nursed in a special unit. The main problem is that before 36–37 weeks babies cannot suck, and therefore have to be fed milk through a tube passed through the nose or mouth into the stomach.

Babies born early are subject to many problems and the earlier they are delivered the more difficult the situation is likely to be (see p. 40).

Many of these babies have profound breathing difficulties in their first week or two as their lungs have not developed sufficiently to cope with breathing air rather than being immersed in amniotic fluid. Other problems abound: intravenous feeding may be needed for a prolonged period, and the baby cannot maintain a stable body temperature or control the levels of sugar and salts in his blood. Resistance to infection is negligible, and some of the drugs and equipment used in treatment may have their own dangers and complications.

Parents usually have open access to their babies in special units. Many smaller units transfer sick babies to a more highly staffed and equipped hospital which might be many miles away. In such a case, you may be encouraged to accompany your baby or you may have to press your obstetrician to allow you to be transferred to the post-natal ward in the hospital treating your baby. Some regional centres, particularly those specialising in heart or brain surgery, may not be able to accommodate you, however, because they have no attached maternity unit.

Separation is always hard but it may be inevitable. The nurses will keep you informed and assist you if you wish to provide breast milk. Make sure you find out the name of the doctor responsible for your baby.

If your visiting times do not coincide with the consultant, ask the sister to arrange an appointment if you wish to discuss your baby with him. The other doctors may be more frequently available but they may have relatively little experience in new-born intensive care.

Other problems

Mature, healthy babies also have problems from time to time. Typical minor events include:

Jaundice This occurs in 1 in 3 babies. Only very high levels can cause harm. To avoid reaching such levels your baby may be nursed under bright blue lights which "bleach" the jaundiced skin.

Rashes Newborn babies do not have perfect skin. Red spots, creamy minute blisters, peeling and flaking are common and generally harmless.

Vomiting Small amounts are normal. The midwives may respond by washing out the baby's stomach of swallowed blood and mucus. More persistent vomiting calls for medical attention.

Low blood sugar Common only in infants of diabetic mothers or babies who are born very small because of an inadequate placenta. Treatment is by frequent feeds, regular blood checks, and – if the condition is severe – intravenous sugar.

Sticky eyes Usually little more is required than a cotton wool wipe. Antibiotic drops are sometimes advised if infection is present.

The loss of a baby

In the Western world, 5 to 10 in every thousand babies are stillborn (that is, they die in the womb after 28 weeks – before then the terms "miscarriage" or "abortion" are used), and a similar number die in the first few weeks of life. If early miscarriages are added in then only about two-thirds of all pregnancies ever result in a normal live baby.

Frequently the cause can be discovered. Miscarriages in the first 3 months are usually due to the fetus being abnormally formed. Many stillbirths are related to an improperly situated placenta or to a period of oxygen starvation of the baby; for example, because of toxaemia or high blood pressure in the mother. The more premature the birth, the more the baby is at risk because of immaturity of his lungs, his inability to control his temperature and blood composition and susceptibility to infection.

To lose a baby is a terrible tragedy, made more so by the difficulty other people may experience in understanding that the feelings of shock and emptiness, guilt and anger are no different from those felt when a loved adult dies. It is common to feel that somebody, either oneself or the doctor, must have been at fault. Thankfully this is rarely the case but any bereaved mother should make sure that she asks for a full explanation from her doctor.

The doctor concerned may ask permission to obtain a post-mortem examination of the baby. This may seem repugnant but it could be the only way to discover the cause of the tragedy and, therefore, whether it is likely to happen again and how this can be avoided.

Parents differ in their reaction to loss of a baby. Some want to see and hold their baby; some do not. The hospital staff may not be sure how to approach this question and you may need to make your wishes clear.

At some hospitals you will be offered a photograph of the baby. This may seem an odd suggestion at the time but many mothers are grateful for this memento. Be prepared for the possibility of distress and depression hitting you weeks later. There may be a local group where you can share your feelings with other bereaved parents (see pp. 138–148 for names and addresses of helpful organisations). Do not forget that if you have other children they may be very disturbed by the event and need to talk about the baby and what his death has meant to them.

Sometimes a baby is found to be abnormal during the pregnancy. This may be after tests have been performed because your previous baby had an inherited defect; or it may be discovered because in your area all women of a certain age are automatically offered tests.

If an abnormality is found, you will be asked whether or not you wish to have the pregnancy terminated. For termination to be carried out in time the necessary tests must start early in pregnancy so that if you think you might be at risk, you should attend an antenatal clinic as soon as possible.

Of course, if you would never consider having an abortion it might be better for all concerned to refuse the preliminary tests.

3
EARLY MONTHS

Developing awareness

A baby develops control over his body in stages, starting with his head, then working down to his arms and trunk, and finally his legs. In his first attempts he can barely raise his head. As the weeks go by, however, he will be able to raise his chest and head while lying on his front. This is an

Babies respond to what is going on around them much earlier than was at one time thought. Smiling between parents and their child provides a rewarding form of communication in the earliest months of a baby's life before he is able to talk.

important stage of his development, because a baby cannot sit up on his own until he achieves control of his head and trunk. Later he will be able to raise both legs off the floor and will eventually support himself by propping himself up on his forearms, probably at about four months old.

Older children are often very interested in a new arrival, especially during the baby's first few days at home, and will show physical affection for him, perhaps bringing gifts of books or toys and being concerned when he cries. Normally this intense interest will grow less after a few weeks, but the older child should still be encouraged to help whenever possible so that he does not feel left out.

Life can be boring for a baby who spends much of his waking hours lying on his back looking at the ceiling. He can take an interest in what is going on around him if he is propped up, but care must be taken that both his back, which is still very soft, and his head are properly supported.

For centuries parents have adapted their clothing to form a support for carrying their babies while travelling or working. Mothers in Lancashire or Wales, for example, until comparatively recently carried their babies wrapped in their long woollen shawls. The sling on the left is a modern version that allows the mother to see her baby. In other parts of the world the traditional methods are still followed. The Peruvian father (opposite, top left) is carrying his child in a back-sling woven in a traditional pattern. A Thai mother (opposite, top right) carries hers in another form of back-sling. In Kenya (opposite, below), two mothers on their way to market use lengths of cotton to form their baby slings: when a baby gets older and heavier it is easier to carry him on the back,

like the mother on the left. The position in which a baby is carried – generally on the breast, hip or back – is governed by the need to balance a load or to keep one or both hands free. In parts of south-east Asia, for instance, a baby is supported on the breasts when a heavy load of kindling is carried on the back. Elsewhere, a baby supported on the hip is balanced by a load on the other side. A mother who needs both hands free will carry her baby on her back.

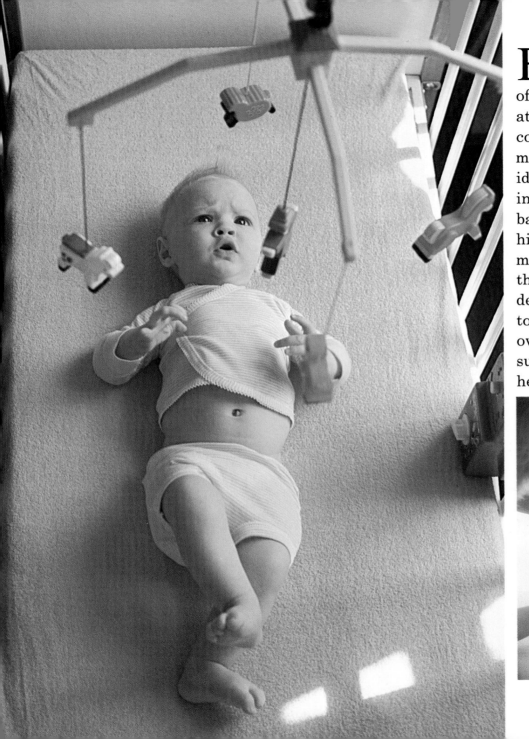

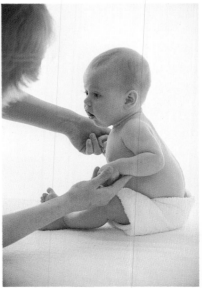

Babies get a great deal of pleasure from looking at objects that are brightly coloured and move or make a noise. Mobiles are ideal. An important stage in the development of a baby's sight occurs when his eyes move to follow a moving object. At about the same time he will have developed enough strength to hold his head up on his own, but will still need support for his back when he is sitting.

3 | Looking after your baby

Before you go home from hospital, you and your baby will be given a special medical examination. Once you are both home, you will not be left entirely on your own to cope. Most countries have qualified nurses, with special training in the care of babies, known variously as health visitors (Britain), clinic sisters (Australia), community nurses (Canada) or public health nurses or Plunket nurses (New Zealand). Their role is basically similar everywhere: to see that you and your child are doing well, to discuss any problems with you and to offer help and advice if needed. They will advise on immunisation and monitor the baby's weight and progress, and will often visit you and your baby at home. (See pp. 138–148 for fuller details of the procedure in various countries.)

As well as checking that your child is receiving appropriate care, your health visitor will tell you where your nearest child-health or "well-baby" clinic is. These clinics may also be known as baby health centres (Australia), community clinics (Canada), "well-child" clinics (US) or health clinics (New Zealand). At them your health visitor and/or a specialist child doctor will check on your baby's progress and on his hearing, eyesight and other aspects of development. While you should always consult your doctor immediately if your baby appears to be ill, these clinics are helpful on occasions when you need less urgent advice – for example, on feeding problems, unexplained crying or nappy rash.

On occasion, you may feel uncertain whether to follow precisely the advice offered. Do not hesitate to mention any doubts you have: for the sake of simplicity the health visitor may have recommended only one method of doing something, but there may well be quite acceptable alternative methods of doing it.

Local authority clinics vary in the way they operate, but the general pattern is that on your first visit, a clerk takes your details and gives you a record card. After that, you discuss your baby with the health visitor. Also on this first visit (and from time to time after this), the clinic doctor will examine your baby. If necessary, he may ask you to take the child to your family doctor, or send you for a hospital check.

Your baby may also be weighed but this is not a vital part of his examination. Other measures, apart from weight, are far more important as guides to the state of his health.

Your next examination
When your baby is about six weeks old, you will probably have another post-natal examination yourself, either at the hospital where he was born or at your doctor's surgery. Many doctors take this opportunity to carry out a cervical smear test to check that the cells in the neck of your womb are healthy.

THE HEIGHTS, WEIGHTS AND STAGES OF DEVELOPMENT described here are average ones. There is no cause for alarm just because the timing of a child's development is slightly different, although marked departure from the average time-table should be discussed with a doctor.

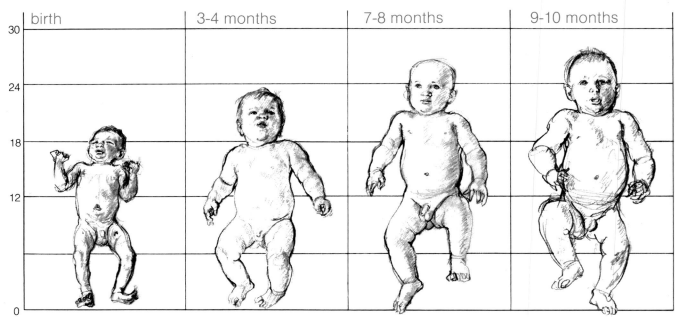

Average height (inches)

	birth	3-4 months	7-8 months	9-10 months
Height	Boys: 19¼-20½in (48-52cm)	Boys: 23¼-24in (58-60cm)	Boys: 26½-27¼in (67-69cm)	Boys: 27¾-28½in (70-72cm)
	Girls: 19¼-20in (48-51cm)	Girls: 22¾-23½in (57-59cm)	Girls: 25¾-26½in (65-67cm)	Girls: 27-27¾in (68-70cm)
Weight	Boys: 7-8lb (3.2-3.6kg)	Boys: 12-13¾lb (5.4-6.2kg)	Boys: 17¾-19½lb (8-8.8kg)	Boys: 19½-21¼lb (8.8-9.7kg)
	Girls: 6¾-7¾lb (3-3.5kg)	Girls: 11½-12¾lb (5.2-5.8kg)	Girls: 16¾-18½lb (7.6-8.4kg)	Girls: 18-20¼lb (8.1-9.2kg)

Ability and behaviour
Can suckle and has a powerful grip, but uses only the fingers. May respond to a sudden loud noise, but not to ordinary sounds. Can see, although objects are blurred. Crying is the only means of expressing discomfort.

Ability and behaviour
Turns head towards sounds. When placed face downwards can lift chin off mattress. Still sleeps most of the day.

Ability and behaviour
Can hold head firmly erect and sit without support. Has learnt to use thumbs to grip. Eyes now move in unison; hears everything and reacts immediately. Puts objects in mouth; two upper teeth appear.

Ability and behaviour
Starts to crawl. Is able to judge positions of nearby objects fairly accurately and will reach out arms for attention. Can tell the difference between familiar and unfamiliar faces. Four more teeth appear.

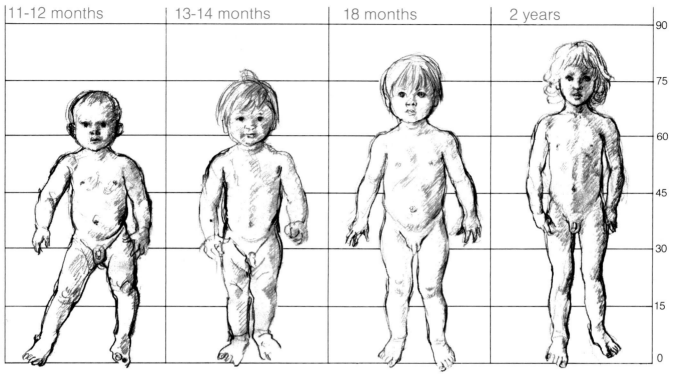

| 11-12 months | 13-14 months | 18 months | 2 years |

Average height (centimetres)

Height
Boys: 28¼-29½ in (71-74 cm)
Girls: 28-29 in (71-73 cm)
Weight
Boys: 21-23 lb (9.5-10.4 kg)
Girls: 19¾-22 lb (9-10 kg)

Ability and behaviour
Stands with slight support; walks holding on to furniture. Says single words. Can push light objects about, close and open doors, and crawl rapidly. First molar teeth appear.

Height
Boys: 29½-30¼ in (74-77 cm)
Girls: 29-30 in (73-76 cm)
Weight
Boys: 22¼-24 lb (10.1-10.9 kg)
Girls: 21-23¼ lb (9.5-10.6 kg)

Ability and behaviour
Walks without support. Feeds himself with a spoon. Is very sound-conscious and can locate source of sound. Can understand much simple language and starts to use one or two words correctly.

Height
Boys: 31¼-32¼ in (79-82 cm)
Girls: 30¾-32 in (78-81 cm)
Weight
Boys: 24½-26¾ lb (11.1-12.1 kg)
Girls: 22¼-25 lb (10.1-11.3 kg)

Ability and behaviour
Walks up and down stairs, one hand holding rail. Can drink from cup without much spilling. Starts to scribble. Asks for pot. Has use of up to 20 intelligible words, but understands four or five times that number. Has 12–16 teeth.

Height
Boys: 33¾-34½ in (85-88 cm)
Girls: 33-34¼ in (83-87 cm)
Weight
Boys: 25½-27¼ lb (11.5-12.5 kg)
Girls: 24-27 lb (10.9-12.3 kg)

Ability and behaviour
Dresses himself but cannot yet fasten buttons. Has started to put words together into short phrases, and to ask questions. Usually dry at night. May begin to play with other children.

75

Toys for the pram and cot

During the first few weeks of his life a baby needs very few toys. At this stage visual, aural and physical contact with his mother are the most important things in his life.

The new-born baby's senses are in good order. He can see, hear, feed, cry, feel pain and experience a whole range of emotions. A new-born baby's eyes probably have a limited focusing ability, restricted to objects close at hand. Distant objects are probably blurred.

Within a few days of birth the baby can distinguish familiar faces from strange ones. Within a few weeks, most babies can turn their heads so as to follow a moving object or figure with their eyes.

A new baby's eyes appear to be attracted more by black and white than by colours. As yet these young eyes are seeing "things" which do not make sense to the baby; he recognises nothing, because he has never seen it before.

At the gazing stage, at a few weeks or a little older, large, bold pictures are useful. One such picture taped to the side of the cot or the nursery wall will attract the baby's attention. An alternative would be large black headlines from newspapers or magazines, or black and white patterns you have made yourself. It is important not to give the baby too much to absorb at once.

After a few days, the baby will have had time to "learn" the picture pattern. Then the picture can either be changed for a different one, or it can be turned sideways or upside-down, thus creating a new interest for the baby. This stimulation can be continued with different patterns and pictures.

Some noises may amuse a baby. An effective yet simple toy is made by filling a cushion with pieces of crushed stiff paper. If this is placed by the baby's feet, he will soon be trampling on it to make a noise.

Before long the baby will begin to show sustained interest in a variety of sights, sounds and movements. He will begin to reach out for dangling objects, but as yet his fingers do not open to try to grasp things. Before this stage is reached, start hanging a few safe objects from a string across his cot. Such objects can include small balls, plastic bottles with small bells inside, plastic measuring cups to click together, or coloured teething rings.

Make certain that these objects are securely fastened, and that they have no small parts which the baby can put in his mouth. Remove the objects when the baby might use them to try to pull himself up.

Mobiles

Mobiles hung over a cot or playpen will stimulate a baby's interest. If you are buying a mobile, choose one that is provided with stiff supporting arcs of wire. If you make one yourself, you can hang a variety of objects of your choice on it provided you keep the balance right. These objects should be brightly coloured, simple shapes in reds, yellows and blues, such as plastic cups, spoons, pieces of bamboo painted with non-toxic colours, and large plastic or wooden beads. If a length of soft yarn is tied between the baby's leg just below his knee and the wire of the mobile, he will move the mobile every time he kicks his feet.

Safe materials

Ensure that the toys you give your baby are safe and suitable. Materials should be stable, clean, soft, colourful and cuddly. Do not swamp your baby by giving him too many toys at once; put some away and then reintroduce them after an interval. (See also pp. 122–123.)

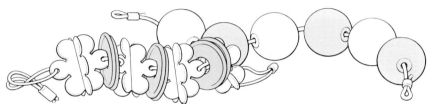

A string of large colourful beads or plastic shapes strung across the pram hood will attract a baby's interest. The beads and shapes can be changed to re-engage his attention.

Coping with a crying baby

In the first few weeks, a baby may cry a good deal; it is often difficult for parents (or even doctors) to be sure of the cause.

Your first thought will probably be that you are not feeding the baby enough, especially if you are breast-feeding. Do not let your baby's crying make you feel that you are failing him with breast-feeding and that you should give it up.

If the baby is really not getting enough milk, feed him more often: your milk supply will certainly catch up with his needs.

A bottle-fed baby who cries a lot, but who has had plenty of milk, may be soothed with a drink of water that has been boiled and cooled.

The temperature of the baby's surroundings can easily affect his sleeping and crying. A baby kept in a warm room – not less than 18°C (65°F) and preferably 21°C (70°F) – is likely to sleep more and cry less than one who is in a cooler room. A wet or dirty nappy is not enough, by itself, to make your baby cry, but if it gets cold he will soon show distress.

Some babies cry when they are undressed, and can be quickly soothed by being wrapped up, or by being held against you. A fretful baby may also be soothed by being carried next to you in a sling.

You may find that your baby cries inconsolably for no apparent reason for an hour or so in the evening, drawing his legs up as though he has colic. Such crying is very common, and is known as "three-month colic" because it usually stops, very suddenly, when the baby is three months old. Doctors disagree about the cause of evening crying, and you certainly should not blame yourself for it. Do not, however, dismiss persistent distress as "three-month colic" – if in doubt, always seek medical advice.

Doctors sometimes suggest that a baby frets because of boredom, loneliness or exhaustion. Certainly, a baby can cry from boredom if he has nothing to look at or listen to. Give him interesting things to play with, such as mobiles, and try to have him with you where he can be aware of you and what you are doing. Talking to him can soothe him; so can singing or humming or playing music.

A baby who is very tired may cry in a desperate-sounding way, and be particularly difficult to soothe. A change in routine, too, can easily upset your baby. However, you can do something to alleviate all these potential causes of persistent crying, once you have recognised them.

Waking at night

A mother who has constantly to pick up and soothe her baby in the early months should not worry that she is spoiling the child. You cannot spoil a young baby. Babies cry for a reason and should be comforted. However if your baby wakes in the night and is not due for a feed, give him a chance to go back to sleep, even if this means that you lie awake for several minutes (but do not leave him for more than a quarter of an hour).

Do not encourage your baby to expect more than a necessary feed, change or short cuddle when you do go to him in the night. If you cuddle him back to sleep, do it without taking him out of his cot, otherwise he may wake up as soon as he is put back, and avoid soothing chatter as the baby will love this and stay awake for more.

Your baby's comforters

During his first 18 months, your baby will develop his own way of comforting himself: it may be a dummy, a bottle at bedtime, a comfort blanket or just thumb-sucking. As he grows older, such comforts become very necessary to his sense of security. The need for comforters often reaches a peak at around two years. A child may still want them when he is three or even four years old, to go to sleep with or just to enable him to cope with tiredness or stress.

Having a well-loved comfort blanket, for example, can keep a toddler happy and willing to enjoy and explore new situations when he might otherwise be anxious and miserable. If your child seems to become dependent on some object or habit in this way, this is normal, and you should understand how powerful and long-lasting these habits can be. Do not expect to be able to throw away the blanket or the dummy before your child is two or three years old – perhaps as late as four or five – because taking away his comforter while he still feels the need of it could cause him great distress.

Some mothers are anxious about whether they should allow a growing baby to have a dummy. There is no harm in a dummy, provided it is always kept clean. However, the alternative of thumb-sucking does have the advantage of helping your baby to explore his mouth and learn to feel. If you prefer your baby not to have a dummy at, say, 18 months old, then it is best not to use one at all.

How your baby changes

As your baby grows up, and his understanding of the world around him changes, the things that make him unhappy also change.

Around the middle of his first year, he will probably change in the way he responds to people whom he does not know. He may become very wary with strangers, and cry if they pick him up or even come near him. This means that he is beginning to distinguish those people who he knows love him and look after him from those he has not seen before.

A baby of ten weeks who cries when his mother leaves him may agree to be comforted by a stranger. An eight-month old baby in similar circumstances is likely to become even more upset if a stranger tries to comfort him. Because of this, it is well worth getting him used to being cared for, even briefly, by someone other than yourself, before this age.

Some babies just do seem to cry and cry, whatever you do. This is the more upsetting if you are a first-time mother, unprepared for the sheer exhaustion of having a constantly crying baby. To make it worse, the baby is liable to sense that you are upset and will cry all the more. This is the kind of situation that drives parents to distraction. See the following section for advice.

COT DEATHS

Between the age of 2 weeks and 1 year, the commonest reason for a baby in the Western world to die is known as the "Sudden Infant Death Syndrome" (SIDS or Cot Death).

About two in every thousand babies die unexpectedly but in about half of these cases a cause is found – usually overwhelming infection. In the other half no cause of death can be found. These are the true cot deaths. There are many theories and much research, but where the defect lies – heart, brain, lungs, or air tubes – remains uncertain.

Nobody needs to be told that it is a devastating thing to happen. Many women never truly get over such a sudden loss of a baby and the lack of a specific cause somehow makes it harder to bear.

In some areas the pathologist discusses with parents what happened; in others a paediatrician or family doctor may do the same. It is reasonable to ask your family doctor to consult an expert on the subject. (See pp. 138–148 for the addresses of organisations that will help.)

The chance of it happening again to another baby in the family is very small indeed but not out of the question. Some families obtain a device which sounds an alarm if the baby stops breathing. There is no hard evidence that any lives have been saved by these machines; they are expensive and prone to false alarms. Nevertheless many mothers feel reassured and sleep peacefully if they have an alarm. Your local hospital paediatric unit may be able to help.

Avoiding cruelty to children

Cruelty to children can take various forms, from physically beating a baby to denying a child affection. It is committed by both men and women. Most people do not like to think of themselves as behaving in an "unnatural" way to a child, but the best of us can do things, when we are under stress, that we would not normally like to admit to.

What causes stress?

There are obvious pressures such as poor housing, debt, unemployment, a handicapped child or the physical or mental illness of someone in the family. There are more subtle ones such as insecurity, feeling unloved or misunderstood, tiredness and loneliness. Single parents are especially liable to stress, as are women who feel they ought to be able to combine having a job and being a "perfect" wife and mother. Many women suffer from pre-menstrual tension. Problems between parents are common: sexual difficulties, the fact that a parent prefers one child to another, a lack of agreement about controlling the child, a lack of sharing of routines. Even the normal behaviour of a child – crying, wetting and soiling, and the resulting disruption of routine and sleep – can cause the stress that makes a parent feel violent towards him. And the continual crying or whining of a child who just will not stop, when you yourself are tired and exhausted, has driven many a parent to the limits of endurance.

What does stress do to us?

Stress makes us unhappy: often irritable, lonely and depressed and liable to magnify small problems into very large ones. It can make us behave in a tense or explosive manner. It can result in physical violence, especially when reasonable verbal methods of communication break down – as, of course happens with a baby, who can't even understand why you are angry. There are mothers, calm and tolerant for much of the time, who become irritable and impatient when pre-menstrual, start hitting a crying child and find themselves unable to stop. Others may not even realise that they are under stress and are burdened with guilt when they have an urge to throw their baby across the room.

Stress does not always manifest itself as violence. Some parents may take out their resentment of a stepchild or unwanted baby by locking it in another room or even in a dark cupboard, while others may find it difficult to show affection and will punish a child by refusing to cuddle it or talk to it – a form of cruelty less obvious than battering but potentially even more damaging.

What can we do about it?

Dealing with stress is easier said than done. The cause may lie outside you, in your partner or child, but you must deal with yourself before dealing with anyone else.

The very first thing is to recognise the problem. Violence between adults is often a warning sign; experience shows that this can spread to the children. It usually begins with isolated, often minor, explosions of anger; then it grows. Serious and fatal injuries to children have usually been preceded by less serious ones. So be alert to any signs of wanting to abuse your child.

Sometimes just recognising the problem helps. Sometimes there is an easy solution, such as changing your routine. If you do feel an urge to hit your child, and are afraid that it is getting out of control, immediately remove yourself physically from the child – go to another room and try to calm down before you cope with the problem.

Talk to someone who will understand, ideally a friend in a similar situation. If there isn't anyone obvious, try joining a mother-and-toddler group. If you have been feeling very isolated and guilty, it will be a relief to find that yours is not the only baby that insists on going on crying when you have done everything in the book to console him, and that other mothers have had an impulse to strike a child that has just asked "Why?" for the thousandth time. If relatives, friends and neighbours prove unhelpful, try your doctor or a professional counsellor. Talk to your partner if you can (although if a lack of harmony between you is one of the causes of your stress this may only increase the problem). There are voluntary organisations that exist specifically to help parents who feel like abusing their children and can be telephoned at any time (see pp. 138–148 for details).

The following may also be helpful as ways of overcoming the problem of stress:

● Recognise the tension and the pressure.
● Identify the things you are doing or not doing that show stress (you may like to make a list).
● Identify which relationship is causing stress and recognise that it may be two-way.
● Do not blame your child (or anyone else) for doing things to you.
● Do not blame yourself for the way you feel.

Others are under pressure too

The stress that you have felt may be the same stress that a friend or neighbour of yours is feeling now. It may help them to talk to you. Most of us don't want to be thought to be poking our noses into other people's business, but if you think a child is at risk, your concerned care for the child will help you to recognise the difference between showing friendly concern and being a busybody. If someone you know is under pressure, an expression of help and sympathy, without any implication of criticism, is likely to be appreciated.

If you are rebuffed but you remain concerned – perhaps the child is bruised, or you hear screaming, or the child disappears for no obvious reason – notify a child care organisation (see pp. 138–148 for addresses) or even the police. If you are really concerned about the health and safety of the child, remember that his life might be at risk: the stakes are too high for you to do nothing.

Getting in shape

Once you have slept, after your baby is born, you will soon start thinking about your figure – and perhaps feel disappointed that it seems almost as bulky as it was when you were pregnant. Do not worry: this state of affairs is normal.

Although the womb no longer contains a baby, it is still bulky, and will shrink only gradually. Also, extra fat will have been built up for use in producing milk for your baby. Whether or not you choose to breast-feed, your body will have prepared itself to do so. If you bottle-feed, that extra fat is not used up in the normal way. (Diet for mothers, p. 60–61.)

Apart from the fat, your pelvic-floor and abdominal muscles are still stretched. To get them back to their previous length and fitness, you will need to do exercises.

Begin on the first or second day, and keep them up, even when there is no one to supervise.

Your partner may try to help by suggesting types of exercises used by athletic men to tone up their stomach muscles. If he does, do not follow his well-meant advice: your stomach muscles are not the same as those of a man.

Keep to the exercises recommended on this and the following pages, and you will soon see your figure return. At the same time, you will also begin to feel fitter, much stronger and more energetic.

FIRST STEPS TO RECOVERY

After the huge physical effort involved in giving birth, it is only natural to want to drift into well-deserved sleep almost straight away. If, despite your exhaustion, you can first manage two simple, undemanding exercises, you will give yourself extra help towards a speedy recovery.

First, your body needs oxygen, so do a breathing exercise to take in plenty of fresh air. This is particularly advisable if you smoke, or if – like most mothers – you have been given a pain-killer or anaesthetic to inhale during labour.

Next, improve the circulation of blood in your legs and feet, which may have become sluggish during labour. At one time, a mother was told not to move about for some time after giving birth, and this sometimes led to circulation troubles.

Even if you cannot manage these exercises (described below) immediately, do them each three times a day after that first deep sleep.

EXERCISE 1: THE BELLOWS

To clear the lungs, lie on your back with your head on the pillow, your knees bent and your feet kept flat.

Place your hands on your stomach. Now breathe out as much air as possible, with your mouth open. Go on squeezing it out, pulling your tummy wall in until you cannot make another sound. Breathe in as soon as you feel you must. Repeat this four times.

If the exercise makes you cough, do not worry: this only shows that you needed this particular exercise.

EXERCISE 2: THE PUMPS

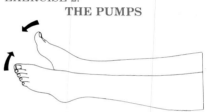

To help circulation, straighten your legs. Bend and stretch toes as far as possible, six times up, six times down.

Keep your legs straight. Bend and stretch your ankles six times.

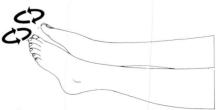

Draw circles with your big toes, six times in each direction.

TONING UP YOUR MUSCLES

It is important to restore your pelvic-floor muscles as soon as possible after your baby is born. The exercise for this, the Underlift, is described below. It should be done frequently throughout the day, before you lift or carry anything.

Always do the Underlift exercise before getting out of bed, or standing – especially for the first time after giving birth – and before getting up from the lavatory. Also, use the Underlift to hold up the pelvic-floor muscles under other strains: when you sneeze, cough or laugh.

This exercise, if done regularly, brings fresh blood into the pelvic area by its squeezing action. It reduces swelling and discomfort, and will assist in healing if there are stitches in the perineum.

The other exercises on this page are to tone up centre-front stomach muscles (the Rock) and sides of the waist (the Hitch). The Twist (p. 82) helps muscles which cross over from ribs on one side to the pelvis on the opposite side.

After each exercise, rest face down with two pillows under your pelvis.

Each movement of these exercises should be performed slowly and smoothly, but the muscles must be made to work. Feel them contract as much as possible, pause, then try to go further, to the absolute limit. In this way, fibres gradually shorten, and your outline improves. If the rhythm is too quick, the fibres do not have time to contract to the maximum possible extent.

EXERCISE 1:
THE UNDERLIFT

Lie on your back, with knees slightly apart. Imagine a tampon in the vagina, and pull it up slowly as far as you can. Feel the tension inside your vagina, and not in your buttocks, thighs or stomach. Hold up tightly for a moment or two, then let go. Once you have learned the exercise in this position, you can also do it on your side, with hips and knees bent, or sitting well back in a chair. Do not raise both legs at once, or try to sit up straight from the lying-back position.

From the third day after your baby is born, also do two additional exercises – the Rock and the Hitch. You should try to do these every day, four times at each session. After one week, do them each six times; after two weeks, progress to eight times. After three weeks, you should do them ten times daily.

Always stop any exercise if you feel too tired to continue doing it.

EXERCISE 2:
THE ROCK

Lie down as if to do the Underlift exercise. Now press the hollow under your waist down on to the bed (or whatever surface you are lying on).

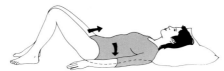

Pull up the pubis towards the ribs, as far as it will possibly go; then try to pull just a little further. You should feel your stomach shortening and also feel the buttocks contracting as your hips lift slightly off the surface. Your waist must remain in firm contact with the surface during this particular exercise and your back should become rounded. Now relax and feel the hollow under your waist return, as your seat drops back on to the surface.

EXERCISE 3:
THE HITCH

Keep one leg straight, draw up the other.

Make the straight leg feel shorter by hitching up the hip on the same side, towards your ribs.

Then make it seem longer, by stretching your foot to an imaginary object just out of reach. Repeat several times, then bend that leg, straighten the other and continue with the same exercise.

Continued overleaf

EXERCISE 4:
THE TWIST

Lie with both your knees bent and your arms stretched sideways, at shoulder level. Keep shoulders flat, feet together.

Now twist one knee sideways until it touches the mattress or the floor. Keep both your knees together as you make the twist. Hold the position for a moment, then twist the other way, leading with the other knee.

Repeat the exercise six times in each direction, rolling from side to side.

Up and about

Once you are really up and about, you can stop the Bellows and Pumps exercises, but you should make it a habit to pull in your stomach wall at frequent intervals.

On the move

Almost from the start, you will need some form of transport for your baby. For easy trips with a very small child, a Moses basket is cheap, light-weight and convenient. But you will also be likely to need a full-size carry-cot, or a pram.

A full-size carry-cot should be one which you can use both as a pram (on a transporter) and as a cot (with or without a stand, which may also be used for holding the bath). It is ideal for transporting a baby in a car (see p. 86). A carry-cot should be sturdy, with strong handles; not so heavy that it is uncomfortable to carry; easy to fold flat for storage; and equipped with rings for attaching a safety harness.

If you prefer a more substantial vehicle, giving a smoother ride, you may decide on a pram. This need not be grand and expensive, but if you do think of buying such a pram, work out where you will keep it in the house, and consider any stairs that you may have to cope with. If you are likely to take the pram on car journeys, check that it will fit in the back. Many modern prams have a separate body and chassis, which you can unclip for easy handling.

In choosing your pram, make sure that the handle is at a comfortable height, and that there are secure points to which to attach a harness. As your baby grows and wants to see more, you can fit in a back-rest; this gives him a gently tilted support until he is old enough to be able to sit up for long by himself.

Sitting up

When your baby is old enough to sit up comfortably for reasonably long periods (but not before), you can use a pushchair. There are two main kinds. One is the sturdy folding type; a version is available that can be adjusted to allow the baby to sit up or lie down, and also to face either forward or back towards you; it can also be adapted for use as a carry-cot transporter. The other kind is the light-weight collapsible "stroller", which can be carried almost like an umbrella when folded up. This too is available in an adjustable version. Both pushchairs and strollers should have safety rings to which the baby's harness can be securely attached. Twin versions of both are available. There is also a double pushchair, either side of which can be adjusted independently. This is particularly useful if you have both a baby and a toddler to cope with.

If your life involves a lot of getting on and off buses, the stroller will be the more convenient type of push-chair. If, however, you expect to spend a lot of time pushing your child along rough country lanes the sturdier folding type may be more suitable for the conditions, because it has bigger wheels.

Convenient extras

There are a number of extras which can make life easier when you are taking your baby out in a pushchair or pram. They include a shopping tray to go underneath the pram; this is much safer than carrying heavy shopping on top of the pram, where it could tip the pram over. You can also buy a pushchair basket which may still be useful later on, if you have a freezer, because it makes a handy freezer basket.

Other extras for pushchairs include a cover-all which will keep your baby dry in showers; it has a waterproof hood, to keep the rain off his head. A transparent waterproof cover to fit over a pushchair is also available, and gives all-weather protection.

There is also a cosy pushchair bag, which does away with the need for blankets (and the risk of blanket corners trailing and getting caught up in the wheels) and which will keep your baby snug and warm. If your pushchair has a centre strap on the seat, you can choose a version which has a separate section for each leg.

Slings and carriers

Prams and pushchairs are ideal for wheeling babies and toddlers along pavements. Sometimes, however, a wheeled vehicle can be a nuisance, and then a baby sling or "back-pack" type of carrier comes into its own.

TYPES OF PRAMS AND PUSHCHAIRS

A full-size carry-cot that can be used as a pram (on its transporter) or as a cot (with or without a stand).

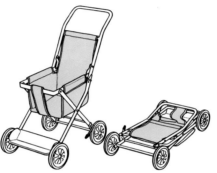

A high-backed upright pushchair that folds to compact size when it needs to be carried or stored.

A type of pushchair that can be adjusted so that the baby can sit up, lie down and face forward or backward.

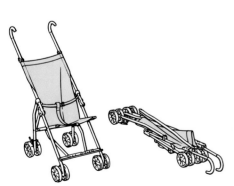

A "stroller" that folds like an umbrella: easy for getting on and off buses.

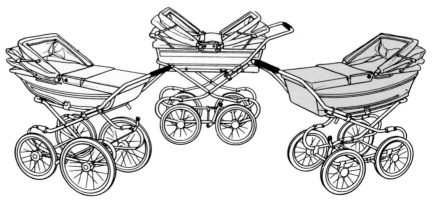

High-built luxury pram with larger wheels (left); pram for twins (centre); and (right) smooth-riding fold-up pram with front and rear springing.

For instance, you may have nowhere to keep a pram at home, or you may have a lot of stairs to climb.

A sling or carrier will enable you to take your baby with you into a crowded shop and use lifts and escalators. With a sling or carrier, too, country walks on unpaved paths, where wheels would bog down, become possible. Moreover, your baby is likely to be happier when he is kept in close contact with you.

Remember that until a baby can hold up his head unaided the sling or carrier must have a head support. (See also the pictures on pp. 70–71.)

Safer car journeys
A baby or young child should always travel in the back seat of a car. It is illegal to hold him in your lap in the front passenger seat, and you put his life at risk if you do so. (See also p. 133.) Ensure, even in the back of the car, that a baby is in a properly secured carry-cot and a child in a safety seat or harness, depending on his age and weight. If a car is involved in an accident, stops suddenly or swerves violently, a child without any safety restraint may be thrown through the windscreen or against a front seat or side of the car.

Tips for happy travel
To make the journey easier for both child and parent:
● Take a waterproof bag containing a moist sponge and baby-wipes, for freshening a child's face or wiping sticky fingers.
● Take disposable nappies or spare pants, and a bag for soiled nappies.
● Take a warm rug, to cover a child while he is asleep.
● Take a potty. This can be used inside the car at a lay-by and, by bringing relief, helps to prevent restlessness and car-sickness.

MAKING THE PRAM SAFE

One of the most important items you buy for your baby will be a safety harness, to keep him from falling out of his pram or high-chair. Even when he is a little older, he will still need the harness when walking outdoors or riding in his pushchair.

It is best to start using the harness before your baby is old enough to sit up, so that he will be used to restraint by the time it becomes necessary for his safety.

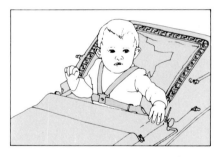

A safety harness is essential for any baby in his pram. Adjust anchor straps so that he cannot stand and tip the pram over.

THINGS TO CHECK
Make sure that your pram has rings for attaching the harness. Also, see that its brakes are really safe, and (if it is a folding pram) that there is a safety device to prevent it folding up by accident. If the pram has a detachable body, always make certain that it is firmly secured to the chassis before use.

At regular intervals, test the brakes, to make sure that they are not becoming less efficient; if they are, have them attended to at once. Tyres should also be checked regularly, and the wheels oiled. If your pram is the fold-up type, check that the safety locking device is working properly.

While your baby is very small, it is advisable to fit a fine-mesh safety-net over the pram, to keep out flies and other insects, and cats. When your baby is able to sit up properly, you can fit a seat on the pram – but never leave him on the seat unattended, in case he upsets the pram.

WHEN YOU ARE OUT
Taking your baby out in the pram, be extra careful crossing the road. Never push the pram off the pavement until you clearly see that no traffic is coming. It is best to step into the road first, and then pull the pram after you, even though this may be slightly awkward.

When you park the pram, do not rely entirely on the brakes to prevent a runaway accident; always park so that if the pram does somehow move on its own, it will run *away* from the road.

Do not pile shopping onto the pram, in case it capsizes. For the same reason, do not hang anything heavy from the pram handle. Never leave it with another child sitting on it, or with a dog tied to it.

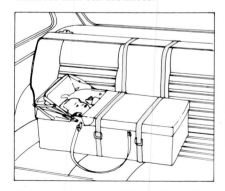

To stop a carry-cot sliding off the back seat, it must be anchored by straps bolted to the car's main frame.

Furnishing the nursery

You will save yourself much time and energy by careful planning of the room where your baby will spend a good deal of his early life. Remember to allow ample storage space, and make sure that heating, lighting, windows, floors and furnishing materials are suitable and safe.

Make sure there are no sharp corners on any furniture and that any paint or lacquerwork, especially on the cot, is non-poisonous and lead-free. Don't paint the room all white. A child needs the stimulation of colours and things to look at and play with.

Space for storage
You will need space for clothes and, unless your bathroom is very large, space to keep all the essentials for nappy-changing, as well as a flat changing surface – the top of a table or chest of drawers will do if you do not want to buy a special unit, but the edges must be guarded so that the baby cannot roll off.

A wide variety of space-saving storage devices is available. These include under-bed drawers, window-seat boxes, linen-box stools and free-standing drawers or boxes of wire or plastic, as well as wall cupboards and shelf units.

Heating the nursery
Ideally a baby's room should be kept at a steady temperature of about 18–21°C (65–70°F). This temperature is easy to maintain if your home has central heating. Keep a check on other forms of heating by installing a wall thermometer, and stand the cot well away from draughts.

Many types of heater are available; make sure that the one you buy is safe to use, and well-guarded. An electric radiator is much safer than a wall-mounted gas or electric fire.

A free-standing electric radiator or convector heater should be stable on its base, and should cut out automatically if it is knocked over or if the airflow becomes restricted in some way. Air vents must not be large enough to allow a child to push objects through them and on to the electric elements, and there should be a three-core flex, properly earthed.

An oil heater is potentially lethal and gives off very strong fumes. If you must use one, it should be designed to go out if knocked over, though you should if possible attach it to a wall or pillar for safety – with, of course, a guard around it. Stand it on a sheet of metal, which will not burn, and always fill it out of doors in case of fire.

Windows and curtains
On whatever floor of the house your nursery is situated, it is essential to put some type of safety-lock and bars on the window. Curtains should be made of flameproof or flame-resistant material.

Covering the floor
The flooring for a nursery needs to be hardwearing, comfortable to play on and easy to clean. It must be capable of withstanding accidents with the potty, occasional sickness and spillages of paint, as well as rough use from wheeled toys of every kind. Loose rugs on a hard surface such as wood-block or ceramic tile are much too dangerous for a nursery. Hard-wearing stain-resistant carpet is suitable, as are semi-hard floor coverings such as vinyl, or cork tiles. Vinyl, in particular, is comfortable to walk on and easy to clean, but can be dangerously slippery when wet.

Arranging the lights
It is important to have good night lighting, not only to reassure your baby but also for your own convenience when you have to attend to him during the night. A dimmer control switch installed on an existing light fitting allows you to vary the light level from just a glow to full illumination; it also enables you to bring up the light slowly, with less risk of disturbing the baby.

A place to sleep
In the early months, your baby can sleep in a carry-cot or in a full-sized cot which will last him for about three years.

The advantage of starting with a carry-cot, or crib, is that when the baby is very small it is easier to tuck him in securely and cosily than it is in a big cot. The lining should be detachable and easy to wash.

In choosing a cot, you should make certain that it is strong and rigid, with safe, child-proof fasteners to prevent the drop-side being accidentally released. Upright bars should be no more than 6 cm (2⅜ in) apart, so that as your baby becomes more active he will not be able to get his head trapped between them. The horizontal top rail should be about 49.5 cm (19½ in) above the top of the mattress, which should be not more than 10 cm (4 in) deep.

A foam plastic mattress is light, which makes cot-making easy, and hygienic, reducing any chance of infection and rarely causing allergies.

With a baby under 12 months old, *do not* use a pillow: it creates a risk of accidental smothering. For children over this age, you can buy a special fibre-filled pillow which is porous (guarding against suffocation), non-allergenic and easy to wash.

Feeding equipment

Whether you breast-feed or bottle-feed, make sure that you have a suitable chair, without arms, that you can sit in to feed your baby.

If you bottle-feed, an electric bottle-warmer or a microwave oven can be useful, especially in the middle of the night. Make sure that it is fully insulated for safety.

It will not be long before your baby is sitting up for his feeds: at 9 to 12 months he will need a high chair. This should be strongly built and not liable to tip over when weight is put on the feeding tray or the arms. The tray should be detachable, for easy washing after meals. As an economy, you can buy a multi-purpose chair which, as the baby grows out of the high-chair stage, converts into a low-level chair and table.

Reclining chairs

From a very early age (say, one month), a lightweight reclining chair is useful. Your baby will enjoy an improved view of everything when he is able to sit half-upright, his back and head supported, and the reclining chair will make a safe play-seat later on. Because it is easily carried, this kind of chair is especially useful for a mother busy about the house, or when travelling.

Most reclining baby-chairs have a stand which can be used to convert the seat into a swing or high chair. They also have attachments for a baby's own safety harness.

The reclining chair you choose should be capable of being adjusted from almost horizontal (for the young baby) to upright (for the toddler). Always put the chair on the floor and never ever on a table-top or work surface. Make sure there is no dangerous equipment near by.

KEEPING A BABY BOOK

A Baby Book is a weekly record of your child's development, enabling you to keep watch on his progress and compare it with the progress of other children in the family, or of other people's children. These comparisons usually confirm how misleading it is to generalise about development. The progress of individual babies varies widely but naturally, without necessarily giving cause for either pride or worry. Nevertheless, a Baby Book is a more reliable record of development than your memory, and it can give warning of slow development in areas where this is important.

Your Baby Book may show weeks on end with no major changes to enter, followed by a sudden flood of changes. This is not a sign that your baby has acquired a whole new range of skills overnight. He has, in fact, been practising and co-ordinating the skills he already possesses, in preparation for his next stage of development. For example, when you see him lying in his cot opening and closing his hands, he is in fact making ready for the time when he will be using his hands to grasp objects.

Your Baby Book will contain as much or as little as you like, but it will normally record your baby's increase in weight and length. If the figures show that his weight is straying outside certain upper and lower limits – that he is overweight, or is not thriving – you will know that there is something amiss, and that medical advice should be sought.

Later on, when the child is standing and walking, you will be able to check that his weight is correct for his height. A toddler can participate in the keeping of a Baby Book if you make a game of it. If you check his growth in height against marks on a wall or board, you can show him where he – or a brother or sister – came up to at the last check, and what point he might reach by the time of the next one. Seeing how far the pointer of a scale swings each time the child is weighed can become almost a game.

Beside some dates will be entries recording when your child cuts his first teeth, when later teeth arrive, and when the full set of 20 milk teeth is complete (by about the third birthday). Here, too, will be a note of when the baby first raises his head (at about 4 months), when he sits up (7–10 months), and when he pulls himself to his feet. The Baby Book will record when he walks (10 months–2 years), uses a potty, becomes "dry" and speaks intelligibly.

Other entries may record the baby's first smile, and the first time he recognises himself in a mirror. Entries such as these may be sentimental rather than useful, but they are no less valued for that in after years.

A baby and the first child

Parents who already have one child are generally concerned about how he or she will react to the arrival of a new baby. They wonder how to prepare the older child for the coming of a "rival" who will inevitably demand most of your attention.

How you cope with this situation will of course depend a good deal on the age of the first child. However, even children apparently old enough to understand that there is a new baby joining the family, who have discussed the idea and even helped to prepare for the baby, may be emotionally upset when the event actually happens.

Even before the new baby arrives, the first child has to cope with upheaval in the family routine if, as is probable, his mother goes into hospital. The upheaval may include being looked after by someone who does not usually do this.

How much the separation from his mother upsets him will vary, not only with the first child's age, but also according to his own temperament, his experience (if any) of being apart from her before, and the kind of care he receives while she is away.

If he is accustomed to being parted from his mother, and if those partings have been made happy times for him, he is much less likely to be upset this time. Even if this is to be the first such separation, you should not need to worry about him so long as he is being looked after by familiar, loving people. As an extra boost to his sense of security, his daily routine should be kept as near normal as it possibly can.

Your child will certainly want to visit you at the hospital. When he does, you should take one or two simple precautions to avoid the unnecessary risk of making him feel jealous of the baby. Ask his father, or whoever is bringing the child to visit you, to make sure that the hospital staff know the special visit has been arranged. Then you will be able to make sure that the new baby is in his own cot, and not in your arms or at the breast, and that you have both hands free for a big welcome.

Do not be in too great a hurry to introduce the older child to the new baby. They will have plenty of time to get to know each other. If you keep glancing towards the baby, waiting for the opportunity to introduce the two, the older child might easily get the impression that you are really only interested in the new arrival.

On this sensitive occasion, pay really close attention to your first child: let him tell you all the interests and excitements of his life at home without you, and show him that you are listening.

When the clear opportunity does come to introduce the baby, it may help if you have arranged an exchange of gifts: the older child can bring a present for the baby, and there can be a present for him "from the baby" waiting in the cot. Remember, though that what your first child needs at this time, far more than any gift, is the reassurance of your love.

If, on this first encounter, the older child seems unimpressed by his new brother or sister – or even antagonistic – do not be worried. He has never been faced with a baby brother or sister of his own before, and he may just be unable to respond

TIREDNESS

What makes all these potential problems seem especially difficult for you is the fact that having just given birth, you will feel tired – and at the same time will be very busy with your baby. (Remember that extreme "tiredness" may be a sign of depression.)

Your sleep is being frequently interrupted by your new baby. Your days, already filled by his demands, may be made more difficult by the needs of an older child who is naturally anxious to be reassured that he is just as important to you as he ever was.

To help you through this difficult patch, it is worth trying to prepare yourself for the needs of your first child *before* you settle down to feeding or bathing the baby. To avoid a sudden inconvenient request for a drink, or the potty, you can get the drink and produce the potty for the older child in advance.

Feeding time for the baby may also be a useful time for reading to the older child. This is a good way to reassure him and make him less likely to feel excluded in some way by the baby.

Remember, too, that you are unlikely to have to cope with the work and the problems all by yourself. Your partner will probably wish to help as much as possible, and this can be a great opportunity for him to become closer than ever to the older child.

straight away. What matters in the end is not what he says or does at this first meeting, but how he and the baby get together as they grow up.

At home with the baby

Although your first child may show great pleasure in his new brother or sister at first, this does not mean that he needs no assurance of your love for him. A child who does not openly show jealousy in words or behaviour may nevertheless feel as insecure as the one who does.

Try to get your child to tell you what he really feels about the new baby, and do not be upset if he expresses jealousy. Help him to understand that because you are very busy with the baby you cannot spend so much time on him as you used to – but that this will not always be so.

However hard he may try to behave normally, during the first two or three weeks your first child is likely to show some sign of at least mild upset over the arrival of the baby. One of the most common reactions is to become "difficult", especially if he is around two years old.

A toddler who feels jealous of the new arrival may envy the baby's privilege of being fed at your breast. He may ask to share your lap with the baby during feeds, or even ask to be breast-fed himself. It is sensible to allow this: the phase will soon pass.

Many children also start having disturbed sleep: they become difficult about going to bed, or start waking in the night. An older child – especially one who shares a room with the baby – may form the habit of waking whenever the baby does, so as to seek a little of the attention being given to his brother or sister. If possible, try to spend a few minutes exclusively with your older child at his bedtime. If he shares a room with the baby, always take the baby out of the room for a night feed.

Some first children show their hidden feelings by a change in feeding habits: the child may refuse to eat, or may make a fuss over particular foods which he used to like.

With other children, toilet-training is sometimes affected. The child may begin having "accidents", or may revert to insisting on being helped by you. Bedwetting can be another sign of jealous stress, and if this happen at a time when the child could be resenting a new baby, keep that thought in mind when you deal with the problem. However, do not automatically assume that the baby is the cause of the bedwetting: this can easily arise from some other cause, such as the stress of going to nursery school for the first time, or an excitement such as being taken away on holiday.

Constructive help

Your first child's reaction to the challenge of a new baby may, however, show itself in more constructive ways. He may display new independence and maturity, start feeding himself, give up the feeding bottle or become reliably dry and proud of it.

Most older children do tend to show a double attitude towards the new brother or sister. Many are very interested during the baby's first few days at home, especially if they visited him early on in hospital and have been telling friends and neighbours all about him. They will show physical affection for the baby, and perhaps bring him gifts of books or toys; they are concerned when he cries. Normally, however, this intense interest will grow less after a few weeks.

As this deeper interest slackens off, it sometimes becomes mixed with a certain amount of aggression towards the baby, although this is not very common at such an early stage of their relationship.

Role of a father

This is the time when the relationship between father and first child can take on a completely new dimension if the father, for once, has sole charge of him. If the father realises that this is when his first child particularly needs him, he will be able to give the love and attention necessary, rather than join you and visiting relatives in picking up and playing with the baby.

When you begin going out for walks, if your partner is not there to help, it may be difficult at first to take both children. However, if the older child was accustomed to being taken for walks before the baby arrived, it will help his self-assurance if you can make the effort to resume this routine.

If you cannot go out yourself, it is still helpful if the walk routine can be kept up with help from a grandparent, friend or neighbour.

Remember, what your older child needs at this time is extra support, love and reassurance. If you can manage to remain patient, and keep a sense of humour amid the seemingly endless flow of childhood needs, this difficult phase will pass.

4
OLDER BABY

Sitting to walking

When a baby reaches the middle of his first year he begins to put things into his mouth. He already finds nourishment at his mother's breast and comfort from sucking his thumb. The next step is to test everything within reach, whether it happens to be a teething ring or his own foot.

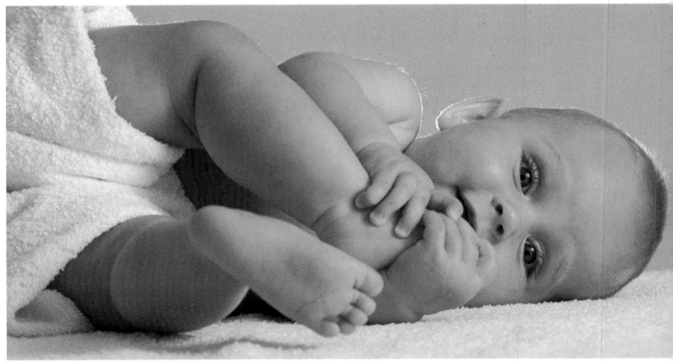

Nearly all babies love physical contact: they enjoy being played with when they are feeling awake and responsive, and being held and cuddled if they are feeling tired and unhappy or otherwise in need of comfort.

A child's first social contacts are with his mother and father. The way in which they play with him, respond to him and encourage him will make all the difference to his future self-confidence with other people.

In his first year a baby does not need another baby to play with. If two babies are placed near one another each will usually carry on with his own pursuits, although probably keeping an eye on what the other is doing.

A baby-bouncer, a saddle suspended by elastic material, enables a baby to develop and strengthen the muscles he will later use when standing and walking. For

him, the bouncing is part of the day's enjoyment, and at the same time he benefits from this exercise. Later on, a baby-walker, a frame on wheels, also exercises his muscles without putting too much strain on them, and provides his first experience of getting around on his own.

Your baby will decide for himself when he feels confident enough to try a few tottering steps. The age at which he does this varies considerably – from, perhaps, ten months old to two years. The first time he lets go of his support, he is liable to fall over. The way in which individual babies react to this also varies a lot. Some are quite unperturbed by their frequent lack of balance. They fall back on

When a baby has learnt to pull himself to his feet, he is able to stand upright if he holds on to something for support.

their bottoms, pick themselves up and start again. Others may take a few steps and wait several weeks before trying again to pull themselves to their feet and stand unaided. But the first moment of mastering the art of independent motion is one of triumph.

4 Reaching the age of mobility

During their first year, anywhere between the ages of six and 12 months, most babies discover how to move around on their own in one way or another. Some pull themselves along on their stomachs, some crawl on all fours; others shuffle along on their bottoms or just roll over and over to reach their destinations.

Your baby's first efforts at moving about the house are fascinating to watch, but they do bring problems for you and potential hazards for your child.

One problem is the difficulty of keeping him (and his clothes) clean. No matter how spotless you try to keep your home, a baby who is crawling or rolling around the floor is bound to become grubby.

In the garden or the park, your newly mobile child is not likely to stay patiently on a rug or mat when there are more exciting things to do. He is likely to pick up and examine everything he finds, so make sure you have a damp flannel or "wipes" in sachets handy.

Whether he wants to crawl about or sit still, he should have a ball, or other simple playthings, to encourage him to increase his mobility.

Although your baby is developing so swiftly, his skin is still very sensitive. If he is out in strong sun or wind he should have at least a light cotton T-shirt or dress and, if necessary, a sun-hat. To prevent sunburn or wind burn, you can use an inexpensive cream on his skin: this can be used for the whole family.

Standing up

The next stage of mobility is standing up, though some babies do this without first going through the crawling stage. This again brings some problems, particularly with regard to safety.

It is essential to make sure that any items of furniture by which your baby may pull himself up cannot tip over and injure him. Once he is standing, he may find a whole new range of interesting items within his reach. Any valued and breakable items, as well as any that might be dangerous, should be removed to a safe height, even if for the time being they seem just out of his reach.

If you have a telephone, this should also be put out of your child's reach: otherwise you could be faced with large bills for accidental long-distance calls. If he seems interested in the telephone, buy him a toy one of his own.

Learning to walk

Once your baby can stand up by holding on to the furniture, he will soon discover that he can also walk with this support, or by holding on to your fingers. This stage of helping him to walk can take up a good deal of your time, and it may be helpful to let him sometimes use a baby walker – a tubular frame on wheels, with a sling-seat, which he can propel along with his feet. However, this is no substitute for your own effort and encouragement, and should not be used for a long period.

The age at which babies begin to walk varies enormously: your own child may start to walk as early as nine months old or as late as two years old. A baby who started by crawling may not bother to walk at an early age, because he can get around quite happily without doing so. Heavier babies often start walking a little later than lighter ones.

Whenever your baby begins to walk, he is likely to suffer a few bumps and scrapes as he toddles around. Do not worry too much about these mishaps; your child's first steps are a milestone in his development, and you will need to strike a reasonable balance between keeping him safe and allowing him to satisfy his natural curiosity and use his growing energy. Just make sure that obvious dangers are moved out of his way, and if he does have a slight accident, be ready with your sympathy and a cuddle.

Now that your baby is standing and walking you will notice that his legs are rather bowed: this is normal, but if he wears a nappy while walking, you should make sure that it is not too bunched-up between the legs, or it may encourage the bowed effect to become unduly exaggerated.

A child who has begun to walk may go back to crawling for a while if he has been ill, or is under stress such as jealousy over a new brother or sister. Do not show annoyance or impatience: he is merely appealing for an extra display of love from you. If he receives this he will feel secure again and revert to walking.

Safety in the home

As soon as babies discover how to crawl, wriggle or shuffle on their bottoms, their new-found mobility opens up a whole new world of discovery – and danger. Nearly half of all accidents in the home happen to children. Most of these children are under five, and many of these accidents can be prevented.

A young baby has little or no sense of danger, and a normal home harbours many possible risks for a child of this age, so simple safety precautions are essential.

A playpen is useful for keeping a mobile baby safe while you answer the door or attend to the cooking; but do not leave him in it so long that it becomes a cage restricting his natural urge to explore. The playpen should have a floor: otherwise, a determined baby can easily move it.

To avoid cuts (as well as damage), keep all china, glass, tools, cutlery, scissors and old razor blades out of reach. Avoid a trailing electric flex or table cloth – toddlers love to pull them, with the risk of bringing an iron, an electric kettle or a pot of hot tea down on their heads. Sockets set four feet or more above floor level make it easier to keep flexes out of a child's reach as well as being more convenient for you.

A child will put anything in his mouth, so take care with small objects. Don't throw things like paper clips into waste-paper baskets, as a

small child enjoys turning out the contents.

In the bathroom, fix the bolt or lock out of a toddler's reach. Small children can easily drown in a few inches of water, so never leave them alone in the bath.

Safety with poisons
On average, 20 toddlers die in Britain alone from poisoning every year.

In the kitchen, keep washing powders, washing-up liquid, bleach and other cleaning materials in their original containers, so that they cannot be mistaken for anything else. Store them on a high shelf, well out of reach. If they have to be within reach, for example in a cupboard under the kitchen sink, fit a child-proof catch on the cupboard door.

In the workshop and garage, the same precautions must be taken with oil, turpentine substitute, paraffin, paint-stripper and similar substances. In the garden shed, take the same care with weedkillers, insecticides and fertilisers.

In particular, *never* keep any poisonous liquids in old soft-drink bottles. Small children will assume that they are for drinking.

The bathroom medicine cupboard should be wall-mounted, well out of reach. Its fastening should be designed so that a small child cannot open it, even if he climbs up to it. The cupboard should have a sloping top, to prevent bottles being left on top and forgotten. Ideally, the cupboard should incorporate a pull-down dispensing tray, so that there is no chance of medicine bottles being left on tables within reach of children.

To children, pills look temptingly

like sweets. Old medicines and pills should be flushed down the lavatory, and in some countries can be returned to the chemist if obtained on prescription.

Safety from burns

Burns and scalds kill about 150 children in Britain alone every year. Thousands more are injured or disfigured.

Keep your children away from fires and make their night-wear from fabrics with low flammability, such as pure polyester and pure nylon. Flowing garments are particularly vulnerable, and pyjamas are safer than nightdresses.

Wherever there is a fire with exposed flames or elements, a fireguard is an absolute necessity. This should be fixed firmly to the wall or chimney breast, so that a small child cannot push it aside. Its mesh should be strong, and fine enough to prevent fingers or inflammable articles being pushed through. It should have a top, so that toys cannot be thrown behind it. An expanding fireguard is adaptable to different fireplaces.

Avoid placing mirrors above fireplaces. The clothing of a child stretching up to look at his reflection can quickly catch light.

In the kitchen, toddlers must be prevented from pulling the contents of cooking utensils on to themselves. A strong and rigid cooker guard – a detachable rail around the top – is best. Failing that, pot and pan handles must always be turned inwards.

Even though natural gas is non-poisonous, an escape can still cause an explosion and a fire. Teach a child never to touch gas taps.

Some electric cookers have rings that remain black when hot. Teach children never to touch them even when cold. The outsides of cookers, too, can get hot enough to burn. Keep hot irons well out of the reach of young children.

In the bathroom, warn children not to touch hot-water taps, which can burn. To avoid the danger of scalds, run cold water first, then add hot water to raise the temperature. Never leave a small child alone in the bath, where he can turn on the hot tap.

If an electric heater in the bedroom or nursery is necessary, a convector heater is preferable to the glowing, radiant type. Make sure that the heater has a cut-out which automatically switches off the current if the heater is overturned; check, too, that the holes in the heater grille are small enough to exclude a child's fingers. Use a hot-water bottle only to warm a child's bed – remove it before he gets in.

Never let a small child light a firework himself, or approach or handle any lit firework. At Christmas, use flame-resistant decorations.

Never allow young children to get hold of matches.

Care with electricity

An electric shock can kill, and even more frequently it inflicts severe burns. Treat electrical points and appliances as possible sources of danger at all times.

Never use a portable electric fire or fan heater to make a cold bathroom more comfortable for a child. Water is an excellent conductor of electricity, so it is easy for a wet

towel flicked on to a heater element to cause a fatal electric shock.

Do not use an electric blanket in a child's bed if he is a bed-wetter.

Put all electrical appliances away after using them. Food mixers, hair dryers and electric drills can injure a child badly if he switches them on, or give him an electric shock if he interferes with them.

To prevent a toddler poking metal objects into electric points, cover unused points with a spare plug, or with a safety cover.

Care to avoid falls

It is necessary to have a safety gate to prevent the baby going up or down stairs. One that is detachable and adjustable can also be used to block an open front or back door in hot weather. The screw fixings of the gate should be of a type impossible for a toddler to undo. The gate must be high enough to stop a child climbing over it, and for the same reason its bars must be vertical.

Once a toddler can climb, upstairs windows become a hazard. Fit a short chain to a dormer window, or a lock to a sash window so that there is no danger of the child falling out.

High chairs should have firm, widely spaced legs so that they are not easily tipped over. Use the child's safety harness to clip him into the chair.

A rubber mat in the bath and a hand-rail on its edge help to prevent bath-time falls.

A toddler's cot should be fitted with fastenings he cannot undo, and the cot sides should be free from crossbars, which will encourage him to climb.

First year of growth

Throughout childhood, the proportions of the body change as growth and development proceed. The newborn baby has a relatively large head and short limbs: this is one of the features that make him look vulnerable and appealing. As he gets older, the rapid growth of his head slows down; brain growth is almost complete at the age of five. At the same time, the legs and arms, which previously were comparatively short, grow longer, in relation to the body.

Centiles

During the first year of life, a baby triples his weight and increases in length by 50 per cent. Babies grow at different rates, and there is no such thing as "normal" weight or length at a particular age. There is, however, a *range* of weights and lengths which are considered normal.

This range is usually represented by a series of lines, called centile lines, on a graph (see right). Centiles are charted from the recorded rates of growth in weight and length of a representative sample of babies, and they show the normal variation in weight and length recorded in 94 per cent of babies.

If a baby's weight falls in the 3 per cent above the 97th centile, or in the 3 per cent below the 3rd centile, then it is likely that there is something wrong with him and a doctor should be consulted for advice. The same

principles apply to centiles of length.

As well as measuring weight and length, most child-health clinics keep a regular check on the growth of a baby's head, during this first year. The head enlarges quickly at this time because of brain growth.

One easily visible feature of normal head growth is the closing of the fontanelle, the soft spot on top, near the front of the skull. This varies greatly in size at birth, and can be seen pulsating with the heartbeat. Many mothers feel unnecessarily nervous about touching the fontanelle, or washing the skin over it, but the brain beneath is fully protected by a very tough membrane. Bone forms rapidly in the fontanelle membrane, and the soft spot gets smaller through the first year, usually closing completely during the second year. There are five small fontanelles, one at the back of the head and two at each side, that close about the end of the first year.

GUIDELINES TO A BABY'S GROWTH

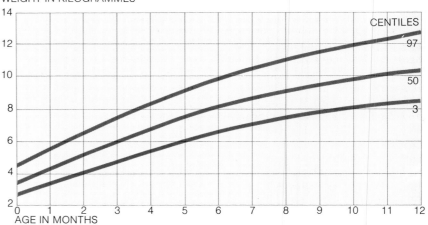

WEIGHT IN KILOGRAMMES

CENTILES
97
50
3

AGE IN MONTHS

This chart shows weight centiles. The top line, the 97th centile, is the upper weight limit recorded in 97% of babies; in other words, only 3% of babies will be heavier than this. The middle line, the 50th centile, is the average weight of babies. Only 3% of babies fall below the bottom line, the 3rd centile, at any given age. Between the centile lines shown, other lines can be drawn on the graph to find other growth rates.

Most babies' growth rates will follow one of these centile lines. Do not worry which centile your own baby follows, as long as he follows one line or another fairly consistently. If he shows a persistent tendency to cross lines, it may mean either that he is getting too fat (if he crosses the lines moving upwards on the graph), or else that he is not gaining as much weight as he should (if he crosses them by moving downwards on the graph).

The first solid food

As long as your baby is comfortably established on breast-feeding or bottle-feeding, there is absolutely no need to attempt to introduce solid foods. Indeed, it can be harmful to start him on solids before the age of about four months, because a baby's digestion and metabolism are not yet ready to cope with anything but milk. They may be overstrained, or respond by becoming allergic to the food that has been given. Also, solid food before this age could lead to the baby being overweight.

By four or five months, however, the iron stored in the baby's liver before he was born is running out, and the small amount present in milk is not enough. So foods richer in iron become necessary. Also, as your baby's nutritional needs grow, you will find it more and more difficult to satisfy his appetite with milk alone. When you reach this stage, it is time to start him off gradually on solid foods. The baby himself will leave you in no doubt as to when he is ready to begin. It may be at about four months, rarely before, or not until six months or even seven – it varies from baby to baby.

How to begin
Do not try to introduce your baby to too many new flavours at once when he begins his adventure into solid food, or you may find that he rejects everything. You can start him off with a small teaspoon of a grain or rice cereal, made up into a sloppy mixture with milk.

The best time of day to introduce solids is at the midday feed. Most babies respond best after they have had their usual breast or bottle-feed, when mother and baby are relaxed and calm. Introduce the foods one at a time, leaving a few days between each new taste. This gives the baby a chance to get used to the new flavour – and allows you the opportunity to identify any food which seems to cause an upset stomach or an allergy. If a new food does upset the baby, do not give him that particular food again without consulting your doctor or health visitor. These reactions are usually temporary, and you will probably be advised to try the food again, in very small amounts, after a month or two. Wheat flour, cheese, cow's milk, eggs and fish are all possible causes of allergies, as are some preservatives. The symptoms generally include a rash, slight temperature or wheezing. It is thought that hyperactivity can also be caused by an allergic reaction. It is best not to introduce such foods until your baby is older than six months.

Do not be surprised if there is a change in the frequency of your child's bowel actions; this change can often occur after mixed feeding is introduced.

Preparing baby foods
As a first taste of solid food, purées of fruit or vegetables, or a baby cereal, are ideal. Bananas are easily digested, as are papayas (pawpaws) which, in their native countries, are among the first foods given to babies.

Citrus fruits are very acid and should not be given except as well-diluted juice until the baby is twelve months old. Strawberries are a common cause of allergy and should also not be given to a very young baby. Babies who are allergic to wheat flour or gluten can have rice flour or millet instead.

It is really very simple and inexpensive to prepare fresh food for your baby, rather than buying proprietary brands. In the long run, this makes it easier to change over to a more adult diet. Cooked fruit, and vegetables such as boiled potato, will need little more than mashing with a fork. If you have a hand blender or electric liquidiser, most foods can be made into purée very quickly (see First recipes for babies, p. 103).

Never add salt or sugar to the food: too much salt can cause dehydration, and sugar will encourage a "sweet tooth", with all its obvious health problems. In any case, a baby's palate is far more sensitive than an adult's, and he simply does not need seasoned or sweetened food.

Occasional problems arise with weaning. Some babies refuse to have anything to do with solids at first; others start well, but later lose their enthusiasm. Refusal to eat solids in a baby's first year is usually the result of a change in routine. In particular, introduce lumpy foods only gradually, because babies often have some difficulty with these.

Before you offer any food to your baby, apart from making sure there are no lumps, see that it is neither too sticky nor too runny for him to cope with. If at the first very small sampling he takes to the new experience quite readily, offer a little more. Most babies quickly get used to a new taste and consistency, and you can gradually increase the amount to suit your baby's appetite.

Manufactured baby foods can be very convenient if you are short of time or are travelling. They are often available in small sample sizes, useful if you are experimenting with a new taste. Do make sure, though, that they are free from added sugar, salt or preservatives.

If your baby refuses a solid food, never try to force him to eat it. Solid foods are quite different from milk, in taste and texture, and swallowing solids involves a different technique from sucking at a bottle or breast. So do not worry if the baby does not seem keen, at first. Try something else – a different kind of cereal, apple purée, or some other kind of strained fruit. If he obviously dislikes solid food, or gets upset, just leave it, and try again a few days later.

You should take care not to give your baby too much food that is fattening. While he has been on a diet of milk alone, he is not likely to have become overweight. Once he begins to change over to a mixed diet, however, he will run the risk of getting fat – and fat babies (frequently described misguidedly as "bonny") all too often grow into fat older children and end up as fat adolescents.

After a few weeks on solids, add another type of food – for example, purée of vegetables or egg yolk. In this way, you can gradually build up his experience of new foods, moving eventually to a good variety by the time he is six or seven months old. By then, his diet can include small amounts of meat, liver, fish and chicken, so long as they are strained or very finely minced.

At about six months old, you will notice that your baby is starting to chew, and that he can easily cope with soft lumps in his food, even before he gets any teeth. Soft pieces of potato or well-cooked vegetables can now be added to his dinner, and it will gradually become less necessary to serve the food in liquid or purée form. But you should still avoid large, hard lumps, which might cause him to choke.

Finger foods

At about the same age, he will begin to put things in his mouth, and you can introduce him to foods which he can hold himself, and chew. Most babies love to feed themselves and be independent. The traditional rusks are ideal to start with, as they go soft fairly quickly. However, most bought rusks have added sugar, even when marked "low sugar", so make your own if you can (see recipe opposite). Finger foods play a large part in a baby's diet at this age. Toast fingers are usually popular, as are sticks of fruit and vegetables such as apples and carrots.

As soon as a baby shows signs of wanting to try to feed himself, let him do so, even though he is bound to make rather a mess at first. He will gradually learn to cope more effectively, and a baby who feeds himself is likely to eat as much as he needs, whereas a baby who accepts all the food his mother forces on him may well become overweight.

There is no need to try to measure out precise amounts of food. If in doubt, give too little at first; and when your baby has finished that, offer him a little more. Even a baby can be put off by the sight of an over-full plate of food. Above all, do not expect your baby to eat up his food in any particular time. Some babies learning to feed themselves may get through a meal quite quickly, while others take their time – just as they probably did while being breast-fed or bottle-fed.

Before long, your baby will be able to cope with small sandwiches and other tea-time foods. Avoid foods containing sugar – such as sweets, cakes and biscuits – because they can contribute to excess weight, as well as harming teeth. Chewing more solid food – as well as toys and other hard objects – can be a great comfort to a baby when he is teething, and will help him to develop healthy gums and teeth.

Until now, milk has still formed by far the major part of your baby's diet. But once he is happy to accept solids, you can begin to replace some of his milk intake. When you do this, you may find that he drops from four to three feeds a day (if he has not already done so), because solids will satisfy his hunger for a longer period than milk alone will.

Eating with the family

By the age of about six months the baby's mealtimes will more or less coincide with those of the remainder of the family, which makes life easier for you. For some of the meals, at least, he will be able to eat the same food as the rest of the family,

FIRST RECIPES FOR BABIES

Here are some basic recipes you can use to introduce your baby to solid food. Do this little by little, starting with a tea-spoon or two once a day, and only gradually work up to a menu such as the one given here. Some babies will have reached this stage by about 6 months, others not until 9 months or later.

On waking: Diluted fruit juice or milk (from breast or bottle).

Breakfast: Baby cereal mixed with milk. Milk to drink (breast or bottle).

Mid-morning: Cooled boiled water or diluted fruit juice (sugar-free).

Lunch: Chicken or fish with vegetables; fruit purée (fresh or cooked) with yoghurt or egg custard. Milk or water, according to feeding stage reached.

Tea-time: Bread-and-butter fingers, with cheese or the yolk of a lightly boiled egg. Diluted fruit juice.

Bedtime: Milk (breast or bottle).

RECIPES

Apple purée
Peel and chop a small eating apple; sim-mer in a little water until soft. Mash with a fork.

Banana or mango rice
Mash a ripe banana or a piece of mango with 2 tablespoons boiled rice. Add a little milk and, if desired, ½ teaspoon honey.

Cheese purée
Sieve or blend 1 tablespoon cottage cheese until smooth, and stir in 1 to 2 tablespoons boiling water.

Vegetable broth
Roughly chop 100 g (4 oz) each of carrots, celery and tomatoes. Put them in a heavy pan with 100 g (4 oz) of split red lentils. Cover with 1 litre (1¾ pints) of unsalted chicken stock (or meat or vegetable stock, or with plain water) and simmer for 40 minutes. Stir in 1 tablespoon un-salted tomato purée. Sieve or liquidise until smooth.

Rusks
Cut thick slices of bread (preferably wholemeal, but without actual whole grains in it) into 1 cm (½ in) cubes. Dip them into vegetable broth or stock. Bake on a greased baking sheet in a low oven (150°C, 300°F, gas mark 2) for about 20 minutes or until crisp. If wished, these can be crumbled and eaten as a cereal with broth or milk.

Carrot purée
Peel and slice carrot, simmer in boiling water until soft. Drain, mash with fork.

Chicken purée
Finely slice or shred 60 g (2 oz) chicken breast, put on plate with 1 tablespoon water or milk, place over pan of simmer-ing water; cover and cook until tender (15–20 minutes). Blend or liquidise with the liquid.

Egg custard
Heat, without boiling, 125 ml (¼ pint) milk and mix slowly into 1 egg yolk beaten with 1 tablespoon sugar. Strain into a double boiler and reheat, stirring the custard until thick. Chill.

Fish with papaya (pawpaw)
Simmer 50 g (2 oz) white fish with 50 g (2 oz) raw papaya in a little water for about 10 minutes. Blend or mash.

even if some of it must be puréed.

Some of the food you prepare for the family may *not* be suitable for babies, however. Unsuitable foods include highly spiced or seasoned meals such as hot curry – this may contain chilli, which is an irritant – or rich foods which contain a lot of sugar or fat, such as stodgy puddings or fried foods. If you are giving these to the family, you should prepare something else for the baby yourself.

If you own a freezer, you can cook larger quantities of dishes suitable for your baby and freeze them in one-meal portions. Then all you have to do when you want to use them is to re-heat them thoroughly.

Drinks
As your baby eats more solid food, he will need more to drink, in the form of water which has been boiled and cooled, or well-diluted fruit juice. These drinks should be offered to the baby between meals.

There are a lot of fruit syrups, such as rosehip and blackcurrant, speci-ally manufactured for babies and older children. They are rich in Vitamin C, but do tend to contain a lot of sugar. These drinks should always be well diluted. In any case, there is nothing wrong with plain boiled water as a drink for your baby, who will get plenty of Vitamin C from his food. A far better way of supplying Vitamin C is to give the baby juice from freshly squeezed oranges, as long as this is suitably diluted. Pure fruit juice for babies, without added sugar, is now available.

Never ever put sugary drinks in a feeder bottle for the baby to suck.

How baby teeth grow

Your baby's first tooth will probably appear when he is four or five months old, although he may have none for the whole of his first year. There is no fixed age at which the first (primary) teeth should come through, and there is certainly no need to worry if your child's teeth appear later than those of other babies. However, by 14 months most children should have some teeth. If your baby has none by the age of 18 months, consult a dentist.

Teething is a normal process in the development of a baby. Some babies seem to produce their teeth with no sign of trouble. Others have flushed faces and reddened gums where a tooth is emerging. They may also be irritable and dribble more than usual.

Teething is wrongly blamed for other disorders. It does not – as some people believe – cause bronchitis, high temperature, severe stomach upsets or any other ailment. If your baby shows any sign of illness, do not blame teething: call your doctor or take your baby to the surgery.

The baby who refuses solids is also likely to drink more. This means that his nappy will probably need to be changed more often.

At about this time, your baby may continually chew his fingers or his toys. This is not due to teething, but is a stage of his oral development.

If your baby does want to chew, give him a teething ring or play-shapes. Encourage him to eat rusks (preferably home-made – see p. 103) and chew raw carrots.

Protecting the teeth

Sugar is an enemy of the teeth. As soon as sugar has been eaten, acid forms in the mouth and begins to dissolve the mineral in the enamel outer layer of the teeth.

Once the mineral is lost, a soft cavity is left in the tooth itself. The destructive process continues, as the next layer of the tooth, the dentine, is attacked. The area of decay expands and reaches the pulp which contains the nerves and blood vessels. This inflammation is very painful. Finally, the pulp will die and pus will fill the inside of the tooth – and can spread into the face.

Sweets and snacks are the most harmful way to take sugar, so far as teeth are concerned. But in whatever form sugar is taken – white or brown, liquid or solid – it means that destructive acid will be present.

Babies are not born with a "sweet tooth" and if sugar is not added to their milk and other foods, they need never grow to like it. To prevent your child developing a sweet tooth, make sure he has enough to eat at mealtimes, and that he is not given sticky buns, cream cakes and sweets between meals. Cleaning the teeth immediately after a meal minimises the harmful effect of any sugar that has been eaten. Ask relatives and friends to help by giving presents other than sweets.

Another danger to teeth, in babyhood, is the practice of giving the child a dummy coated with honey, syrup or jam. This keeps the sugary substance in close contact with the baby's front teeth as he sucks. It can quickly cause decay as soon as the teeth come through the gums. For the same reason, never use a miniature feeder filled with sugary drinks or syrups, and never let a toddler take a bottle of sugary milk to bed.

As soon as a child can use a spoon to feed himself, he is old enough to

DEVELOPING TEETH IN A BABY

In the months before your baby is born, he will begin to develop teeth from a core of cells in the centre of the jaw on each side, upper and lower. These cores grow backwards through areas which will eventually harden into jawbones. Cells break off from the cores and form toothbuds – one for each of the 20 milk teeth and 32 permanent teeth. As the time of birth approaches, the milk-tooth buds develop into tooth shapes until at birth all but the roots have formed. By the time your baby is four or five months old, his first teeth may break through the gums.

6-week-old embryo

12-week-old embryo

16-week-old fetus

24-week-old fetus

32-week-old fetus

At a baby's birth | Tooth breaks through

start trying to brush his own teeth. Until then you should do it for him. Start brushing his teeth as soon as they appear; try to treat it as a game and assume he will enjoy it. Special baby fluoride toothpastes are available that contain no sugar. Many young children do not like toothpaste, but at this age it is enough to brush with water.

Children of this age cannot be expected to clean their teeth thoroughly, so, after the toddler has had his turn, you should always supervise and then finish the task for him.

Strengthening the teeth

Apart from avoiding too much sugar and making sure the child's teeth are kept clean, they should be strengthened against acid attack.

If a child takes in some fluoride each day his adult teeth hidden in the gums will acquire enough to reduce decay. Ask your dentist how much fluoride your child needs: your water supply may already contain fluoride. If your child needs more, it can be given in tablets – crushed in a milk feed or dissolved in a Vitamin C drink – or in drops added to the milk or other drink. An older child can chew the tablets. For extra protection, after the age of three, the dentist can paint the teeth with fluoride.

Your child should get to know the dentist before he has any trouble with his teeth. A good dentist will take the trouble to make friends with the child, and probably give him a "joyride" in the dentist's chair. Six-monthly visits from the age of three can also be helpful in preventing tooth decay.

HOW THE FIRST TEETH APPEAR

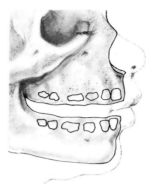

At birth

Usually, no teeth are through when the baby is born. Incisors working out through the gums (see profile, left) are marked A and B, canines C, molars (double teeth) D and E on plain view, right. They will not appear in that order.

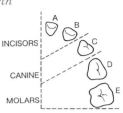

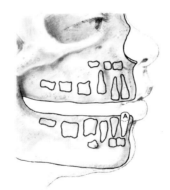

At five to six months

First are usually the lower central incisors (lower A). Next, the upper central incisors (upper A) or the lateral incisors (upper and lower B). The first molars (D) should show by 12–15 months, canines (C) by 16–20 months, and second molars (E) by 20–24 months.

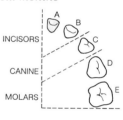

At three years

A full set of 20 baby teeth (primary teeth) should have come through by now: eight incisors (A and B), four canines (C), eight molars (D and E). The 32 permanent teeth are steadily growing in the gums.

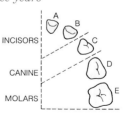

A garden for all the family

There are two differing family views about a garden. Parents may regard it as a place to grow fruit, flowers and vegetables, and as somewhere to sit on hot summer days. Growing children, however, look upon it solely as their private playground. You can have an attractive, productive garden while still leaving play space for your children, but planning should be done at an early stage, looking ahead to the years when children are mobile.

Adapting the garden
These are the basic features of your garden that will need attention:

Lawn You will have to postpone any plans for a lawn of bowling-green standard while children want to use it as a cricket pitch or as a site for an Indian camp. If you are sowing a lawn when your first baby is still in his pram, ask your seed merchant for a special hard-duty seed mix. The resulting grass will withstand punishment for years, and any bare patches can be re-seeded in autumn.

In an established lawn, buy turf in autumn to cover bare spots. Move a swing every autumn to a different part of the lawn. If possible, get rid of all flower beds in the middle of the lawn to make a large play area.

Garden pool If you move into a house that already has a pool, drain it before your first child can walk. Even a shallow pool is a potential killer. Do not use the empty pool as a sandpit because it will soon become waterlogged. Instead, fill it with pot plants or cover it with planks of wood until the children are older.

Sandpit Make a sandpit on well-drained soil in a sunny part of the garden. Cover the sand with poly-thene, held down with bricks or stones, when the children have finished playing; otherwise the pit will soon be fouled by cats. In autumn clear out the sand, keeping some for odd building repairs and spreading the rest on the garden. Fill the pit with fresh sand in the spring.

Flower beds Avoid using stakes to support plants. A child can all too easily ram one into his eye. Instead, buy special grow-through supports obtainable from garden centres.

Greenhouses Any gardener must be prepared for damage to glass from a mis-hit ball. You might, however, hang a nylon-mesh screen on stout supports on the most vulnerable side of the greenhouse. Use polythene or PVC cold frames and cloches.

Paths If you are moving into a newly built house and have an opportunity to design the garden, try building a path that runs round the garden with interesting bends and corners. Plant shrubs at strategic points so that a new view opens as you turn a corner. Meanwhile, children can enjoy racing on their tricycles and pedal cars.

Pets and your baby

If you have one or more family pets, there is no reason to feel that you must get rid of them just because you are expecting a baby. Pets are part of the family, which should not be broken up just because a new member is on the way.

However, you will need to plan for the day when the baby arrives, when pets will have to play a less important role in the family than they have been used to. This is particularly necessary for a hitherto childless couple who until now have lavished affection on their dog or cat.

Once you bring your baby home, you will have enough work on your hands without having to cope with pets who have not been prepared for the alteration in their routine. For this reason it is important that any necessary change in the pet's life is made well before the baby is brought home for the first time.

Your dog
If your dog has been allowed into your bedroom – perhaps even to sleep there – he will have to be taught that this is no longer permitted. The dog should be given a basket or box in another room, preferably the kit-chen, and get used to sleeping there.

You may have to endure a night or two of hopeful whining, scratching and barking, but he should soon become accustomed to his new sleeping arrangements. He will easily settle in if he is led to his sleeping place at about the same time each night, and when he finds that his initial "complaints" have no effect.

It is essential not to let the dog feel that the new baby is responsible for his being banished from your bedroom, or to feel jealous about the fuss made of the child. You should make a special effort to "fuss" the dog a little more than usual while he is getting used to the baby.

During pregnancy and for a while afterwards, you may need to make special arrangements for the exercising of your dog, if you have not the time or energy to do this yourself. Exercise, important for a dog at all times, is even more important now; an under-exercised dog is a bored dog, who becomes jealous more easily and may become aggressive as a result of that jealousy.

Part of the dog's exercise, once you have brought your baby home, may be walking with you when you take your child out in his pram. The dog will need to be taught to walk so that the lead does not get caught up in the pram wheels. Never leave the dog tied to the pram while you are shopping: this is a recipe for disaster.

Very occasionally, despite all precautions and adequate exercise, a dog may become extremely jealous, and this may show itself in the form of aggression. He is unlikely to be able to vent his aggression directly on the baby, but he may show it towards you instead. The aggression and jealousy may pass after a while; if, however, it does not, then you will have to reconcile yourself to the need to part with the dog, no matter how much he may have been one of the family until then.

It is much more likely that as your dog becomes accustomed to the presence of your baby, he will become over-protective, and show aggression towards people outside the immediate family. This protectiveness can be embarrassing when displayed towards close relatives or family friends, but will normally fade away quite quickly, and is unlikely to create any lasting problems.

Your cat

Cats, too, can be jealous, but normally of each other. The real danger of allowing them into the room where your baby sleeps is their tendency to choose the cot or pram as a comfortable place to sleep. They will not be put off by having to share their sleeping place with the baby – indeed, they will appreciate the extra warmth. There is then a serious danger that the cat will settle on the baby's face and cause suffocation.

A cat is intelligent enough to accept exile from the bedroom very quickly, to all appearances. But he may also show great cunning and determination in slipping back through the doorway unnoticed. The answer to this problem is to place a net over the cot or pram.

Remember that other people's cats may get into your home, or into your garden when the baby is out in his pram. Always put a net on the pram when it is in the garden, even if the baby is not in it: this prevents any cat getting into the habit of trying to sleep there. A good fine-mesh net has the additional advantage of keeping flies and insects away.

Health risks

The chief risk to health is toxocara, a roundworm whose eggs are found in the faeces of cats and dogs. A child playing in contaminated areas can easily be infected. Symptoms are usually mild or non-existent, but very occasionally serious eye disease and even blindness can result. Dogs and cats should be wormed every six months. It is a good idea to have your pets' health checked by a veterinary surgeon and to have any necessary vaccinations done before your baby arrives.

From the beginning, discourage the dog from licking your baby. When the baby begins to crawl, teach him not to go near the pets' food or drinking bowl. Apart from the question of hygiene, even the best-intentioned dog may resent an attempt to share his dinner.

As your baby changes to solid foods, neither dog nor cat should be allowed to finish off his leftovers. The dog may begin to consider the entire meal as *his* food, and decide not to wait until it is offered. The cat may form the habit of jumping up to join in the child's meal.

While your baby is young, it is important to watch your pets for fleas and other parasites and any signs of skin trouble. If you suspect such problems, consult a veterinary surgeon. Fleas and mites from dogs and cats can cause skin infection in people. A more common problem, however, is an allergic rash caused when the child is hyper-sensitive to animal parasites.

Looking after a child

Many women return to work about six months after the birth of their child. Even if you do not work, you may at some period be prevented by accident, illness or some other domestic crisis from looking after your child yourself. In either case, you will obviously want to ensure that your child has the best possible care.

Unless you can afford the considerable expense of employing a private nanny, probably your choice will be between a child-minder (who looks after other people's children in her own home) and a day nursery (or crèche, day-care centre or child-care centre – various names for places where children are cared for in fairly large groups).

The latter may be government supported or run privately, either for profit or by a charitable organisation. They are all similar in the services they offer, but the hours of child care, the ages of the children (very few cater for under-twos), the charges and the quality of service vary considerably. Charges may be related to your ability to pay, while some crèches are provided for a nominal fee by companies as an incentive for young mothers to work for them.

Child-minders in Britain should be registered with the local authority (see p. 146) and are liable to inspection. Although registration is not in itself a recommendation it is a starting point when you are looking for a child-minder. As they are often the only available means of care for very young children they do tend to get very booked up.

Some staff in nurseries and day-care centres – but by no means all – will have had some training. An untrained child-minder, on the other hand, has fewer children to cope with and may be in a better position to provide the sort of mothering most children need.

When inquiring about child care, you should visit a centre or a child-minder's home during working hours. Do not be put off if the premises look slightly scruffy, but do beware of any place that appears dirty.

How much stimulation will your child get from play and toys at the centre or child-minder's home? Looking after his physical needs alone is not enough. Though education is not the primary aim of these child-care services, every child needs stimulating play and attention from adults to help to develop his body and mind.

The mother at home
Even if you look after your child at home you may want him to have the chance of meeting and playing with other children of his own age. Play-groups (for under-sixes) and Mother and Toddler groups (for under-threes) are a very successful way of meeting this need. Your child benefits from the company of other children and you can share your problems and experience with other mothers.

Toys for the older baby

When your baby begins to grasp things, it is time to give him a suitable rattle. Initially this should be tied within his reach to enable him to hold and release it, yet be able to grasp it again. An ideal rattle contains a revolving wheel that makes a noise when the wheel is turned.

At this age a baby can put small objects into his mouth, so anything that is given to him to play with should be small enough to hold, but not so small as to be easily swallowed. It is also very important that the materials he is handling can be safely sucked.

It is important from the start that you should play games with your baby. Ideal games are the ones that encourage him to co-ordinate hand and eye movements. A bunch of keys, or something similar, shaken and passed across the cot in front of a baby will attract his attention and encourage him to follow the object with his eyes. Rattles and squeaky balls brought within reach of his hands will encourage him to coordinate hand and eye, and eventually to grasp and hold the objects offered to him.

Exploring by handling
Very soon the baby begins to use both hands to fondle things. He can

handle rings, rattles, balls, teddy bears, dolls, large cloth building cubes and small picture books, and he can transfer an object from one hand to the other. A large, deeply indented plastic ball with a squeaker makes a very interesting toy at this age. Its shape makes it easy to handle, and yet the shaped surface prevents it from rolling too far away when it is released.

Other toys suitable for this age group include teethers, hand bells on a wooden handle, a string of large wooden beads or cotton reels painted in non-toxic paint, securely sealed tins of stones, peas or beans, or other things to rattle, and washable rubber or plastic animals and plastic dolls. A medium-sized cardboard box filled with odds and ends makes an excellent plaything.

Even as young as six months, babies can really enjoy "board books". By twelve months, they

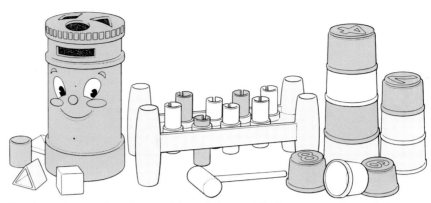

The letter-box teaches the matching of shapes. The hammer and pegs help hand and eye co-ordination, and the beakers nest together or build into a tower.

enjoy manipulating toys: matching shapes and fitting them together, as well as knocking them down. Do not swamp your baby by giving him too many toys at once; put some away and then reintroduce them after an interval.

While toys are essential to a baby's development and well-being, nothing can take the place of the time spent by his mother and father playing with him.

Safety with toys
A great deal of publicity has been given to dangerous toys, so most adults are aware of at least some of the hazards.

Many large toy manufacturers work to stringent specifications and carry out continuous and rigorous tests ensuring safety. Much work is also going on to develop agreed standards of safety. These standards will help to ensure that, in the future, toys are designed and manufactured to avoid all known hazards.

In the manufacture of the best-made toys no toxic substances are used, and inflammable materials are avoided. Clockwork mechanisms and other moving parts are fully enclosed, and exposed metal parts are free from sharp edges. Wheels are securely attached, and apertures are tested for size and shape to make certain that a child's fingers cannot become trapped in them.

Always examine a toy before giving it to a child. It should match a child's stage of development; and some play needs adult supervision. Here are a few points to watch:
● Eyes in dolls and teddy bears should be firmly fixed.
● Do not give construction kits to very young children – they can easily swallow small pieces.
● Wooden toys should have smooth edges to prevent splinters.
● Rivets and screws should be free from burrs and sharp edges.
● Play with sand or water should be supervised. Thrown sand can get into a child's eyes, and spilt water makes a floor slippery.

Babies enjoy gripping large plastic or fabric dice, and specially shaped rattles and teethers. The "whirly" toy has rattles on three separate stems for baby to box with.

Helping your baby to talk

Even before your baby is born, he can hear the sound of your voice and your heartbeat. By the time he leaves the womb, he already associates these sounds with food, warmth and security – and he will continue to do so.

From the beginning, your baby learns to communicate with you – his first and most natural teacher. His first lesson will be that your presence means comfort for him.

As early as the sixth week you can see how your baby's expression changes when he sees you coming or hears your voice. Soon he will begin to communicate by smiling, cooing, babbling and kicking. These are all part of his development towards learning to speak.

As a new mother, wishing to give your baby the greatest possible encouragement towards proper speech, you will need to know what is happening in these early stages. While a baby is aware of surrounding noise from the moment he is born, he will not usually show any reaction to the sound of your voice until about the third week. Once he does so, he will begin to take notice of you as the person who looks into his cot, picks him up, feeds him, changes his nappy and generally makes him feel warm and comfortable.

During his sixth week or so a baby should begin to smile, and he will be responding to his mother in particular. By the age of four months, he will be cooing and chuckling: these are the early signs that he is beginning to recognise and join in the society around him. Though he still cannot talk, he will have other ways of communicating with you – by touching you, pulling, pushing, or grasping your finger.

First attempts at speech

Even before your baby manages to pronounce his first real word, his "baby talk" will come more and more to resemble speech. You can encourage him to imitate speech patterns, with rising and falling intonations, while he is still producing only an expressive babbling sound. With your encouragement, your baby will learn to control the movements of his tongue, lips, palate and vocal chords.

At about six months, your baby will probably "talk" less often, but more effectively. He will experiment with "Ma" and "Da", which at this stage are mere sounds and not an attempt to say "Mama" or "Dada". Later he will begin to say each sound twice over, or more, producing "Ma-ma" and "Da-da".

Although these sounds are almost universal among children around the world, if you show interest and approval when he says his first "word", he will be encouraged to say it again. From there it is a short step for him to identify "Mama" and "Dada".

As your baby progresses in his efforts at real speech, you will probably find yourself talking with him more and more, especially when you are feeding, dressing, undressing or bathing him. At this stage, many mothers join in the child's baby talk. This has often been criticised, on the ground that a child who grows accustomed to using baby talk will have to "unlearn" it, in order to start learning proper speech.

Do not be put off by such criticism, if you and your child are happy using baby talk. The exercise of imitating adult speech sounds is a valuable one for the baby, even when he does not understand what they mean. Also, it is natural to talk and sing to your child, and there is no need for you to feel embarrassed about doing so in the company of others.

At about nine months, your baby will realise what some sounds mean: this applies especially to his own name and to such words as "No" and "Bye-bye", which are usually accompanied by some recognisable facial expressions and gestures.

By the time your baby is one year old, he should have built up a useful vocabulary of single words. These may include such expressions as "No more", "Sit down" or "Give me" – although as far as the baby is concerned they are all just single pieces of sound, as if each of them were a single word.

Your baby will also have learned to understand some simple instructions and respond to them, even though he cannot yet know why he should do so.

Even at this early age, it is well worth reading aloud and singing to your baby. He will not understand the words of the story, rhyme or song, but he will enjoy the sound and rhythm of them.

When to see the doctor

Children are subject to numerous minor complaints; overcoming them is part of the process by which the body builds up its defences against disease. But even though many ailments are not serious, whenever you are worried about your child's health – if he looks or behaves differently from normal – it is best to consult a doctor.

Visiting the surgery
When you do feel a doctor's advice is needed, it is not always necessary to ask the doctor to call. Often the best step is to telephone and tell him or his receptionist what the child's symptoms are. The doctor can then assess the degree of urgency and tell you whether you should bring the child to his surgery, or whether he will visit you.

Taking your child to the surgery is usually the quickest way of seeing a doctor. Do not be afraid to take a child with a fever out of doors; taking him to the surgery will make him no worse.

It may sometimes happen that you feel you have an emergency on your hands, yet you cannot reach your doctor, or he cannot visit you for some time. In this case you should take your child by car or taxi to the nearest hospital. On pp. 170–173 there is a detailed description of what going to hospital in an emergency entails, and what you can do to make things easier for you and your child.

Going to hospital
There are certain circumstances in which you should take your child immediately to hospital: these include severe injury or burns, a broken bone or the swallowing of poisons (see p. 179).

If you do have to rush your child to hospital, and you have a telephone in the house, tell your doctor first. He can warn the hospital that you are coming, and tell the doctor in the Emergency Department any previous medical details concerning the child which might help. If your child has swallowed poison, don't forget to take the container to hospital.

How to interpret the symptoms
There are certain symptons which can be listed as indicating that your child should see a doctor without delay. But just because a particular symptom shown by your child is not on the list, because it is not usually serious, do not be deterred from seeking medical advice if you feel that something is wrong. For example, a baby can have meningitis without displaying specific symptoms, but you yourself will realise that he is not behaving normally and know that things are not as they should be.

One sure sign that something is wrong with a baby's health is sudden loss of appetite. The usual reason is an infection which can cause a very serious illness within hours.

The best sign of health is energy, and it does not matter how little a child eats so long as he is energetic. The body takes first what it needs for growth, and only the "spare" calories are available to fuel the child's running around.

Diarrhoea
Diarrhoea, especially if accompanied by vomiting, can be very serious in young babies because of dehydration from loss of body fluid. The mere passage of green stools is not, in itself, a cause for alarm. If the child is otherwise well and happy and taking his feeds, green stools can be ignored. However, green stools in a baby who is off colour and off his food are very serious.

Constipation
A child is constipated if the stools become hard and dry and are painful and difficult to pass. Infrequency of bowel movement does not necessarily mean constipation. Do not make the mistake of regarding a daily bowel action as vital. Insistence on pot training and on the daily bowel action can lead to "stool holding" or excessive bowel control, and is often associated with stomach aches. It is normal for a breast-fed baby to go many days between bowel actions. The mother's milk is so adjusted to her baby's needs that there is minimal residue.

Mothers are often more alarmed by constipation than by diarrhoea, but constipation by itself is never serious. Occasionally, however, it may be associated with vomiting and screaming attacks or, if the child is old enough, by a complaint of abdominal pain. This is serious, be-

111

cause the cause could be intestinal obstruction or appendicitis. Constipation by itself, however, is not a cause of abdominal pain.

Screaming and fits

Sudden screaming bouts in babies, when associated with pallor (most babies go red in the face), are very serious. The cause is likely to be an intussusception, meaning that one portion of the intestine has been propelled forward into the part of the tube immediately in front, thereby causing an obstruction. Screaming after immunisation which is clearly different from normal crying must be reported to the doctor.

A convulsion, or fit, is always frightening, especially if you are alone. But don't panic and rush to the telephone or for your neighbour, because your child might vomit and choke while you are out of the room. Children never die in a convulsion unless they inhale their vomit and drown. Lay the child on his side in the recovery position (p. 182), so that if he vomits he cannot choke. Stay with him until he comes round, so that he immediately sees you.

Fortunately, convulsions in young children seldom last more than a minute or two – through it seems like an age. They are usually associated with fever (see below) and as the child gets older and his brain more stable he no longer reacts in this way. The tendency to feverish, or febrile, fits often runs in familes, and does not lead to epilepsy.

Fever

Whether a child's feverishness should be regarded very seriously depends on associated symptoms. If he is perfectly rational and is able to drink without vomiting, it is not an emergency, but it is right to tell your doctor. Possibly the child has a throat or ear infection, or is about to come out with a measles rash.

The situation is different if you know that your child is liable to feverish fits. In this case you should give one aspirin and start the process of tepid sponging, which you will have been taught by your doctor or at the hospital on a previous occasion.

Equally serious is the condition of the child who becomes delirious with the fever. He needs to be stripped and tepid-sponged at once, and the doctor should call as soon as possible.

Fever is a protective reaction of the body as part of its defences against infection. It is only when it gets out of control that the situation is serious. Babies may be so seriously struck by an infection that their heat-regulating mechanism is disturbed. Instead of developing a fever they become cold. The baby must then have extra warmth, and a doctor must be called immediately.

Eyes, ears and nose

A foreign body in the eye causes redness and pain. If watering from the eye washes the foreign body beneath the eyelid you may be able to remove it with a clean handkerchief. Make no attempt to remove a foreign body from the cornea, the clear part of the eyeball, but take your child straight to hospital.

Children often poke objects into their ears and nose. Removal usually requires a doctor's skills and instruments. Discharge, either of pus or of blood, from one nostril is most often caused by a foreign body. Discharge from one or both ears is more often due to infection in the middle ear. This can lead to deafness; never pass it off as a "runny ear".

Other symptoms

Rashes are seldom serious, except in some cases of measles (see p. 161) and chicken pox (see p.153), and for meningococcaemia. This is most dangerous when mauve patches develop as well as red spots. You must take the child quickly to hospital.

Difficulty in breathing, whether due to asthma in a child or croup in a baby, is always alarming. Both respond well to treatment.

You should also consult a doctor if your child develops a limp.

Urinary symptoms, such as pain felt in passing urine, associated with urinating more often than normal, require a visit to the doctor. Try to take a specimen of urine in a bottle which has been sterilised by boiling. A change in colour of urine is important. Blood in small quantities turns the urine brown; it requires a lot of blood to make the urine red.

Lastly, there is one emergency in which you will not even have time to call the doctor. This is when your young child chokes on some solid piece of food, such as a rusk, and goes black in the face. You should try to get it out with your fingers but if this is not possible then you must immediately hold him upside-down and thump his back hard to dislodge whatever is stuck in his windpipe or larynx. To prevent this, never leave your child alone when he is eating food liable to choke him.

5
TODDLER

Playing and learning

When a child becomes mobile an entire new dimension is opened up to him. He is now on the point of leaving babyhood behind, to become a sociable, observant, inquisitive and active participant in adult life. His natural curiosity will impel him to explore everywhere he can and he will need constant supervision. Stairs are an invitation to adventure, and should always have a safety gate fitted. At home or in a playgroup, a toddler will encounter a host of new experiences. He will look and listen with fascination as adults introduce him to books and television.

Fitting together the pieces of a jigsaw puzzle requires a degree of hand control and visual co-ordination which is achieved by a child's second or third year. The dexterity acquired will be helpful when he starts learning to write.

Looking at a book is an absorbing occupation. If a child is used to being read to by a parent, and he looks at the pictures and text while he listens, he will quickly learn to associate the written symbols on the page with familiar words.

After two weeks of regular visits to a pool, even a young child will often enjoy splashing around with only a pair of armbands for support.

Once a child can walk, much of his time is spent in boisterous activity. This both burns up surplus energy and practises skills such as climbing and pedalling.

Learning how to get on with other children is an important part of a child's social education. It will be more enjoyable if they share an interest – most children, whatever their age, like playing with water, and a well-run playgroup will ensure that the children have congenial occupations.

Children love splashing paint on paper. The blobs of paint reveal a dawning colour sense. At first these have meaning only for the child, but they will develop into recognisable shapes and patterns. This enjoyable activity is also part of a child's preparation for writing.

5 Drawing and painting

Between his first and fourth birthdays, a child leaves babyhood behind to become a sociable, observant, inquisitive and active participant in adult life. At home or in a nursery school or playgroup, he looks and listens as adults introduce him to books and television, laying the foundations for reading and writing. At the same time the child begins to draw and paint what he sees.

Almost all young children produce drawings and paintings in an orderly and easily recognisable progression. By observing the stages in a child's progress in graphic skill, his parents can learn a great deal about him.

Right hand or left hand?

Hand movements are controlled by the brain – the right hand by the left side of the brain, and the left hand by the right side of the brain. Children who use the left hand in preference to the right are simply showing that the right side of the brain is dominant. Most children are born right-handed, but there is no cause for concern if your child shows an inclination to use his left hand. Although it may sometimes be inconvenient to be the "odd man out" in a world geared to the right-handed person, a left-handed child can be as skilful as a right-handed child.

A baby is ambidextrous – that is, he uses either hand equally well – but at this stage he is still developing his grasping powers. It is not until the child is a toddler, and begins to develop skills such as drawing or picking up small objects, that the dominance of one hand begins to reveal itself.

Watch the child as he brushes his teeth, throws a ball, uses a spoon or turns a door knob. When one hand appears to be the dominant one, you should encourage him to practise with that hand.

On no account should the child be made to draw, write or paint with the right hand if the left hand appears to dominate. To try to do this is in effect to try to change the child's nerve connections, and switch the controls from one side of his brain to the other. This may bring on nervous difficulties affecting the child's speech development.

From scribbles to drawings

At about one year, a child with a pencil or crayon begins to scribble; later he moves on to straight and curved lines, and finally to drawings of things he sees. When a child first discovers paint, he makes blobs; then follow patterns, and lastly paintings that are pictures. This stage-by-stage progression is common to all children all over the world, and tells the observant adult much about the physical and mental development of the individual child.

Young artists normally start with illustrations of people. This is because the people around them are the closest and most powerful influences in their experience so far. A child's

119

TODDLER

progress towards depicting a human figure is shown on the right.

Even the first illustration here (1), a scribble by a 15-month-old boy, is far from meaningless; the child has discovered that the crayon in his hand will make a mark if he presses it to the paper, and he has developed sufficient muscular control to place the marks within the boundary of the paper. In other words, his physical control is developing as it should.

While (1) shows a skein of lines produced perfunctorily by simple backward and forward strokes, (2) shows lines travelling in various directions, beginning and finishing at different points. This design could not be produced by perfunctory movements. Each line – particularly the circling one – is evidence of a higher degree of co-ordination between hand and eye and a much more sophisticated muscular control than is evident in (1).

Figure (3) is a logical development from (2), consisting of circulating lines only. This kind of scribble is typical at about two-and-a-half to three-and-a-half years, though it is more appropriate to think in terms of "stages" rather than "ages" because so many other factors affect the child's performance. Among them are his home background, and the age at which he first takes a marking implement in his hands.

Art from scribbles
At the scribbling stage the child watches himself working, with the crayon in his hand – playing with it, gliding it over the paper, listening to the sound it makes. He is fascinated by what he does, rather than setting

1 Pure scribbling, with back-and-forth strokes.

2 Separate lines show improved co-ordination.

3 Circulating lines: co-ordination better still.

4 With the first oval, scribbling becomes drawing.

5 With features added, oval becomes a face.

6 Lines added to face symbolise limbs.

7 A sense of number: two legs only.

8 Adding a body: lengthening the legs.

9 Adding a body: the legs are joined.

10 First effort, experimenting with paint: a shapeless blob.

11 "Organising" paint: several blobs placed in relation to one another.

12 One way forward: a picture emerges. Cow, pond and trees?

120

out deliberately to draw something. A child may see, or believe that he sees, a form developing among the lines, and he may name it.

Always listen while a child is working. A tangle of lines may prompt a ramble of words, in which he is both practising verbal skills and giving voice to his developing imagination. Listening to these words enables a parent to get to know the child better.

The big step forward

Figure (4) represents a major development. There is no question, now, of the child simply watching something happening on the paper. He has begun with a concept in his mind which he expresses as a single oval. He is no longer scribbling, but setting down a purposeful statement in line – in other words, a drawing.

Once the child has developed the graphic skills necessary to make the oval, it is a short step to add features to it to make a face. As soon as the face appears, at about three to four years, the child's imagination surges into action. He may add three spots to the face and say "It's a boy with chicken-pox". The face reminds him of his brother's spotty face, and he relives the experience through his drawing.

While drawing, the child externalises his most significant thoughts, giving a parent insights into his personality and reactions. The art content or realism of the drawing is unimportant by comparison.

Making pictures

The "face" will sooner or later sprout a fringe of lines symbolising arms and legs, and a new phase begins. Hitherto the child has operated spontaneously, working from within himself. But now he will gradually become more outward-looking. His preoccupation with the face will give way to awareness that people have bodies. His sense of numbers will develop, and he will realise that people have only two legs. He often achieves his first "body" by shrinking the head and lengthening the legs (8), and then joining the two legs (9). Once the figure is established the child quickly invents various ways of completing it.

All these figures continue to represent the child's fantasies. His family's history is revealed, his television heroes are celebrated, his school friends come to life. At the same time he becomes increasingly aware of factual detail, and realism gains at the expense of imagination. As a child grows older, he becomes more dependent on visual imagery than on mental imagery, and this change-over gradually influences his drawings. For example, he will add hairstyles and clothes that mirror those worn by the person he is drawing.

Taking to paints

There is a clear distinction between the drawing of young children and their painting (figures 10–12). Any work expressed with lines may be defined as drawing, while any work carried out in areas of colour or tone can be called painting; in each case the medium used is immaterial. For instance, figure (4) was made with brush and paint, but this does not make it a painting.

Drawing is also quite a different experience from painting for the child. He uses drawing as a descriptive picture-language, whereas his painting is an opportunity to play with and enjoy the laying, mixing and "splurging" of colour and pigment. Watch a three-year-old standing in front of his first easel, with paint, brush and paper. See how he dips and plops and dabbles and scrubs and splashes. His first "painting" may be no more than one shapeless blob of a single colour (10), but however it turns out, he will very likely fantasise and tell you that it is a bus, a man, an elephant. At first these blobs have meaning only for him, but they will develop into recognisable shapes and patterns.

Whatever the child says, the fantasy is more important than the painting, especially in the earlier years. Be prepared to look beyond what your child puts on the paper. If, for instance, he has four pots of colour to work with, he will have to choose a colour before he can start. He is compelled to make an aesthetic choice, and the training of his colour sense has begun.

At the same time the child gains complete freedom of self-expression. He can spread paint and experience it blazing back at him, without anyone scolding him. He may be so swept away by the magic of spreading blue paint that he will cover 36 large sheets of paper with it, simply because he likes blue. When he completes the 36 blue sheets he may repeat the experience with green.

In figure (11), several shapes of paint are placed so as to relate to each other – clearly a step forward from (10) in that the shapes are "organised" on the paper. The related blobs of paint that a child puts on paper reveal a dawning colour sense. As his skill increases, a child may move on to turning areas of colour into more or less recognisable forms, as in (12) where the lowest shape is clearly some four-legged animal.

Alternatively, the child may progress towards more and more elaborate arrangements of related shapes and colours, usually called painting patterns. Most children seem to have an inborn sense of pattern, but while some will concentrate on painting patterns, others will specialise in pictures.

The adult's role

A child's drawing and painting yield intimate knowledge of his own private world, so long as they are allowed to develop naturally and without interference. The adult's role is to provide drawing and painting materials, then stand back and observe. You can ask a child to tell you what he is doing, but do not urge him if he prefers not to talk. Above all, never help him. To do this is to run the risk of having him come to ask you for help every time. The really young child works spontaneously, and he works best when unaided.

All children produce paintings, all children produce drawings, and many children produce works containing mixtures of both. To go further forward they will have to cross the great divide which separates the inward-looking, spontaneous young child from the more mature, outward-looking, self-critical individual of school age.

Learning with toys

All through babyhood and childhood, each new development of a child's skill and understanding is seen in new ways of play. Watch a one-year-old playing with his mother's kitchen or toilet articles. He begins to use the objects appropriately, recognising what they are for. He will pick up a brush and brush his hair with it; he will put a wooden spoon in a saucepan and stir, where earlier he would just bang with it.

Later, you will notice a child beginning to pretend. He will make-believe that a building block is a car, making a "brmm-brmm" noise as he runs it along the floor. He will pretend that his blocks are food, and gesture as if he is eating them.

This new way of playing is closely linked to a child's new understanding of words. Just as he can use a block as a car, so he is able to use words as symbols of what he is doing or thinking. In the beginning of pretend-play, we see the start of the child's understanding and use of language. At the same time as he starts to play in a make-believe way, he is becoming very good at understanding what you say to him.

The child is also fascinated by pictures in books, which he is beginning to understand as representations of objects that he recognises and that are part of his experience. In his second year he enjoys looking at books and pictures with his parents, and loves to "name" the things that he sees. It is an ideal way for him to discover new words.

Children also gain great pleasure at this age from "representational" toys: doll's-house furniture, little cars, playpeople and other toy versions of familiar everyday objects. It is with this sort of toy that the first make-believe games often begin.

As the child's skill in talking increases, he plays in another new way, with words. Listen to a two-year-old playing on his own, or chatting to himself in bed, and you may hear sequences of words, rhymed and linked in a way that seems to be both practice and play.

There are many other new ways in which a child begins to play during his second year. Earlier, towards the end of his first year, he becomes very interested in putting objects into other objects, taking them out, piling them up, knocking them down and so on. This sort of play gradually builds up the child's understanding of differences in shape, and of the relationships between shapes. Then in his second year, he *knows*, without trying, that a solid disc cannot be threaded on to a post with stacking rings. He has worked this out by thinking about it. Other, similar problems are dealt with in the same manner.

From early in the second year, children often play games that involve grouping things according to their shape or size. They will take the crayons out of a box and carefully line them up in parallel. They will try poking a crayon through holes of varying shape and size. They will drop something through the mesh of a fireguard, then methodically repeat the game with objects of different shapes and sizes. It is not surprising that the toys that the child enjoys at around 15 months often involve stacking, "posting" or matching shapes. Later on you will see how a child's interest in counting begins.

Watch children of 18 months to two years playing with plastic cups or bath toys in water. They will pour water from one container to another, push the cups under the water and let them bob up, empty them and make them float, dribble water into them and make them sink. They will try out endless variations, and discover which objects float, which sink, and which make the biggest splash.

This sort of game, and the "messing about" in a sand-pit which children enjoy so much, helps them to learn about the physical properties of objects. Children learn most quickly and effectively by doing things themselves, rather than by an adult standing over them and telling them how to do them. At the same time, remember that a child cannot develop fully and normally without some participation by his parents.

Their willingness to play with their child, and to show him books and pictures, increases what he learns from play.

Choosing a toy

Because play is an essential part of a young child's mental and physical development, the best playthings are those which encourage and stimulate his natural curiosity. A good plaything does not have to be expensive, but before buying or making a toy for a child ask yourself the following questions:

● **Is the toy right for the child?**
A toy must be chosen to suit a child's particular interests and aptitudes. If, for example, he shows no interest in or taste for constructional toys, they should not be forced upon him.

● **Is the child ready for the toy?**
Although there is an *average* age at which a child is ready to progress from one kind of play to another, the age at which an *individual* child does so varies considerably from one child to the next. If your child seems to be developing a little more slowly than average, do not worry, and do not try to force on him a toy for which he is not ready. A toy should always be suited to a child's stage of development rather than to his age in years.

● **Is the toy easily broken?**
How much a toy will be enjoyed – and for how long – depends on its ability to resist wear and tear, and on its appeal to a child.

● **Is the toy safe to be sucked?**
A toy should be too large to be swallowed. Any material used in a toy should not break up or splinter when

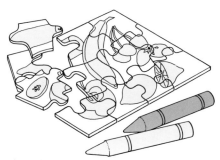

Simple jigsaw puzzles give a child a sense of achievement, but crayons encourage creativity still more.

chewed. Many regulations governing the safety of toys are in force in Britain, but parents should still exercise care when they are making a choice.

● **Is the toy easy to keep clean?**
All toys should be hygienic, so give some thought to the ease with which a toy can be kept clean.

If in doubt when choosing a toy, consult the manager or assistant. In any shop with a reputation to maintain, you will find the staff both knowledgeable and helpful in giving you advice.

Toys and play materials
In his second year, a child's mobility is rapidly increasing. This helps him to gratify his insatiable curiosity. Both mobility and curiosity – walking and exploring – should be encouraged with toys.

The child enjoys push-and-pull toys, which encourage walking backwards as well as forwards, and a large ball to kick and run after. Other toys foster a child's manipulative skills and exploring instinct – bricks to build and stack, simple jigsaw puzzles, small posting boxes, containers for water and sand play. To develop his creative inclinations, a child should be given large, chunky crayons or fun paints.

Many other toys and materials will encourage a child to "make-believe". They include:
 Dolls and teddy bears
 Interlocking cubes
 Pyramid rings
 Toy telephone
 Wooden animals
 Simple musical instruments
 (tambourine, castanets, drum)

Building a vocabulary

From 18 months your child may be able to name many objects around him; his conversation will become more sophisticated, with some "sentences" of two or three words. If he is not quite so advanced at this age, do not worry: many babies progress much more slowly than others and some do not begin to speak until the age of three. Also, a child who starts talking early may make slower progress later on, and a slow starter may suddenly spurt ahead.

It is not until your child is about two years old, and has built a vocabulary of 300 to 400 words, that he begins to merge language with thought, and begins to frame such questions as "What is it?' and "Why?"

From now on, the increase in a child's word-power is spectacularly swift. At the same time he will show a steady improvement in walking, running, balancing and using his hands.

At about this age your child will still not be able to speak a whole sentence, even if he can say each of the words that make it up. But he will begin to show a remarkable ability to pick out the vital words in a sentence that you speak to him.

For example, he may not be able to repeat "Mummy is going to the shop", but he will perhaps say "Mummy shop" – seizing on the two key words from your sentence.

When you are with your child, talk and listen to him constantly. Say funny words, just to make him laugh; teach him that learning words and saying them can be fun. If he is used to seeing adults using the telephone, give him a toy one of his own; it will be a great encouragement to him to talk.

As your child's speech abilities expand, even a routine shopping trip can be enormously educational for him. This is an opportunity that can be missed if you go by car, rather than by walking or wheeling him along the street so that he can see and hear all the sights and sounds.

Forming sentences

By three years old, your child should know about 1,000 words and be able to form real sentences. At this stage, your child's grasp of grammar will not be very strong, but there is no need to worry. He is using his logic to form tenses, plurals and so on – and the English language is riddled with seemingly illogical exceptions to the basic rules.

Logically, for example, the past tense of "I eat" should be "I eated", and the plural of "mouse" should be "mouses". Your child cannot work out these exceptions by sheer reasoning, but he will eventually learn simply by imitating adults.

Do not worry either if your child invents his own words for various objects. This is not a form of laziness: it is a good sign that he is working at learning to use language.

Parents of different nationalities who want their baby to grow up speaking two languages will confuse him if they both give two names for everything. This confusion can be avoided if one parent speaks in one language and the other parent in the second language.

As your child's ability to use words grows ever more quickly, you can help by following two rules:

Never show boredom with his chatter, however ceaseless; it is all-important to him as he explores the new world of language.

Always answer his questions, no matter how many he asks. Nothing is more frustrating for an inquiring child than to be told: "Be quiet, I'm busy."

The role of TV and radio

A harassed mother is not left solely to her own devices in "entertaining" or satisfying her children's thirst for activity and experience. Television and radio both offer a variety of carefully structured and well-presented programmes designed to assist the mother in the social and educational rearing of an energetic and ever-inquisitive child.

Try planning your day so that you can make viewing or listening a shared experience with your child. A good programme will be planned in such a way that you can develop its content on your own, and extract from it every aspect of interest and educational value for the benefit of your child. Again, you can arrange to have at hand materials for further expression of the programme's main theme. Paper and coloured pencils or crayons should be available, together with plasticine or other soft modelling materials, so that you can then follow up ideas that have been suggested in the programme.

Enjoying a story

From an early age, children love to look at bright pictures. This interest is one of the first steps towards the development of their ability to read and write. For a child who learns to love books of pictures – perhaps on tough cardboard or linen pages – will soon want to know about the words which accompany them, and then to learn how to read them for himself.

For your child's sake, do all that you can to encourage his interest in books. See that there are bookshelves for his sole use which are easy for him to reach, and introduce him to the local library. A good librarian will make sure that there is a stock of short, simple stories with brightly-coloured and interesting illustrations, which can be read aloud to children (or which a child can try to read for himself).

What parents can do

The parents' role in introducing books is an important one. Do not confuse "interesting" a child in reading with "teaching" a child to read. The latter is a highly complex operation which is best left to those who are specially trained to undertake the task. Much harm has been done in the past by well-meaning parents, particularly those with children who are undoubtedly bright, in attempting to teach reading.

Nevertheless, there is much that a mother and father can do in ensuring that the basic groundwork of the pre-reading processes has been established. Constant development and reinforcement of spoken language will give the child the incentive to start associating the written symbolic forms with the sounds he has grown to know.

Every child should be surrounded by colourful and attractive books in the home, and these should be easily accessible so that he can take them without asking, and study them as often as he wishes.

Read often to him from "his" books. Ensure that he is sitting beside you, so that he, too, can see the written words and the pictures.

Do not be afraid to read interesting stories over and over again. Children love repetition and delight in anticipating certain sections of vivid and colourful prose. They have retentive memories for stories, and can remember word for word what is being said to them in story form.

They will apparently "read" from a book because they have memorised the contents of the page. This is a positive aid to the beginning of reading; motivation is taking place, and confidence is established.

Tell stories as often as possible, either well-known nursery stories and fables, or simple "jingles" and rhymes, particularly rhyming stories. When you can, make up stories around familiar objects and experiences, and ensure that the central character in many of them is the child. Always involve the child by finishing such sessions with free-expression drawing. Have at hand plenty of paper and coloured crayons, or pencils of a size that can easily be gripped by small hands.

You might start the drawing session with such words as: "Let's draw a picture of the story – there is the giant – shall we make him big? Yes – with long arms and long legs, big hands – big feet – here is his stick. He lives in this castle here – on the top of this mountain – surrounded by tall trees." Each successive statement is accompanied by an addition to the drawing. "Now would you like to try? First the giant's head . . ." and so on. It will also help to write in small printed letters (not capitals) the essential words under the objects drawn – giant, leg, castle and so on.

Children will more easily develop good reading habits if they see their parents constantly reading. This encourages them to understand that there is something about books and the written word which is both pleasurable and useful. People read for two reasons – either as a means of obtaining information, or simply as an enjoyable experience. Introduce your child to both types of reading in the choice of his books.

Learning to read

A child often starts to recognise individual letters from his building blocks. There are many variations of lettered cards and plastic letters which he can use when he starts to put words together.

Sets that associate pictures with names are useful in play, and some can be placed on the wall as part of the decoration of a child's room. The "snap" card games, linking a name with a picture, help the child in quick recognition, and also add the excitement of competition.

Caring for a sick child

Knowing your own child more intimately than anyone else, you will be the first person to realise that he is unwell. You can take the temperature of a child when he is old enough to hold the thermometer in his mouth. A clearer indication of illness is shown, however, by a child going off his food. Whether or not you call the doctor the greater part of nursing a child back to health is usually done at home.

Nursing at home

When a child is to be nursed through an illness at home, his greatest need is the companionship of a parent. During the daytime, this will probably be provided by you.

A baby or toddler wants warm physical contact and reassurance, so it is important to sit comfortably with him, talking or singing to him. Have some of his favourite "quiet" toys at hand; do not worry, however, if he shows no real interest in them, as this phase will pass.

Often when a child is sick, housework suffers. Try not to worry over this. The house will still be there when your sick child is up and well again, but your chance to draw close to him at a critical time will be gone.

Your normal night's sleep may be disturbed by a fretful child. So when he is contented or asleep, take the chance to relax rather than rush round trying to catch up with the jobs which have been neglected. The father or other members of the family can take over from time to time to give the mother a break.

A child is less frightened of illness if he is given a simple explanation of what is happening to him. Tell him that treatment or medicine is necessary to help him get better. Be honest with your child and answer his questions truthfully, so that his confidence in the adults looking after him remains intact.

Sick children seldom need to remain in bed for long, if at all. If your child feels like being active, do not prevent him from getting up unless your doctor specifically advises this. If the child has to be immobile for a long time, try to give him a change of beds: for instance, let him use a settee in the living-room, where he can be with you and the rest of the family. The settee can be near the window, so that the child can see what is going on outside. Being left by himself will certainly not speed recovery, and may even make a child feel worse than he really is.

Fit children are naturally active and curious. If illness prevents them from getting out and about, they will still need stimulation and amusement – at least from the moment they start to recover. So a sick child must be given plenty of satisfying things to do. Adults "talk out" their problems, but children often "play out" their feelings and feel better for doing it. So don't worry if your child's favourite teddy bear takes a beating from a frustrated toddler – it may be his way of getting the frustrations out of his system.

If a sick child can play as naturally as possible it helps to reassure him that he is in working order, and this contributes to his recovery. A variety of simple activities produced at intervals is much more satisfying to a child confined to bed or house than one expensive toy that can quickly lose its charm. Some sick children go back to an earlier phase of play and repeat the same activity over and over again. Others, like adults, cannot concentrate and will avoid activities which demand effort.

Nearly every child has a special "comfort toy" – it may be a chewed-up fragment of blanket or a worn-out teddy bear – which will be particularly precious to him when he is ill. Babies' toys can be hung across cot or bed from a tape or toy rail so that they are within reach. Older children can have a box of special favourites beside them. They will need a tray or bed table for such playthings as model cars or marbles, or for drawing or painting.

After covering the bed with a plastic sheet, you can give your child plasticine or finger paints, or make dough out of flour and water for modelling; salt can be added to the dough to stop him from eating it.

Medicine and food

Giving medicine to children is seldom a problem nowadays, since most medicines have a pleasant taste. Tablets are best crushed and given in a spoonful of fruit juice. Assume your child will take the dose willingly; if he is reluctant, give him special praise for being brave.

When children get over the first stage of illness and their condition improves they often become more restless and demanding, and nothing seems to please them. Parents are there to absorb the grumbles along with the gratitude.

Feeding can pose problems during convalescence. It is best to provide small amounts of food fairly often. Soups, yoghurts and strained fruit are more appealing than heavier dishes. Serving them in an attractive way, perhaps on specially decorated plates, can boost flagging appetites. There is no need to worry if your child does not eat much, so long as he drinks plenty of fluid. He will quickly make up for the food he has missed as soon as he has fully recovered.

Keeping a child amused

Infectious diseases may mean that a child has to be isolated from brothers and sisters. This is lonely and boring for a child. He will need as much of his parents' time as they can spare him, and frequent changes of play activity. It may be necessary to disinfect toys afterwards, in which case they have to be washable. Books can be covered in plastic so that they can easily be wiped clean.

A child with a limb in plaster, or immobilised for other reasons, needs special consideration. Everything possible should be done to compensate for the loss of movement. Babies can be carried about and taken out in prams; they can be put in hammocks, or lie on rugs or cushions on the floor. Older children can be taken out in pushchairs, and can be moved from bed to floor and from room to room for a change of scene. Simple trucks or trolleys on wheels or castors can be made at home, and provide a new and interesting way of moving about the house.

Treat your sick child as if he were slightly younger than his actual years, allowing him extra privileges and understanding, and you will find he will quickly gain enough strength to fend for himself again. Treated in this way, illness can be a positive experience, binding you and your child even more closely together.

Preparing for hospital

Four children out of every ten in Britain are likely to be admitted to hospital once before they reach the age of seven. It is therefore important for parents to talk to their children about what happens in hospital. Sometimes the sight or sound of an ambulance may provide a lead for talking about hospital. There may be an opportunity to visit someone in hospital, so that your child becomes aware of what hospitals look like. When some of the facts are known in advance, it is much less frightening for a child if he has to go to hospital himself than if everything is left to his imagination. Take care neither to make it sound too frightening nor to pretend that it is entirely pleasant. Emphasise that although some things hurt, everyone in hospital is doing his best to make him better.

An emergency visit to hospital is obviously a challenge even to the most calm of mothers, but try to concentrate on practical matters. Take a special toy, blanket or bottle, if this will help to comfort your child. Make sure he is well wrapped up for his journey. Get a message to your husband or a close relative so that someone can come to the hospital to support you (see also pp. 170–173).

Fortunately, not all visits to hospital begin as emergencies, and often it is possible to prepare your child well in advance. Some hospitals supply booklets or comics with pictures of ward scenes for you to look at with your child before he is admitted. Your local library will probably have books which explain in simple terms what life in hospital is like. Read these to your child and talk about what is going to happen. Reassure him that his visit will help him to get well, and that you will help him to get used to the strange place and the new people.

Generally, children of pre-school age find hospital most distressing when they are alone. Even a small baby can sense when his mother is not there, and may become afraid. The effect of a child's separation from his mother may even be worse than that of the illness. Most hospitals now allow unrestricted visiting for parents, and many provide rooms for parents of young children to stay in. If it is at all possible, stay close to your child for at least the first few days after he goes into hospital.

Gradually your child will adapt to the strange environment, and it will seem less threatening. Also he will begin to recover physically, and become more naturally buoyant. At this point you can begin to resume your normal activities. But visit your child often, and when you leave tell him honestly that you are going, even if this does cause tears. Tell him exactly when you will return, and keep your word.

Feeding a toddler

By his first birthday, a child will be eating virtually the same food as the rest of the family, although in smaller quantities, except for milk, which will still play an important part in his daily diet.

The wider the variety of foods to which you can introduce your baby at this age the better. Not only will he be healthier nutritionally, but also he will be less likely to develop food fads later on: you will not face the problem of fussy eating when he is away from home.

You should give your toddler vitamin drops until at least his second birthday. Even later than that, he can benefit from these extra vitamins – but take care not to exceed the recommended number of drops per day, because too much of some vitamins can be harmful.

How much is enough?
Many toddlers go through a phase of eating very little. Although they seem to thrive, their mothers may worry, feeling quite understandably that an active, growing child needs plenty of nourishment. But do not worry needlessly. There is enormous variation in how much food different children need; even if your child is eating half the amounts consumed by other children of the same age, he may still be getting enough for his individual needs.

As long as your child seems fit, healthy, happy and active, is not losing any weight and is growing well, you can be sure he is getting enough food. If you get upset or annoyed when he refuses or leaves food, meal-times will become a battle, and make the situation worse. You cannot *make* a child eat, and it is wrong to try, if he clearly shows that he has had enough.

If reasonable encouragement does not help, it is best to take the food away and carry on as normal. Do not, however, let him fill up with sweets and biscuits: make it clear that meals are the time for eating. You may be simply giving him too much food; if your child has only a small appetite, try giving smaller portions. Again, if your toddler will eat only fish fingers or baked beans (both of which are valuable as food), it is better to give him those than to keep on producing food which he refuses.

Phases like these pass quickly if you stay calm and do not make a big issue out of them. The problem is often simply that the child is discovering his independence, and after he has asserted this to his satisfaction he will become more co-operative once again.

One reason why you should never force a child to eat food which he does not want is that it may make him overweight, both now and in later life, by altering his eating habits and attitudes to food.

It is also a waste of time to try to teach table manners to a child who does not yet know why it is a good idea to be tidy with his food. A baby will probably enjoy playing with his fingers in the food, and dropping it on the floor, just as much as eating it.

If you let him experiment a little, he will probably grow out of it soon enough. But in his second year, you can begin to discourage him from playing with his food by showing your displeasure at having to clean up after him. If your toddler eats with the rest of the family, he will note their disapproval, too, and want to eat as they eat. But remember: it is more important to be friends with your baby than to try to teach him table manners.

The overweight toddler
Weight problems are best dealt with by preventing them. If you follow the patterns of sensible eating outlined here, your child is unlikely to become overweight. You should *not* try to slim your toddler (or baby) unless your doctor or clinic advises you to. A lot of babies get rather podgy after starting solids and before they crawl or walk; but as soon as they become more active they slim down rapidly, as long as you keep a watchful eye on what they eat. If more positive action is necessary, cut down on cereal foods and fats – but do not exclude these foods altogether from your toddler's diet.

Sweet foods and drinks are definitely out for an overweight toddler, while plenty of fruit and vegetables will help to maintain sufficient bulk in the diet. Prepare your own baby foods so that you can keep complete control over what goes into them.

Do not look for any rapid weight loss in your toddler; usually it is sufficient to hold his weight steady, or just slow down the rate at which he gains weight, for a few months, so that he slims as he grows.

MEALS FOR OLDER BABIES

As your baby grows older you can introduce him to an ever-widening range of interesting new tastes. Here is a selection of recipes for dishes that are both full of flavour and nourishing, from breakfast muesli to savoury meals and light puddings. By cooking them yourself you can ensure your baby does not eat anything he would be better off without. Don't use sugar; if you really want a sweet taste try a little honey instead. Salt water for simmering or boiling very lightly; don't add extra salt to food, and be careful of products such as meat extract, which can be very salty. A day's menu could be:

Breakfast: 15–30 g ($\frac{1}{2}$–1 oz) cereal with milk; boiled or scrambled egg; milk to drink.

Mid-morning: Diluted fruit juice; an apple or a pear.

Lunch: About 100 g (4 oz) meat and vegetable stew; a small boiled potato; 1 tablespoon green vegetables such as beans or peas. Fruit yoghurt (without sugar).

Tea: 1 slice of toast with cheese; diluted fruit juice with vitamin drops.

Bedtime: Milk to drink.

RECIPES

Cheese and egg bake
Beat 1 egg in 100 ml ($\frac{1}{4}$ pint) milk; stir in 1 tablespoon grated cheese. Bake in moderate oven until set – about 20 minutes – or steam. Serve with a vegetable.

Baked apple
Remove core, replace with sultanas, bake in usual way. Take out the sultanas and the flesh of the apple and mash together. Serve with yoghurt or egg custard.

Baby muesli
Mix together the following: 2 tablespoons flaked oats, millet or brown rice; 1 tablespoon ground almonds (check there are no large pieces – ideally grind them yourself for freshness and maximum food value); 1 eating apple, grated or finely chopped; 1 tablespoon raisins, well soaked; and a squeeze of orange or lemon juice. If you want a sweeter mixture, liquidise the raisins in a little water.

This can be stored, chilled and tightly covered, for up to 48 hours.

Meat and vegetable stew
Chop or mince 50 g (2 oz) lean beef, lamb or chicken. Add chopped carrot, potato and celery and a skinned, de-seeded tomato. Just cover with water and simmer for 30 minutes. Serve with a vegetable, e.g. cauliflower.

Potato and liver hash
Boil a small potato. Pulp or blend 50 g (2 oz) liver (preferably not pork liver as it is so strong-tasting), removing any tough tissues. Put on a lightly greased plate over a pan of boiling water; cook until liver changes colour. Mash with potato.

Moong dhal
Wash 50 g (2 oz) yellow split lentils well. Cook them with a cardamom pod and a 1 cm ($\frac{1}{2}$ in) piece of cinnamon in a cup of water for about 45 minutes or until pulpy. Cook some rice in twice its volume of water for about 40 minutes, letting it just simmer. (This method of cooking ensures that water-soluble minerals and vitamins are not thrown out with the cooking water.) You may need to add a little extra water after 25–30 minutes if the rice seems to be too dry.

Remove the spices and mash the lentils lightly with a little of the rice.

Fish with rice
Cook 50 g (2 oz) rice as directed in the previous recipe for moong dhal. Mix 2 tablespoons rice with 1 tablespoon freshly cooked white fish. Melt a little butter in a pan and stir in the rice and fish. Top with mashed hard-boiled egg yolk or with grated cheese, if desired, and serve with a green vegetable.

Tomato sauce for pasta
Soften some sliced or chopped onion in a little oil. Add a small tin of tomatoes and cook gently for 10–15 minutes. Stir in some freshly chopped parsley.

Avocado flip
Mash a soft, ripe avocado with enough unflavoured yoghurt or cottage cheese to give a light consistency. Add a squeeze of orange or lemon juice to stop it discolouring.

Apricot mousse
Cook apricots and make into a purée. Beat 1 egg yolk into 2–3 tablespoons purée. Add a few drops of lemon juice and bring the mixture to the boil slowly, at the same time stirring. Remove from heat; stir in 1 tablespoon natural yoghurt. The mousse can be eaten warm or cold.

Ground rice pudding
Bring to simmering point 2 tablespoons of ground rice in 1 cup of milk. Stir for a couple of minutes, simmering, until the mixture is thick. Blend to ensure there are no lumps.

You can add a 2.5 cm (1 in) piece of cinnamon stick or vanilla pod to the milk for flavour, but remove it before blending. This is good made with ground brown rice and can also be made with millet flakes, both of which are available in wholefood stores.

Caring for young feet

Foot care is especially important in the first three years, when a child's growth is fastest. In this formative period soft bones can be bent out of shape by ill-fitting stretch-suits, socks or shoes.

Allow your child to go barefoot indoors as much as possible when he is crawling and beginning to walk. If bootees or socks are necessary for warmth, make sure there is ample room for the toes to wriggle. Some nylon stretch socks may not stretch enough: cotton or wool mixture socks are best for children.

When your child is walking, take him to a shop that specialises in children's shoes, where a trained fitter will measure his feet for width and shoe size.

Always have both feet measured, because one foot may be a different shape and size from the other. Your child should stand for the measurement to be taken, then his feet will spread under his weight and the fitter will be able to make a better assessment of the size and width of shoe that is needed.

Choose shoes with laces or straps across the instep to allow for adjustment without any restriction on the feet. Shoes with leather uppers may be more expensive than those made from other materials, but they will prove better value. The leather yields to the shape of the foot without any pressure, and it "breathes" to make it more comfortable to wear.

Return to the shop to have your child's feet measured every eight to 12 weeks in the first two years, and every three to four months as your child grows older.

Do not keep shoes for "best" wear, because they will get little use before they are outgrown. Do not hand shoes down to another child, because the leather will have taken the shape of the foot of the first wearer.

Parents often worry unnecessarily that their toddler seems to have flat feet. This impression is often due to a pad of fat on the inner sides of the soles, which disappears as the child grows.

It is also normal for toddlers to have bow legs. A bulky nappy may not only make a baby look bow-legged, but may actually increase the natural tendency for him to be so. This condition usually disappears by the time he is two.

Many normal toddlers turn their toes inwards when they first start to walk. Some parents fear that their child will always be "pigeon-toed". In fact, babies walk in this manner simply because it helps them to balance better, and the tendency usually disappears later.

POINTS TO REMEMBER WHEN BUYING A TODDLER'S FIRST SHOES

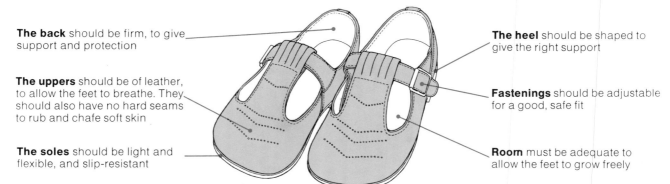

The back should be firm, to give support and protection

The uppers should be of leather, to allow the feet to breathe. They should also have no hard seams to rub and chafe soft skin

The soles should be light and flexible, and slip-resistant

The heel should be shaped to give the right support

Fastenings should be adjustable for a good, safe fit

Room must be adequate to allow the feet to grow freely

Take trouble when buying shoes for a toddler. Ask the fitter if the shop stocks half sizes and a variety of widths.

Make a note of the points to look for listed above before going to buy the shoes.

Problems of the toddler

In the period between a child's first and third birthdays, he develops new powers of understanding and independence which transform his behaviour. Not only does he learn to talk, and to understand much of what you say to him, but the way he thinks about the world changes dramatically.

Even as the toddler discovers his own personal powers and capabilities, however, there are moments when he is desperately dependent on his mother for security. The child's need to be closer to his mother can sometimes be exhausting for her. When the child is tired, frustrated or upset in some way, his need for the familiar people in his world becomes particularly apparent, and he shows that he is still a baby.

Some one-year-olds and two-year-olds are extremely shy and clinging. What can be done about it? Since extreme dependence often reflects fear of being separated from his mother, it is not going to help the child if you force him to be apart from you. Periods of extreme dependence do not usually last more than three or four months; the best course is for the mother to try to increase the time she can devote to the child, and to be patient and reassuring.

Often the child will be content in the company of another member of the family – the father or a grandparent, for instance. This relative may be able, in turn, to introduce the child to other people. A grandparent can sometimes leave a child with a neighbour, or at a playgroup, when for the mother to do this herself would involve too painful a separation. By about three years old, most children are less worried over new situations and separation from their mother; they are also better able to wait for attention.

In some families the mother is upset by the extent to which her toddler expects to be played with and amused. A battle of wills often develops between mother and child, the toddler tirelessly keeping up a string of demands while the mother tries hard to finish her work. Mothers often talk of the time around 18 months as the beginning of that "terrible 'no' stage", when suddenly a child starts refusing to do what is wanted, and firmly asserts himself, with or without words.

This sort of independence is an assertion of the child's growing awareness of himself as an individual. Even if he is much more difficult to deal with than he was a little earlier, it is a consolation to realise that this reflects a development in his growing-up.

Fears and fads
This mixture of dependence and independence can make the one-year-old and two-year-old child difficult to handle – a loving, rewarding and entertaining companion, but also an exhausting and demanding one. It is a period, too, when fears, temper tantrums, food fads, sleep troubles and nightmares, toilet-training difficulties and shyness are all common and quite normal.

At this time, differences in temperament between children are pronounced. Some, for instance, may have a number of marked fears. These may be fears of particular noises, of aircraft, of the dark, of having water on the face or the hair washed, or of particular programmes on television. It is best to provide calm, low-key reassurance, to avoid confronting the child with what frightens him, and gradually to talk and play your way round it.

Screaming outbursts of anger, usually called temper tantrums, are also common at this age. If your child has a tantrum it is obviously best to remove him from other children, especially if another child was involved in the onset of the tantrum. As the tantrum subsides, a hug and a kiss and a distracting game with you may help. The best course is to try to work out what leads to the tantrums and, if possible, to forestall them. A tantrum is often caused by sheer frustration: a child may strive to be independent, but his powers of co-ordination are not yet developed enough to give him, for example, the full control he wants to manipulate his toys. What he needs most is sympathy.

Food fads are extremely common up to the age of three. (See p. 128.)

Sleeplessness
Sleeping difficulties are also common among toddlers. They may take the form of regular waking in the night, or difficulty in going to sleep.

Often the child who is a bad sleeper at 2½ years has been a short sleeper from birth. If the child wakes persistently and both parents are becoming tired and irritable, it is worth consulting a doctor. He will advise on whether medication will help, and how much should be given.

Sometimes the habit of sleeplessness is very difficult to break. If you become very tired, it is worth trying to get an occasional "night off" by getting a grandparent or some other familiar adult to comfort your child when he wakes.

Make sure you have a fixed hour for bedtime, and adhere to it. Be firm about getting your child to bed at the right time, but try to make it a cheerful and peaceful occasion.

There is a great variation in the age at which children become dry by day and night. Most children become dry at night between the ages of two and three years. Some, however, do not become dry until well after three; boys in particular are often late in becoming dry. Children may be dry at night before they have stopped wetting in the day. Even if your child still wets his bed at four years, it is by no means abnormal.

Pot training

Training a baby to control his or her bowels and bladder is a needless cause of anxiety to many parents. Sooner or later all children become clean and dry – five-year-olds do not normally need to wear nappies.

There is no point in starting to train a baby until he or she can sit up easily. By this age – nine months or so – the baby will probably have settled into a pattern of passing a motion once or twice a day. Often this happens at regular times, such as shortly after his mid-day meal.

There is no "right" age at which to start training; different patterns suit different families. Sit the baby on the pot for five minutes or so. If he passes a motion, praise him; if not, put him in a nappy and wait for the next time. Soon he associates the feel of the pot on his bottom with the feeling of passing a motion, and increasingly often the first sensation becomes the stimulus for the second.

Let the control of the bowels become well established before starting to train the baby to control his bladder. Again the principle is to sit the child on the pot in the hope that he will by chance pass water. Give praise for success but do not make an issue about a dry pot.

By the age of 15 months or so a baby should be able to learn simple words for passing urine and bowel motions. When teaching him these words remember that he or you will need to use them in front of other people for some years, so short, inoffensive terms such as "wee" have much to recommend them.

During the second year the child begins to acquire voluntary control of the bladder, and may start to signal to you when he needs the pot. Imitation is a great help in learning to use the pot or lavatory; a boy can watch his older brother or father and learn from him.

Most children grasp the idea of pot training quickly enough. It is then infuriating when they lapse, soiling a nappy within a minute or so of a fruitless ten-minute squat on the pot. Never scold a baby for this. Some-times it happens when the child is under stress – perhaps he is just learning to walk, or another baby has been born into the family and he is jealous, or his father has been away from home. Patience and perseverance are the best ways of dealing with this situation.

Small children love talking about their excreta, and sometimes they play with faeces or urine. The mother should make an effort to suppress any disgust she may feel, since this may cause the child to feel distressed about "dirtying" his clean pot, and set him back in his pot training. A simple explanation that grown-ups don't talk about excretion, having other things to discuss, is the best response to endless chat about the subject from your child.

You may feel that your two-year-old or three-year-old is deliberately not using the pot in order to draw attention to himself and provoke you. He may in fact be calling for extra attention and loving, and you should try to give him these at the same time as being firm about the use of the pot.

Share your problems

To sum up, patience and a sense of humour are the most valuable qualities of a mother who has to cope with a difficult toddler. The difficulties will pass, endless though they seem.

Young mothers can benefit from sharing with each other both the problems and the pleasures of their children. Furthermore, the young child becomes happy in the company of other children and their mothers, and may also grow accustomed to brief separations from you.

Travelling with toddlers

In some ways, travel with a toddler is simpler than travel with a baby. Since the toddler can share adult food and mealtimes, you can take a quick and easy picnic meal for the journey. Avoid a lot of sweets, sticky buns and other foods which tend to be messy, such as oranges. Take lots of cool drinks – diluted fruit juice or squash – as toddlers become very thirsty in any form of transport. Make sure you also have a waterproof bag or two in case of sickness.

Depending on what stage your toddler has reached, you will need either spare nappies (disposable or ordinary), or a potty and spare pants. If you are travelling by car, allow time for stopping at least every two hours; do not set yourself too tight a schedule. Your toddler will appreciate the chance to run about for a few minutes and may well have a sleep when he returns to the car.

Staying happy on a journey
It is important to know how to amuse a lively toddler while you are travelling. Short journeys are not too difficult, as most small children enjoy watching the world go by and commenting on the passing scenery. This, combined with plenty of conversation, will probably keep the toddler occupied – but be careful not to let yourself be distracted from your driving.

For a longer journey, it is a good idea to supply your toddler with toys, books or other amusements. A favourite cuddly toy can be a great comfort, especially if there are delays in traffic jams. A surprise parcel, containing a small present, will hold a child's attention for some time.

Even if you have a radio fitted in your car, it may not be possible to find a programme that will keep your toddler interested. You may find more useful a cassette player which will play tapes of his favourite nursery rhymes, music or stories.

Most parents lack the strength of voice to sing or tell stories above the noise of a car engine. A familiar voice or other sound on tape will soothe a restless toddler, and possibly lull him to sleep. A cassette player can still be useful to play at bedtime after the journey is over.

One way of keeping a small child happy and occupied on a long journey is to arrange for him to have the company of another toddler. You do, however, need to be reasonably sure that the two children will not quarrel with one another.

Safety in the car
A child should always travel in the back seat of a car, in a safety seat or harness (see also p. 84). It cannot be too much stressed that if a child sits or stands unrestrained in a car, a sudden halt or collision, even at comparatively low speeds, can be lethal both to the child himself and to the other occupants of the car.

The correct choice and fitting of safety equipment is critical. Some equipment will injure a child's soft bones if he is catapulted forward; other types allow him to be thrown over the front seat and through the windscreen. Still other designs do not allow for the fact that a child has a large head in relation to his body, so altering his centre of gravity. The result, possibly, is injury to his face and head.

Always buy equipment that has been thoroughly tested to ensure that a child cannot be catapulted forward or injured in a crash or emergency stop.

For toddlers weighing up to about 18 kg (40 lb) – until about the age of five – use a safety seat. It should have side wings for added protection, and the back should be high enough to allow for growth. The correct design supports a child's head. For older children, use a harness.

Never use a safety seat or harness that is simply clipped to the upholstery, or fixed with screws to a flimsy part of the car. The straps must be bolted to the main car frame according to the manufacturer's instructions.

If you ever do have to carry a child without safety equipment, remember:
DON'T share a seat belt with a child. It is designed to restrain your weight, and no more.
DON'T let a child stand on the floor or the seat while the car is moving. A swerve or sudden stop is likely to throw him off his feet.
DON'T let a child put a hand out of the window. This is dangerous for the child, and an accident may be caused because other drivers think that you are signalling.

Foreign travel

Provided that you plan ahead and take some elementary precautions, foreign travel with a child can be as happy and relaxed as travel at home. Your travel agent will tell you what visas and types of immunisation are required.

Book early – and shop around

When making reservations, leave time to look about for the best "buy" – and do so carefully. Nearly every carrier – airline or shipping line – offers concessionary fares for children, and many take babies free. But one airline's bargain flight may not include a seat for your child, who will have to sit on your lap for the whole journey; while another may exclude baggage allowance, creating excess weight that must be paid for.

Remember that the outside temperature at foreign airports may be very different from that in the aircraft. If cold is expected, take extra clothes and blankets for a child. If the weather is going to be hot, take lightweight garments, and avoid plastic pants. As for a journey at home (see p. 133), take favourite toys, changes of nappies or pants, a potty, a plastic bag for soiled linen, and plenty of tissues.

At many city-centre terminals and airports, and also on many ferries, there will be nursing or changing rooms, and facilities for heating food and drink.

The best food for a small child in the air is the food to which he is accustomed. A baby can be breast-fed in a modern aircraft regardless of altitude. If he is bottle-fed, take dried milk rather than rely on fresh milk obtained on the journey, which may be unsafe in some climates. If a baby is used to fresh milk, accustom him to dried milk before the flight.

You must feed, wash and change your baby yourself, but milk and baby foods that you take with you can be heated to the required temperature by the cabin staff. On some flights the staff will provide special meals, if you make your needs known at the time of making your reservations. Some shipping lines, too, offer children's menus.

Do's and don'ts in flight

Some aircraft are fitted with safety belts for babies and small children, but at take-off and landing, a baby must be held securely on your lap. Never strap your safety belt around both yourself and your child.

To relieve pressure in the ears, give a baby a drink, and an older child a sweet to suck. Do not put cotton wool in their ears.

The child travelling alone

To travel on his own, a child will need his own passport (see p. 138–48).

Given adequate notice, the carrier will arrange to look after and entertain your child during the journey. Some carriers take charge of babies and toddlers; others do not. Airlines make a charge for the service, but some shipping lines provide it free. All carriers require a declaration from you authorising them to take care of your child.

At airports you must arrange for an adult to hand over and collect your child. This person should always wait until the flight has left, in case of cancellation or delays.

The years of steady growth

Between the ages of one and five years, the rate at which a toddler grows in weight and height gradually slows down. During this period children will also slim considerably, often becoming quite thin by the age of four or five.

Proportions change, with the legs and arms getting longer relative to the body. Posture goes through changes that sometimes cause concern, although they are quite normal. For example, a toddler tends to have slightly bowed legs, the appearance of flat feet and a marked forward curving of the spine in the lower back; this makes his stomach stick out and often gives the mistaken impression that it is swollen.

Although the growth of the skeleton is slowing down, other parts of the body still grow rapidly – as, for example, the lymphoid (glandular) tissues, which include the tonsils and the glands in the neck. The tonsils become very large, and the neck glands can usually be felt, as can glands in the armpits and groin. This is part of the normal development of the body's protective mechanism against infection.

Teeth continue to appear during this period (see p. 104). By the age of three, the child should have all 20 of his milk teeth.

By one year old, your child should be on a varied diet. He may still be fond of his bottle, but most of his nourishment should now be from meals which he should be able to munch and chew efficiently. He can now cope with all kinds of foods, and there is no need for the specially restricted diet of a very young baby.

During the second and third years, since he is not growing so fast, your child needs rather less food. A fall in his appetite is normal. However, all growing children need more protein, relative to their size, than adults do. The diet should therefore contain a daily source of protein such as egg, cheese, chicken or liver, as well as the protein found in cereals and other plant foods. It will do no harm to give supplementary vitamins, although as the rate of growth slows down, your toddler should be getting enough in his normal mixed diet.

The amount of food eaten varies from child to child. It also varies with the same child, from time to time. It is impossible therefore to say exactly how much a child should be eating. The best guide to whether your child eats enough is whether his or her growth is normal. Remember that milk is a food, and some children insist on it even after the first year.

The developing toddler needs fewer calories than he did during his first year, mainly because of the slowing down in growth, and because his body deals more efficiently with the calories he gets. As the child begins to move around more, a greater part of his calorie intake is expended in the energy he uses in his activities. He also uses up some of the fat stores laid down in his first year.

Patterns and preferences in eating which a child develops between the ages of one and five may persist throughout life. So try to arrange reasonable family meals, with a good variety of foods, and make sure your child joins as far as possible in "sitdown" meals with the family, at regular meal times.

Try not to fall into a habit of rushed breakfasts (or no breakfast at all), and sandwich lunches. Discourage your child from having snacks, and do not let him get used to expecting sweets as a normal part of the daily diet. A diet containing too many sandwiches, snacks, sweets and cakes, as well as being monotonous, contains too many calories in the form of starch or sugar, which will make the child fat and also rot his teeth. Encourage him to eat fruit, nuts and vegetables.

Fats are the subject of a good deal

GUIDELINES TO A CHILD'S GROWTH

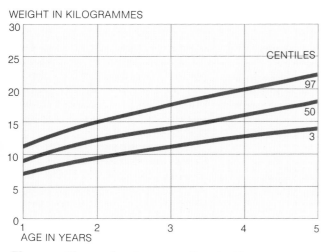

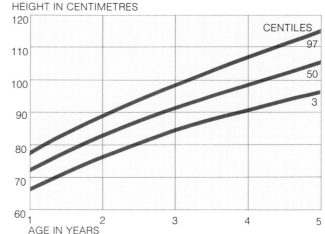

These centile graphs show growth rates for an average child (50th centile line), bigger than average (97th) and smaller (3rd). There are others between these. Whichever your child follows, he should keep roughly to his own line.

of controversy, because of possible harmful effects on health, and in particular their relationship to coronary thrombosis (heart disease). Most experts agree that the fats likely to cause health problems are the so-called "saturated" fats, found in meat-fat, butter and cream.

On present knowledge, there does not seem to be any reason to stop children eating such foods altogether, but it is probably sensible to discourage large amounts of cream and foods fried in animal fats. Instead, use vegetable oils, preferably corn oil, or oils which are labelled "rich in polyunsaturates".

Your reward for the effort of providing good, varied meals at regular intervals will be a child with, at the very least, a healthy set of teeth. There will probably be, in addition, even more important long-term benefits to his health.

Becoming less dependent
At the age of two to three years, a child is rapidly developing independence, in all sorts of ways. He will be keen to assert himself. About this time of life, "no" can be the most interesting word, and its use by the questing toddler is often deeply satisfying to him. This may well show itself in arguments at meal times. It is best, however, not to make an issue of a dispute over food, because such a battle can all too easily become a habit which produces distress all round.

It does not matter if your child refuses to eat much at one meal; he will make it up at another. Strong likes and dislikes are quite usual during this period when a child is asserting his independence.

There is really no point in trying to make a child eat something that he rejects very strongly. You may succeed in getting him to eat it – but it may not be worth the effort, since he is quite likely to be sick after you have achieved your "victory". Left to himself, your toddler may accept the disputed food later on.

Getting ready for school
By law, every child in most countries must begin school at the age of five. Before that arbitrary age, however, many children are thirsting for the kind of learning that parents cannot give.

A few schools may start children at four, but even this is not early enough for some children. That is where public and private nursery schools and playgroups come in.

A nursery school is a self-contained unit offering pre-school education for children of three and four, often on a half-day basis to begin with. A nursery class is much the same, but is usually attached to a first or infant school. Staff in schools or classes provided by the local authorities will be trained, but qualifications are not everything. Experience counts for a lot, and a happy, stress-free and purposeful atmosphere is also important. A visit to the school during working hours is the best way to form an impression, and your suspicions should be aroused if this is refused.

Learning through play
At nursery-school age, learning is still an informal business. New arrivals are welcomed into a relaxed and cheerful atmosphere, and mothers are expected to stay with them at first. Much of the children's classroom activity is more like play than work. The aim is not to start them off learning letters and doing sums, but to lay the foundations for such work.

Nursery teachers try to improve children's grasp of language by encouraging them to talk. They also try to develop their understanding of colours and shapes. This is where the children are involved in counting games, and they play with sand, water, bricks, clay, dough and paint.

Teachers also give them an idea about time ("We have tea at four o'clock") and length ("Teacher's foot is longer than your foot"), and size ("This bag is bigger than that bag").

The children explore personal relationships, learning to share, take turns, and play together. They still have a lot of growing to do, so they need activities that develop both co-ordination and muscles.

At nursery school, they learn to use a paint brush, felt pen or scissors – a competence that will help towards good co-ordination of hand and eye later when they are learning to write. Meanwhile, they take part in games to develop their muscles.

The playgroup alternative
Playgroups (often privately organised) try to develop children's capacities in the same way that nursery schools do. The best of them are in no way second-best to nursery schools, and indeed playgroups can offer something that nursery schools do not: the involvement of parents with the early education of their children.

6
INTERNATIONAL

Facts & figures

Australia

Antenatal care (see also pp. 15–20)

Most women have their first routine antenatal check-up within the first 8–12 weeks of pregnancy. This and subsequent visits will take place at a public hospital antenatal clinic, unless you wish to make arrangements under a health insurance scheme to see your own obstetrician in his consulting rooms. The Medicare scheme will cover you for visits to the hospital antenatal clinic, but you will have to accept being seen by whichever doctor is on duty. The doctor who will attend to you there, although he may never be the same one twice running, will probably be a trainee obstetrician under supervision from a consultant.

Maternity benefits

At your first visit to the antenatal clinic, you should learn whether you are entitled to receive any social welfare benefits while pregnant and after the birth of your baby. These vary according to your family income and other circumstances, and full details, including rates of payment, are available from any Social Security office. You will find their addresses and telephone numbers in the Commonwealth Government section of your telephone directory.

If you have been working continuously for the same employer, either full time or regular part time, for 12 months or more, you will be entitled to unpaid *maternity leave* of up to 52 weeks.

You may resign from your job while on maternity leave provided you give the usual notice, but you cannot be dismissed.

Some employees, such as those in public service where women are paid their full salary for up to 12 weeks, may be covered under different State or federal awards or agreements.

Special provisions apply if you have a miscarriage or stillbirth.

Registration of birth

The law concerning the registration of births agrees in broad outline in all Australian states, although it varies in some minor details. Every birth has to be notified to the Registrar (the Registrar-General's Office in Queensland, Western Australia and Northern Territory; Births, Deaths and Marriages Office in the Australian Capital Territory; the Registrar-General's Division in Tasmania; Births, Deaths and Marriages Registration Division in South Australia; and the Registrar of Births, Deaths and Marriages in New South Wales). In some cases, if more convenient, notification may be lodged with the local court house, which issues a birth certificate and forwards the information to the Registrar's office. In any case the relevant form can be supplied by the hospital where the baby is born and help in completing it is often given by the hospital social worker, who will witness your signature.

A birth must be registered within a specific time limit, which varies from state to state: e.g. one month in New South Wales, two months in Queensland.

If the parents are married either the father or mother should register the birth; if they are not married, only the mother is obliged to do so, although if the child is to be registered in the father's name, particulars and the father's signature may need to be witnessed by a justice of the peace.

Post-natal care (see also p. 73)

While you are still in hospital after the birth, your midwife will be available for advice, and in some circumstances a paediatrician (child health specialist) may examine your baby. If you have any health problems later, you should turn first to your doctor or to the clinic sister at your local baby health centre.

In most cases the clinic sister will have visited you in the hospital before you were discharged and will have made an appointment for your first visit to the baby health centre. Thereafter you will make regular visits to the centre, weekly at first, then fortnightly, then monthly.

Child-care services (see also p. 108)

Private minding is by far the commonest type of child care, often because there is no alternative. In some states it is illegal to look after more than two children for payment without a licence.

The family day care scheme, often run by a voluntary group or by your local council, organises child care in private homes, under the supervision of a co-ordinator who matches the children to the homes available. There may be up to four children in the one home, aged from 0 to 5 years or older, after school hours or during the school holidays. This scheme is cheaper than a day care centre, but the homes will not be as well equipped and it is difficult to check the quality of care.

Pre-schools and kindergartens provide only a part-time service, taking two- to four-year-olds for limited periods throughout the day, possibly just for the morning or the afternoon. Many involve the parents in their management and activities and are not really designed for the working parent.

There are various other part-time services available, but these vary from district to district, and often require parent participation. Neighbourhood children's centres may be run by a committee made up of parents and staff, and so can take on the role of a community centre.

Immunisation (see also pp. 159–60)
Immunisation is available free or at a nominal charge against diphtheria, tetanus, whooping cough, poliomyelitis and measles. Booster injections of combined diphtheria and tetanus with Sabin oral vaccine are given at 18 months, at pre-school and, in some states, again on leaving school (or at 15 years). Girls have a German measles (rubella) injection at about 11 years old. A mumps and measles vaccine or one for mumps

only is available in Australia, but as it is not part of the immunisation schedule it must be paid for.

In emergency (see also pp. 170–71) Follow the instructions given at the front of your local telephone directory and dial the appropriate number (000 in most towns and cities). Don't hang up until the operator makes it clear that he or she has all the information needed.

Poisonous animals
Snakes. There are about a dozen species of highly venomous snakes in Australia. Positive identification of them by an untrained person is difficult, but a knowledge of their distribution narrows down the possibilities, and helps doctors to choose the appropriate antivenom. In Queensland, for instance, a casualty is injected with polyvalent antivenom, which will neutralise the venom of all seven poisonous snakes found in that state. (See p. 186 for treatment.)
Spiders. There are two poisonous spiders in Australia: the redback spider, common to all states, and the funnel-web spider, found only around Sydney. Antivenoms are available for both species. (See p. 186 for treatment.)
Ticks. Bush ticks are normally found in rainforests east of the Great Dividing Range. They attach themselves to the skin of humans and can inject a poison which has a paralysing effect. (See p. 186 for treatment.)
Marine animals. Three venomous marine animals should especially be avoided: the blue-ringed octopus, a small brown, attractive creature

which develops sparkling blue rings when disturbed; the box jellyfish or sea wasp, found in tropical waters, which is almost transparent and has up to ten metres of trailing tentacles; and the stonefish, so-called because it looks like a stone, which lies buried in sand or camouflaged against rock, with its poisonous dorsal spines uppermost.

Treatment for bites or stings from them is as follows.
Blue-ringed octopus: as for snakebite (p. 186), by pressure immobilisation. Mouth-to-mouth artificial respiration (p. 184) may be needed. Get the child to hospital quickly. Box jellyfish: do not attempt to remove tentacles or rub the affected area. Douse liberally with vinegar and if necessary give heart massage (p. 185). Seek medical help urgently. Stonefish: relieve pain by immersing the affected part in hot but not scalding water. Treat as for a box jellyfish sting (see above).

Travel abroad (see also p. 134)
Children under 16 can be included on the passport of either parent, but not on both, in which case they can travel only in the company of the passport holder.

Separate passports can be issued to children of any age, but the application must be approved by their parents if they are under 17.

With the exception of yellow fever any necessary immunisation can be carried out by your doctor, or at any one of the immunisation centres run by the Commonwealth Health Department in all state capitals. Yellow fever immunisation is available only at these centres, and is not valid until ten days after the injection. So don't leave it until the last moment, and remember that, although you may be visiting a country that does not demand yellow fever immunisation, it is required for re-entry into Australia.

EARLY CHILDHOOD ADVISERS

Sydney:
Office of Child Care 230 0811
Contact Children's Services
Switchboard 212 4144
Brisbane:
National Association for
Community Based Children's
Services 345 6208
Adelaide:
Early Childhood Resource and
Advisory Unit 271 9705
Hobart:
Department for Community Welfare
30 3660
Melbourne:
Community Child Care 419 1148
Victorian Playground Association
329 6464 or 329 6277
Perth:
Lady Gowrie Child Centre 450 5411
Darwin:
Community Welfare Division
27 5022
Canberra:
National Association for
Community Based Children's
Services 82 2604

USEFUL ADDRESSES & TELEPHONE NUMBERS

Association for the Welfare of Children in Hospital

NSW (02) 635 4785	Tas (002) 34 4625
Qld (07) 378 1701	Vic (03) 836 8723
SA (08) 228 9427	WA (09) 385 9830

Australian Multiple Birth Association

NSW (02) 621 2424	Vic (03) 762 3487
Qld (07) 208 3992	WA (09) 409 8921
SA (08) 353 1518	NT (089) 32 1940
Tas (002) 29 5070	ACT (062) 58 7925

Australian Red Cross Society

NSW (02) 290 2622	Vic (03) 616 9911
Qld (07) 832 2551	WA (09) 321 0321
SA (08) 267 4277	NT (089) 81 4499
Tas (002) 34 3477	ACT (062) 47 8675

Childbirth Education Association of Australia

NSW (02) 57 4927	Vic (03) 509 9985
Qld (07) 343 5862	WA (09) 321 4821
SA (08) 276 9810	NT (089) 85 4084
Tas (002) 31 1332	ACT (062) 82 3614

Nursing Mothers' Association of Australia

NSW (02) 477 5934	Vic (03) 877 5011
Qld (07) 261 1916	WA (09) 339 1613
SA (08) 339 6783	NT (089) 27 9461
Tas (002) 29 5461	ACT (062) 58 9828

Parents Without Partners

NSW (02) 682 6677	Vic (03) 836 3211
Qld (07) 44 8567	WA (09) 325 4575
SA (08) 51 6660	NT (089) 27 2218
Tas (002) 34 7172	ACT (062) 48 6333

St John Ambulance Association

NSW (02) 212 1088	Vic (03) 67 5576
Qld (07) 52 2092	WA (09) 277 9999
SA (08) 274 0331	NT (089) 27 4444
Tas (002) 23 7177	ACT (062) 95 3777

Canada

Antenatal care (see also pp. 15–20)
This may take place at a doctor's office, a hospital clinic or a community health centre. The disadvantage of antenatal care in a hospital is that you tend to be seen by a series of different doctors, and there is no guarantee that you will see the same one twice running. Moreover, you may not know in advance which doctor will deliver your baby.

In Canada, antenatal care is supervised by doctors and nurses. Except in remote regions of the country, midwives cannot practise because they have no legal status. Virtually all births occur in hospitals. (N.B.: children under 12 are not permitted to visit Canadian hospital wards. There are areas where they can visit with the mother but not with the newborn.)

Maternity benefits

You are eligible for *maternity benefits* from Employment and Immigration Canada if you have worked in an insurable employment for 20 out of the 52 weeks preceding the birth of your baby. The period of eligibility begins either 8 weeks before the estimated date of birth or the week the baby was born, whichever is earlier, and can extend for up to 15 weeks. Benefits equal 60% of normal insurable earnings. In 1985, the maximum benefit was $276 a week. If your employer also provides benefits, you may receive up to 90% of your usual income. Mothers without insurable income who may be in need can ask their local social services for assistance.

There are no special benefits for a mother of twins. However, a mother of three or more babies is eligible for special provincial benefits.
Family allowance: Health and Welfare Canada provides monthly support payments for all dependent children under 18 resident in the country with at least one parent who is a

citizen (or landed immigrant) living in Canada (1986: $31.58 per month). *Child tax-credit*: this was introduced to help low- and middle-income families (1985 tax year: up to $384 for each eligible child).

Registration of birth
Generally, every birth in Canada has to be registered with the provincial department of health or with the vital statistics division (usually a branch of the health department). In some provinces, the hospital authorities register births. But in others, one of the parents must register the birth of the newborn at the local town hall or municipal offices within a specified period after the birth.

Post-natal care (see also p. 73)
When you leave hospital with your baby you can arrange for a community nurse to visit you at home. She will direct you to the nearest community or "well-baby" clinic.

Child-care services (see also p. 108)
These include day-care centres which must meet provincial minimum standards. Some centres offer full-day, weekday services. Others have only half-day services. One centre may limit its care to babies, while another will take pre-school children between the ages of 2 and 5.

Day-care homes are not licensed but may be inspected and supervised by the local social services department. These homes may be a good choice for infant and for lunch and after-school supervision. A working mother may be entitled to financial assistance if family income is low or if she is the child's sole support.

Immunisation (see also pp. 159–60)
Children in Canada are given free immunisation against polio, whooping cough, diphtheria, tetanus and measles.

In emergency (see also pp. 170–71)
Dial 0 or 911 (if that number exists in your area). Follow the emergency telephone procedure in your telephone book or the instructions of the operator. Don't hang up until the operator makes it clear that he or she has all the information needed.

Poisonous snakes
The only Canadian poisonous snakes are pit vipers, such as the massasauga, prairie and timber rattlesnake. (See p. 186 for treatment.)

Travel abroad (see also p. 134)
Children under 16 can be included on the passports of either parent, but obviously can travel only in the company of the passport holder. Children travelling on their own will need passports of their own.

Your doctor can arrange for any necessary immunisation to be given.

USEFUL ADDRESSES
Canadian Foundation for the Study of Infant Deaths
P.O. Box 884,
Toronto, Ontario,
M4T 2N7
(416) 488-3260
Canadian Institute of Child Health
Suite 165,
17 York Street,
Ottawa, Ontario,
K1N 5S7
(613) 238-8425

Canadian Red Cross Society
95 Wellesley Street East,
Toronto, Ontario,
M4Y 1H6
(613) 923-6669
Compassionate Friends of Canada
685 William Ave.,
Winnipeg, Manitoba,
R3E 0Z2
(204) 787-2460
La Leche League of Canada
Garlough Road,
Williamsburg, Ontario
K0C 1H0
(613) 535-2255
(information and support for women who are breast-feeding)
Parent Co-operative Preschools International
481 Queens Avenue,
London, Ontario,
N6B 1Y3
(519) 439-6751
Parents Anonymous
P.O. Box 843,
Burlington, Ontario,
L7R 3Y7
(216) 637-9773
Parents of Multiple Births Association of Canada
283 7th. Ave. South,
Lethbridge, Alberta,
T1J 1H6
(403) 328-9165
Parents Without Partners
205 Young Street,
Toronto, Ontario,
M5B 1N2
(416) 363-0960
St. John Ambulance
312 Laurier Ave. East,
Ottawa, Ontario,
K1N 8V4
(613) 236-7461

New Zealand

Antenatal care (see also pp. 15–20)
Most women go for their first ante-natal check-up when 8–12 weeks pregnant. This and subsequent visits may take place at a hospital, in your GP's surgery or in your specialist's surgery. Many hospitals provide a "progress book" in which details relevant to the progress of your pregnancy are recorded at each visit.

One disadvantage of antenatal care in a hospital is that you tend to be seen by a series of different doctors, obstetricians and midwives.

Antenatal care can be given by a domiciliary midwife and your GP, with the baby being delivered in hospital by your GP. You may also choose to have your baby at home. In this case, the midwife visits you early on in your pregnancy and will be present at the birth. She may also deliver your baby.

Maternity benefits
The following benefits, which are reviewed at six-monthly intervals, are available through your local social welfare department.
Emergency Sickness Benefit: single women may qualify for this benefit, ranging from $92 to $115 a week, during the last three months of their pregnancies.
Family Benefit: payable tax free in respect of each child, regardless of income (1986: $6 a week). This benefit can be received in lump sums. In respect of a first child, it can be obtained as a one-year advance. An advance on the second year's benefit can be had in order to buy a suitable car-seat for the child. After a child is 12 months, you can also get an advance of up to $4000, covering the entitlement until the child is nearly 14, in order to help buy or build a home.
Domestic Purposes Benefit: single parents may qualify for this benefit to enable them to stay at home and care for the children (1986: $185.76 a week in respect of the first child and an additional $10 in respect of each other child).
Drugs and Laboratory Tests: while pregnant and for one year after giving birth, mothers do not have to pay for most drugs prescribed specifically because of their antenatal or post-natal condition, but do pay a $1 dispensing fee on each item. All laboratory tests connected with motherhood are free.

Mothers in certain types of employment – such as those in the Civil Service, for instance – are entitled to paid *maternity leave.* Check your position with your employer.

Registration of birth
By law, every birth has to be notified to the local Registrar of births and deaths within 48 hours in cities or towns or within 7 days in more remote areas. This is the responsibility of the occupier of the premises where the birth has taken place, whether it is a hospital or a private home. The Registrar also sends registration forms to the parents. If the parents are married, either the father or mother should then register the birth; if they are not married, only the mother is obliged to do so (the father's name may be recorded if both parties agree).

If neither parent is able to register the birth, the occupier of the premises where the baby was born, or a person present at the birth or in charge of the baby, must register it.

Post-natal care (see also p. 73)
A public health or Plunket nurse usually calls automatically after she has been notified of the birth by the health department. She will direct you to your nearest health clinic.

The following benefits are available through your local social welfare department.
Multi-birth assistance: if you give birth to two or more babies at a time, you are entitled to free home help for up to three months.
Motherhood training: if required, nurses will be provided, at no cost, to train mothers in mothercraft skills.
Help with disabled infants: guidance and financial assistance is available for those with children who are physically or mentally disabled.

Child-care services (see also p.108)
Anybody paid in cash or kind to mind more than two children under 7 is legally obliged to be licensed by the Department of Education.

Child-Care Centres may be located in special buildings or in private homes. Charges vary, depending on the centre's policy and on parents' means. Subsidies are available from the Department of Social Welfare for parents with limited means. The centres usually take children from the age of about 2 but some accept them from about 6 weeks old.

Immunisation (see also pp. 159–60) Children in New Zealand are given free immunisation as follows: triple vaccine (whooping cough, diphtheria and tetanus) at 6 weeks, more triple vaccine and polio at 3 months and 5 months, measles at 15 months, double vaccine (diphtheria and tetanus) and polio at 18 months, polio at 5 years.

In emergency (see also pp. 170–71) Dial 111, whether for fire, police or ambulance. In most areas, thanks to modern technology, the operator answering you will be able to identify your number immediately.

Poisonous spiders Two venomous spiders may now be found in New Zealand – the katipo and the red-back which has arrived on ships from Australia. All hospital boards hold anti-venom serums to counter bites from these spiders. (See p. 186 for treatment.)

Travel abroad (see also p. 134) Children under 16 can be included on the passports of either parent but obviously can travel only in the company of the passport holder. Children travelling on their own will need passports of their own.

Your doctor can arrange for any necessary immunisation.

USEFUL ADDRESSES
Auckland Family Counselling Service
33 Owens Road, Epsom, Auckland 3
Tel: Auckland 687-632
Bereaved Parents Group
P.O. Box 4267 Auckland
(branches in most areas)

Birthright Inc
P.O. Box 6032 Te Aro, Wellington
(to help children of solo parents)
La Leche League
P.O. Box 2307 Christchurch
(information and support for women who are breast-feeding)
Maori Women's Welfare League
Waitatarau Community Centre
Hepworth Street
Freemans Bay, Auckland
NZ Child Abuse Prevention Society
P.O. Box 37151 Parnell, Auckland
(to assist people who fear they may harm their children)
NZ Home Birth Association
P.O. Box 7093 Wellesley Street
Auckland 1
Tel: Auckland 768-245
Parent Help or Parent Line
Listed in most areas under Personal Emergency Services in local telephone directories.
(to assist people who fear they may harm their children)
Plunket Society
P.O. Box 6042 Dunedin North
(also see local telephone directories)
Pregnancy Help
P.O. Box 5077 Christchurch
Tel: Christchurch 528151
(to help single pregnant women in temporary difficulty)
Red Cross Society
P.O. Box 12140 Wellington North
Tel: Wellington 723-750
(also see local telephone directories)
St. John Ambulance Association
P.O. Box 10043 Wellington
Tel: Wellington 723-600
(also see local telephone directories)

South Africa

Antenatal care (see also pp. 15–20) This may take place in your obstetrician's or GP's surgery, at a provincial hospital clinic or a municipal health department clinic.

By law, you are not entitled to paid time off work in order to have an antenatal check-up, but most women are able to come to some sort of arrangement with their employers.

Women covered by medical aid, and those who can afford it, usually see private obstetricians. Provincial hospitals and municipal health departments run antenatal clinics throughout South Africa. Fees are considerably lower than those of private obstetricians and are worked out on a sliding scale according to your income; however, you will probably be seen by several different obstetricians and midwives.

You may also have your baby at home. If you are seeing a private obstetrician, speak to him about this. Otherwise, approach your local municipal health department. They employ private midwives who carry out deliveries at home, but your antenatal check-ups will take place at your local municipal health department clinic.

Maternity benefits These are available only to women who contribute to the Unemployment Fund. By law, a woman (or man) employed in any job, other than a government post, which pays less than R1800 (1800 South African Rands) a month (1986), must contribute to the fund. It is a nominal amount, worked out on a sliding scale according to your income.

You are entitled to 45% of your ordinary weekly earnings for a maximum period of 18 weeks before your baby's due date, and eight weeks after this date. If the child is stillborn, you will be paid the benefit for only four weeks after the birth. Maternity benefits are subject to the number of weeks that you have contributed to the fund. The formula is one week's benefit for every six weeks' contribution.

Registration of birth

A white, coloured or Asian baby's birth must be registered within 14 days, with the Registrar or Assistant Registrar of births at the local office of the Department of Home Affairs. In a rural area, the birth may be registered with any justice of the peace or policeman. Parents of black babies must notify the local commissioner, and must register the birth at the local office of the Department of Constitutional Development and Planning.

The birth must be registered by either the mother or the father. If neither parent is able to go to the office of the Registrar of Births, the Registration of Birth form may be collected by a person nominated by the parents. The form must be completed, signed and returned immediately. In exceptional cases, a person who was present at the birth, or the occupier of the dwellings where the child was born, may register the birth. An illegitimate child's birth

must be registered by the mother – the father has no obligations in this regard.

Post-natal care (see also p.73)

You can choose to take your child to a private GP or paediatrician, a provincial hospital clinic or a municipal health department clinic. Divisional council health departments, while not offering antenatal care, do have post-natal clinics for babies.

Child-care services (see also p. 108)

A childminder, paid or not, does not have to be registered. However, a crèche or nursery school has to be registered with the Department of Education's Nursery School Section. Crèches and nursery schools at work places are not common for the private sector in South Africa. Some mothers working in government services, for example at a hospital, are able to have their children looked after for them. Most crèches and nursery schools accept children between the ages of 2 and 6 years, but some start taking babies from the age of 3 months.

Nursery schools are usually privately run and will have been inspected by a municipal or divisional council health inspector. Staff generally consist of qualified pre-primary school teachers and nurses, although there is no legal requirement concerning qualifications.

The Department of Health and Welfare runs crèches and nursery schools, where a nominal fee is charged according to the parents' income. The care of the children is seen to by teachers, social workers and nurses.

Immunisation (see also pp. 159–60)

Immunisation is free at municipal or divisional council health department clinics, but you may prefer to take your child to a GP. During the first month, BCG immunisation is given against tuberculosis, which is still a serious problem in South Africa. The 3-in-1 injection immunises against diphtheria, whooping cough and tetanus, and is given to your baby at 3 months, $4\frac{1}{2}$ months and 6 months. Immunisation against polio is given orally with each of the 3-in-1 injections. Immunisation against measles is given when your baby is 7–9 months of age.

In emergency (see also pp. 170–71)

Emergency numbers are found at the front of the telephone directory and they vary throughout the country, except for the Flying Squad which always has the number 10111. While an ambulance may be called, you can usually get help more quickly if you can take your child to the nearest hospital or doctor's surgery yourself.

Poisonous snakes

There are two main categories of poisonous snake in South Africa: cobra-type snakes, and adders (see p. 186 for treatment).

Invest in a handbook on snakes if you are going into the veld. You should, in any case, read up on snakes in the particular area that you live in. Give your children some practical rules to follow – for example, they should never walk barefoot in the veld. Also, they should never step over a large rock or log without knowing what is on the other side. If your garden has bushveld on its borders keep your grass short, and do not leave rubble lying around. Long grass and rubble make perfect hiding places for snakes. Also, rubbish left in the open will attract rodents, which will in turn attract snakes.

Travelling in South Africa and abroad (see also pp. 133–34)

When travelling in South Africa, it is important to remember that certain illnesses such as malaria are associated with some parts of the country and special precautions are often necessary before, during and after a visit to such an area.

Most children under sixteen who are travelling with their parents (South African passport holders) are included in one of their parents' passports. A child travelling without a parent must have his or her own passport. Immunisations necessary for travel abroad are carried out at your local District Surgeon's office.

USEFUL ADDRESSES

Association for Pre-School Education Care and Training
2nd floor Industria House
350 Victoria Road
Salt River 7925, Cape
Tel: (021) 47-2546
(information on pre-school crèches and nursery schools)

Breast Feeding Association
c/o Child Care Information Centre
cnr Liesbeeck and Sawkins Roads
Rondebosch 7700, Cape
Tel: (021) 66-8363

Child Care Information Centre
cnr Liesbeeck and Sawkins Road
Rondebosch 7700, Cape
Tel: (021) 65-4104 ext nos 13, 14, 15

Child Safety Centre
c/o Child Care Information Centre
cnr Liesbeeck and Sawkins Road
Rondebosch 7700, Cape
Tel: (021) 65-4104

La Leche League
(information and assistance to mothers who are breast feeding. Look under "La Leche" in your telephone directory)

Life Line
(free confidential advice for problems. Branches are found in all the major centres – look them up in your telephone directory)

Mother's Help Line
c/o National Childbirth Education Association
32 Odendaal Road, Aurora
Durbanville 7550, Cape
Tel: (021) 99-1684 and (021) 58-4591
(for any mother needing a sympathetic ear for her problems. It is a 24-hour service, manned by volunteers)

Natural Childbirth Unit
Maternity Section
Johannesburg Hospital
Parktown 2193
Johannesburg
Tel: (011) 643-0111

Parents of Twins Association
Consult the Life Line Directory of Services (see Life Line above).

SA Red Cross Society
Red Cross House
77 De Villiers Street
Johannesburg 2001
Tel: (011) 29-2441
(first aid courses)

St John Ambulance
cnr Loveday and Leyds Streets
Johannesburg 2001
Tel: (011) 725-3380
(first aid courses)

The U.K.

Antenatal care (see also pp. 15–20)
This may take place at a hospital, in your GP's surgery, or at a community health centre or clinic. You are entitled to take paid time off from work. You will be given a "co-operation card" on which details relevant to the progress of your pregnancy are recorded at each visit.

One disadvantage of antenatal care in a hospital is that you tend to be seen by a series of different doctors, obstetricians and midwives, and there is no guarantee that you will see the same one twice running. However there are alternatives: *"domino schemes"*, under which antenatal care is given by a midwife and your GP, and the same midwife comes into hospital with you and delivers your baby; and *GP units* (not available everywhere), where you are entirely looked after by your doctor and midwife, and your doctor will come and supervise the birth of your baby in hospital.

You may also choose to have your baby at home. In this case, the midwife visits you early on in your pregnancy and will also be present at the birth. She may deliver your baby, even if the doctor is also present.

Maternity benefits

The following benefits are all available through your local social security office. Your GP can give you the necessary claims forms.
Maternity Grant: a lump sum (£25 in 1986), payable after you are 29 weeks pregnant, plus extra if you are on

supplementary benefit. (This is due to be abolished in April 1987 and replaced with a means-tested grant.) *Maternity Allowance*: payable weekly for 18 weeks, starting 11 weeks before the week your baby is due but payable only if and when you stop work (1986: £29.45 per week). *Child Benefit*: payable tax free in respect of each child, regardless of income (1986: £7.10 per week). *One Parent Benefit*: an additional benefit for the first child in the family if you are a single parent (1986: £4.60 per week). *Prescriptions and Dental Treatment*: free while pregnant and for one year after giving birth. If you are on supplementary benefit, free milk and vitamins are also available while you are pregnant and until the baby is 5 years old.

If you work, you may be entitled to paid *Maternity Leave*: 90% of your usual pay, less the maternity allowance, is payable by your employer for 6 weeks. You may also have the right to return to your job.

Registration of birth

By law, every birth has to be notified to the Registrar of births and deaths for the sub-district in which the child was born within a certain time limit (6 weeks of the birth in England, Wales and Northern Ireland, 3 weeks in Scotland). If the parents are married, either the father or mother should register the birth; if not, only the mother is obliged to do so (the father's name may be recorded if both parties agree).

If neither parent is able to register the birth, the occupier of the premises where the baby was born, or a person present at the birth or in charge of the child, must register it. In Scotland and Northern Ireland, a relative may register the birth.

Details of the birth must also be sent within 36 hours to the District Health Authority, normally by the doctor or midwife, but in the case of a home birth by the father.

Post-natal care (see also p. 73)

A health visitor usually calls automatically after she has been notified of the birth by the district health authority, and should make regular calls over the next five years, to keep an up-to-date record of your child's health. She will tell you about your nearest clinics: every local authority area has its own child-health clinic, but in addition, more and more family doctors now run their own "well-baby" clinics for mothers and children. Vitamin drops and milk feeds are available from these clinics and are generally considerably cheaper than elsewhere.

In certain circumstances you may be entitled to a home help. Your local social services department will be able to help you.

Child-care services (see also p. 108)

Anyone paid in cash or kind to mind children under 5 years of age for more than 2 hours a day is legally obliged to register with the local authority.

Council nurseries charge varying prices, depending on the council's policy and the parents' means; places are allocated by the local social services department, normally on the recommendation of a social worker. They usually take children from the age of about 2 but can accept them from 6 weeks old. Private nurseries must register with and be supervised by the local council. The person in charge is usually required to be a trained nursery nurse.

Immunisation (see also pp. 159–60)

Children in Britain are given free immunisation against polio, whooping cough, diphtheria, tetanus and measles.

In emergency (see also pp. 170–71)

Dial 999, whether for fire, police or ambulance. Don't hang up until the operator makes it clear that he or she has all the information needed.

Poisonous snakes

In Britain, the only poisonous snake is the adder, which is distinguished from the harmless grass snake by the zigzag marking down its back. (See p. 186 for treatment.)

Travel abroad (see also p. 134)

Children under 16 can be included on the passports of either parent or even of a relative, but obviously can travel only in the company of the passport holder. Children who are travelling on their own will need to have passports of their own.

USEFUL ADDRESSES

Association for Post-Natal Illness
7 Gowan Avenue,
London SW6 6RH
01-731 4867

Association of Breast-Feeding Mothers
131 Mayow Road,
Sydenham, London SE26 4HZ
01-778 4769

British Red Cross Society
9 Grosvenor Crescent,
London SW1X 7EJ
01-235 5454
(first aid courses)
"Foresight"
The Old Vicarage, Church Lane,
Witley, Godalming,
Surrey, GU8 5PN
042879 4500
(pre-conceptual care)
Health Education Council
78 New Oxford Street,
London WC1A 1AH
01-631 0930
La Leche League of Great Britain
BCM 3424,
London WC1N 3XX
01-404 5011
(information and support for women who are breast-feeding)
The Miscarriage Association
18 Stoneybrook Close,
West Bretton, Wakefield,
West Yorkshire, WF4 4TP
092485 350
(information and support for women who have had a miscarriage)
National Childbirth Trust
9 Queensborough Terrace,
London W2 3TB
01-221 3833
National Society for the Prevention of Cruelty to Children
67 Saffron Hill,
London EC1N 8RS
01-242 1626
Parents Anonymous
6 Manor Gardens,
London N7 6LA
01-263 5672
(24-hour telephone service for parents worried that they may abuse their children)

Pre-School Playgroups Association
Alford House, Aveline Street,
London SE11 5DM
01-582 8871
St John Ambulance
1 Grosvenor Crescent,
London SW1X 7EF
01-235 5231
(first aid courses)
Society to Support Home Confinements
Lidgate Lane, Wolvingham,
Bishop Auckland D43 3HA
0388 528044
Stillbirth and Neonatal Death Society
Argyle House,
29–31 Euston Road,
London NW1 2SD
01-833 2851

The U.S.

Pre-natal care (see also pp. 15–20)
This may take place at a doctor's office, a hospital clinic, or a community health center. Most women see doctors in private practice, but if in need of financial assistance may receive free or nearly free pre-natal care. To find out if you are eligible, contact your state health department or local Medicaid office.

In the U.S., pre-natal care is supervised by doctors and nurses, and sometimes by midwives. Nurse-midwives must be certified; certified or licensed midwives are legal in several states. Although some births occur at home or in childbearing centers (out-of-hospital birth centers), most occur in hospitals.

Maternity benefits
Employers are required by law to treat pregnancy as a disability, so that a pregnant woman receives any disability benefits her employer offers. Disability leave for pregnancy and childbirth is usually several weeks, but the precise amount of time depends on the woman's health. A few states have disability insurance programs, which ensure that eligible women in those states receive disability benefits. Contact your state department of labor for information. Maternity leave beyond disability benefits is up to the individual employer.
Tax Dependency Exemption: a tax deduction is allowed for each dependent child. (1986: $1040.)

Registration of birth
Every birth in the U.S. has to be registered with the local (usually county) health department, which then reports to the state health department. Hospital authorities register births unless the child is born outside the hospital, in which case the person delivering the baby is responsible for registering the birth.

Post-natal care (see also p. 73)
Post-natal care is supervised by doctors, nurses, and occasionally nurse-midwives and midwives. Most states have "well-baby" and "well-child" clinics for those requiring them. Contact your state health department for information.

Child-care services (see also p. 108)
Child-care services include day-care centers, often to be found in schools,

churches and community centers. Day-care homes, on the other hand, are privately run in people's homes. In most states, day-care facilities with more than a specified number of children must meet state standards and be licensed. Most facilities offer full-day, weekday services, but some may have only half-day services. One center or home may limit its care to babies, while another will take children between the ages of 2 and 5. Certain federal funds may be used by local agencies for day care.

For those working parents paying for child care, at least part of the expenses may be taken as a tax credit.

Immunization (see also pp. 159–60) Under the Medicaid program, low-income families can qualify for free or low-cost immunization against diphtheria, tetanus, whooping cough, polio, measles, rubella (German measles), mumps, hemophilus influenzae type B (Hib) and tuberculosis. In addition to these sponsored immunizations, some school health services and public health clinics offer free or reduced-rate vaccines. U.S. schools require certain immunizations before entry, but those required differ from state to state.

In emergency (see also pp. 170–71) Dial 0 or 911 (if that number exists in your area). Follow the emergency telephone procedure in your phone book or the instructions of the operator. Don't hang up until the operator makes it clear that he or she has all the information needed.

Many poison-control centers now exist in the U.S. Find the one nearest you by checking your phone book's emergency phone numbers.

In less urgent cases help may be found at a nearby health center or the emergency room of the nearest hospital.

Poisonous snakes
The only U.S. poisonous snakes are rattlesnakes, copperheads, water moccasins (cottonmouths), and coral snakes.

Treatment for bites from the first three is the same. If the bite is on an arm or leg, apply a light constricting band on the side of the bite nearest the body but do not cut off circulation. Wash the bite area with soap and water and immobilize it. Do not use ice or cold compresses. Make a $\frac{1}{4}$ inch deep cut with a sterile blade through each fang mark in the direction of the length of the limb. Do not make cross-mark cuts. Draw out venom with suction cups or suck it and spit it out. Seek medical help immediately.

For treatment for bites from coral snakes, see p. 186.

Travel abroad (see also p. 134) Children, regardless of age, will need passports of their own to travel abroad. Your doctor can arrange for any necessary immunization.

USEFUL ADDRESSES
American Academy of Pediatrics
141 Northwest Point Blvd.
P.O. Box 927
Elk Grove Village, Illinois 60007
American Red Cross
17th and D Sts. N.W.
Washington, D.C. 20006

Association of Birth Defect Children
3526 Emerywood Ln.
Orlando, Florida 32806
Informed Homebirth/Informed Birth and Parenting
P.O. Box 3675
Ann Arbor, Michigan 48106
Mothers Are People Too
c/o ASPO/LAMAZE
1840 Wilson Blvd., Suite 204
Arlington, Virginia 22201
Mothers at Home
P.O. Box 2228
Merrifield, Virginia 22116
National Association of Childbearing Centers
Rt. 1, Box 1
Perkiomenville, Pennsylvania 18074
National Committee for Prevention of Child Abuse
332 S. Michigan Ave., Suite 1250
Chicago, Illinois 60604
National Organization of Mothers of Twins Clubs
5402 Amberwood Ln.
Rockville, Maryland 20853
Parents Without Partners
7910 Woodmont Ave., Suite 1000
Bethesda, Maryland 20814
Retarded Infants Services
386 Park Ave. S.
New York, New York 10016
Share
c/o St. John's Hospital
800 E. Carpenter St.
Springfield, Illinois 62769
(support for parents who have suffered the loss of a newborn baby)
The Compassionate Friends
P.O. Box 1347
Oak Brook, Illinois 60521
(support for parents who have experienced the death of a child)

7
CHILDREN'S HEALTH GUIDE

ADENOIDS

The adenoids, two small lymph glands at the back of the nose, can become enlarged in children with minor throat or nose infections.

The role of adenoids, like that of tonsils, is to trap germs and destroy them. If they become enlarged, they can interfere with the passage of air through the nose, prevent mucus draining away properly, and cause the child to breathe only through the mouth. Enlargement can also block the Eustachian tubes, which connect the middle part of the ear with the back of the throat, causing infection and pain in the middle ear.

A doctor may give antibiotics to treat the infection, and nose drops to reduce the swelling of the lining membrane of the nose. If adenoids repeatedly become enlarged a doctor may recommend their removal, and this is a relatively minor operation.

ALLERGY

A child with hay fever, asthma, nettle rash or eczema probably has an allergy, meaning that his body is sensitive to something eaten, inhaled or touched. Allergy-producing substances, or allergens as they are known, are all around us. They number several hundreds, including animal hair, feathers, house dust, pollens, and foods such as milk, eggs, wheat, shellfish, strawberries and chocolate.

The tendency to develop an allergy sometimes runs in families, although a child's particular allergy is not necessarily exactly the same as that of one of his parents.

The mechanism by which an allergic attack takes place is complicated. In hay fever, for example, the child breathes in pollen. Because he is sensitive, the pollen becomes an irritant to his body. In response, the body cells produce antibodies, in the same way as the body reacts to infection from bacteria, viruses and other germs. The next time the allergen enters the body, the antibodies are already present and neutralise the invaders. As part of this process, however, histamine and other chemicals are produced; it is these that are responsible for many of the distressing symptoms of allergies, including the familiar streaming eyes and sneezing of hay fever.

There are three courses of treatment open to a doctor trying to help a child who has an allergic disease. Firstly, he tries to identify the substance to which the child is sensitive so that it can be eliminated from his environment. Secondly, he may give medicines or drugs to prevent the allergic attack, or at least to reduce its severity. Thirdly, if the allergen cannot be avoided, the doctor may desensitise the child to it.

In trying to discover what causes an allergic reaction, the doctor will want to know exactly when the attacks occur, in what surroundings they take place, and whether other members of the family have allergies. He will usually then carry out skin tests. These involve making a series of small scratches on the child's back or arm, into each of which a different allergen is introduced. If the reaction is positive, a weal surrounded by a reddish area forms at the site of the scratch within 20 minutes. A large variety of allergens may have to be tried before the troublesome ones are discovered.

Once the cause of the allergy has been discovered, the sufferer must try to avoid it. For instance, if the allergy is caused by the hair of a pet, the child must where possible be kept away from the animal responsible. If the cause is a certain food, drug or article of clothing, this must be avoided. In the case of dust allergy (due to a mite that lives in house-dust), the house must be vacuum-cleaned regularly in preference to sweeping, which only raises the dust.

In many cases, such as summer hay fever, the allergen cannot be avoided. Then the doctor will probably prepare a programme of desensitisation. This consists of a series of injections that contain an extract of the allergen, or allergens, to which the child is sensitive. They are increased in strength over a period of time, so that step by step his resistance to the allergen is built up. If, however, the child shows a harmful reaction to any dose, the following dose is reduced.

ASTHMA

A disorder of the bronchial tubes leading to difficulty in breathing. It can be caused by an infection of the nose, sinuses, bronchial tubes or lungs. A more common cause is an allergic reaction, which is often inherited. (See ALLERGY.)

In allergic asthma, the child may be sensitive to pollen, animal hairs or feathers, insecticides, or certain foods, drugs and chemicals. The tiny house mite, found in house dust, contains a protein to which a child may be allergic. When he comes into contact with any mites, the chemical substance histamine is released into the child's system, triggering off the allergic reaction. Bedding containing feathers or hair are not only common allergens, but also harbour the house mite.

Another possible cause of asthma is emotional stress – brought on, perhaps, by starting at a new school, by worry over examinations, by fatigue, or even by pleasurable excitement.

In a typical asthmatic attack, the child will have difficulty in breathing, will feel a tightness in his chest, will wheeze, and will sometimes cough. There is usually a feeling of suffocation which can be extremely frightening to the child. Towards the end of the attack, thick mucus may be coughed up.

Non-allergic asthma is treated by a doctor, who may prescribe antibiotics to bring any infection under control. Allergies cannot be cured, but the severity of the symptoms can be reduced. The child should be given a series of tests to try to identify the allergens involved. A course of injections may then be prescribed to reduce the child's sensitivity. Breathing exercises, under the supervision of a physiotherapist, may also help. Inhalants, or injections, may be used to relieve an attack.

BITES AND STINGS

Most insect bites and stings cause very minor irritation; relief of this is the only treatment needed. Calamine lotion is soothing, and cooling the skin with a cold compress helps.

Children should not scratch bites, as this may lead to infection.

Nettle stings can be treated with calamine lotion or antihistamine cream.

For snakebite and more serious stings (wasps, bees, hornets, jellyfish), see First Aid, p. 186.

BLISTER

An accumulation of fluid under the skin, often caused by burning or rubbing. Serious burns (see p. 176) have to be treated by a doctor. Blisters caused by rubbing, such as by a badly fitting shoe, are less serious, but they must be protected so that they are not accidentally opened to admit infection. Put a gauze dressing or adhesive plaster over the blister until it heals. Do not interfere with it in any other way.

BOIL

A boil is caused by a germ, the staphylococcus, that enters the outer layer of skin through a hair follicle, the channel through which each individual hair grows towards the surface. A germ will enter the follicle more easily at the point where the skin has been rubbed, such as at the back of the neck or on the buttocks.

The bacterial infection becomes a raised tender area. Usually, within two or three days, it comes to a head and bursts to discharge pus, a yellow matter. A single boil will be painful but not serious. The consequences can be grave, however, if bacteria enter the bloodstream and cause blood poisoning. For this reason, never squeeze a boil to try to bring it to a head. This can spread the infection to nearby hair follicles, starting more boils. Hot fomentations also encourage boils to spread.

Left alone, the boil will heal itself. The use of dressings impregnated with antibiotics may help to reduce the spread of the infection.

Consult your doctor if the boil does not come to a head, or if there are red streaks running from the area of the boil. This means that the infection is spreading to what may be a serious extent.

BRONCHITIS

Bronchitis in children usually occurs in its mildest form, known as "wheezy bronchitis", and does not normally appear after the age of five.

Bronchitis is an infection of the tissues that line the air tubes branching out into the lungs from the windpipe. The wheeze is caused by the child breathing through tubes that are inflamed, full of mucus, and in a state of spasm which makes them narrow.

The wheezy sound of a bronchitis attack is sometimes confused with the symptoms of ASTHMA, but asthma attacks suddenly, whereas wheezy bronchitis occurs following a cold, or else in combination with a chest infection.

The treatment of wheezy bronchitis is aimed mainly at making the child cough up the mucus. Cough medicines are ineffective. By using physiotherapy parents can help their children to bring up mucus, but the parents first need instruction from a doctor or physiotherapist.

It does not matter if the child swallows the mucus instead of spitting it out: both are effective, although swallowing the mucus may cause vomiting.

BRUISES

The many knocks that children take often cause small blood vessels to be ruptured without the skin being broken. The bleeding under the skin shows as a black or blue mark.

Minor bruises, even those accompanied by swelling, heal without special treatment, although cold, wet compresses speed the healing process and help reduce pain. A severe bruise should be examined by a doctor.

A "black eye" has an alarming appearance, but does not harm the eye. It consists of bruising of the tissue around the eye. There is swelling for a few days, and discoloration may last longer.

BURNS AND SCALDS

Trivial burns and scalds under 2.5 cm (1 in) in diameter should be treated by immediately immersing the area in cold water, or holding it under cold running water. If done at once this reduces the pain, and also cleans the skin quickly. Do not touch the affected area, or try to remove anything sticking to it. If a blister forms, cover it with a medicated adhesive dressing; do not prick the blister. Keep the dressing dry. If necessary, give the child an aspirin tablet to relieve the pain.

Larger burns and scalds are serious; they require first aid (see p. 176) and medical attention. See also SUNBURN.

An electric shock can make a burn that is small in area but deep and slow to heal. If it has not healed in a couple of days, consult a doctor.

CHAFING

The rubbing of clothing against the skin, or the rubbing together of two moist skin areas, causes this soreness of the skin. It is most common in the armpits, buttocks and groin, and should be treated by washing the chafed area, thoroughly drying it, and then dusting it with talcum powder.

CHICKEN POX

An acute, highly contagious disease that is caused by a virus and marked by eruptions on the skin. It mainly affects children under ten, and is one of the mildest of infectious fevers.

The eruptions appear as dark red pimples, first on the back and chest, then spreading to the face, scalp and arms. The disease generally lasts about two weeks after the first appearance of the spots. It produces a mild fever, severe irritation leading to a desire to scratch the spots, and loss of appetite.

If a doctor confirms a case of chicken pox, the child should be put to bed if he feels unwell, and kept isolated until all the blisters have formed scabs. Try to stop the child from scratching the spots, for this could lead to secondary infection and scarring. To help reduce this risk, cut his fingernails short and make sure that his hands are thoroughly clean.

To relieve the itching, dab the spots with calamine lotion, which will help to dry them and reduce the irritation. It can also help if the child is given a warm bath in which a cup of bicarbonate of soda has been dissolved. An antihistamine, prescribed by a doctor, can also be

helpful. If the blisters show signs of infection, inform the doctor.

With a baby change the nappies frequently, or the spots will not dry out thoroughly and will become liable to infection. If possible, leave the nappy off so that the skin is exposed to the air.

Few people can catch chicken pox more than once, but the same virus that causes chicken pox in children can cause shingles in an adult. As a result, an adult with shingles can give chicken pox to a child.

COLDS

The common cold is a virus infection of the lining of the nose. It is never the result of a child being chilled by wet feet, sitting in a draught, or anything else. In fact, keeping a child excessively warm seems to bring on a cold rather than deter it.

The symptoms of a cold include a discharge – clear or sometimes thick and yellow – from the nose, and a cough caused when these secretions irritate the back of the throat. There may be VOMITING, loss of appetite, and a FEVER (which causes shivering). The ADENOIDS and tonsils may become enlarged; this is not a bad sign, but an indication that the body is fighting the infection.

Babies are more distressed by colds than older children, as they cannot breathe so effectively through their mouths. Nose drops should be given to allow the baby to

breathe through his nose more freely. Babies are also more likely than older children to get lung complications such as pneumonia. For these reasons a doctor should be consulted, and visitors or other children with colds should be kept away from the baby.

COLD SORE

An infection caused by a virus, *herpes simplex*, which leads to sores around the mouth and nostrils. It rarely affects babies, but can attack children aged from one to five.

The sores last approximately ten days, and will disappear of their own accord. During the ten days, however, the sores will be extremely painful – particularly in the first attack, which starts with white ulcers forming inside the mouth and on the tongue.

After a first attack, sores may appear whenever the child's resistance is lowered, especially when he has a cold, although the cold is not the primary cause. A doctor may prescribe an antibiotic ointment to reduce secondary infection.

COLIC

Some babies cry regularly for long periods, drawing up their legs and often passing wind. By the time they are three months old these crying

153

sessions tend to stop. That is why this unexplained crying is known as "three-month colic".

It was once believed that babies behaved in this way because they swallowed air while feeding. In fact, babies always draw up their legs whenever they cry. The passing of wind, whether up or down, is due to increased pressure on the abdomen. If a baby is well and has been fed his crying indicates that he needs comfort from his mother.

CONSTIPATION

The frequency of a child's bowel movements depends on the individual child's habits, diet and physical make-up. His bowels move whenever they need to – in some children more than once a day, in others daily, or even only once every three or four days. The belief of some parents that any child's bowels should be opened at least once a day can have the opposite effect. A child may then hold on to his stools and become constipated. The bowels do not need to be trained to work regularly because there is a natural mechanism to perform this function.

No direct treatment of the "constipation" caused by such stool-holding should be undertaken because this only aggravates the problem. Parents should ignore their child's bowels, thereby leaving nature to do its work.

Diet has no part to play in the management of chronic constipation in children.

Temporary constipation which may accompany a feverish illness is a different problem. This is due to the fever and to the fact that the child is eating less. It will correct itself when the illness passes.

COUGH

A cough is not itself a disease – it is a symptom, a protective reflex action of the windpipe or the bronchial tubes to get rid of mucus or other obstructions, and has many possible causes. Inhaled dust, or a piece of food lodged in the windpipe, can cause a bout of coughing.

Plenty of hot drinks, and lemon or blackcurrant pastilles, may help to relieve a cough. Do not dose a child with a strong cough medicine intended for an adult. If a cough lasts for more than a few days consult a doctor. He may prescribe the occasional teaspoon of a soothing cough linctus.

If the cough is accompanied by a sharp pain in the side, it could be a sign of inflammation of the lungs, and a doctor should be called.

CRADLE CAP

A thick brown layer of crust that may cover a baby's scalp or appear in patches. Cradle cap may occur as the result of insufficient washing of the "soft spot", the anterior fontanelle (see p. 100), in the mistaken belief that vigorous washing can damage the brain. It may also occur because the skin itself is naturally greasy.

As soon as the flakes appear, wash them away with a solution of 1 teaspoon of sodium bicarbonate to 1 pint of water. Sometimes the crust can be removed by soaking it overnight with olive oil. This will help to loosen the flakes of skin, so that they can be gently lifted off with a comb in the morning. If the crusts are stubborn to remove, or the skin beneath the crusts is inflamed, seek advice from a doctor.

Cradle cap that has become established may be cleared up within a day or two with a special anti-cradle cap shampoo. Rub this into the scalp as an ointment at night, and use it again as a shampoo in the morning. If the crusts reappear, repeat the treatment.

CROUP

This acute infection of the vocal cords is most likely to occur in children between the ages of two and four. It is most common in winter and spring, and normally occurs in the first instance at night.

The first symptom is difficulty in breathing. Each breath is accompanied by a high-pitched croaking noise. A rasping cough – often compared to the bark of a seal – develops. Call a doctor without delay if the child has difficulty in breathing, indicated by a rapid, heaving movement of the chest.

To relieve the spasms while waiting for the doctor, moist warm air is helpful. Prop the child up on pillows, and increase the humidity by allowing the steam from a boiling kettle to circulate in the room. Alternatively, start hot water running in the bathroom basin and bath, and keep the child in the room where he can inhale the steam. Whichever treatment is used, it is important to stay with the child to calm his fear and to make sure he does not scald himself.

The doctor may prescribe antibiotic or sulphonamide drugs to control the infection, and an expectorant to relieve the blocked air passages. He will advise you on how to help your child if another attack occurs.

CUTS AND GRAZES

Apart from gently washing away any dirt and dried blood from around the wound, minor cuts and grazes are best left to themselves. A dressing is needed only to help to control bleeding and to prevent germs from entering before a scab has formed.

A scab is the body's own barrier against infection. Washing a scab or rubbing antiseptic ointments over it will not provide additional protection, but only soften the scab and weaken the barrier.

Many children expect to have a plaster put on the smallest of cuts, and this simple treatment can help to keep the child from crying. By covering the wound, however, the healing process can be slowed down, so do not leave a plaster on for too long.

Any small white or yellow patches on a scab, which mean that a wound has become slightly infected, will usually clear up of their own accord. You need only be concerned if the child complains of pain, or if the skin in the area of the wound becomes inflamed. If red streaks spread out from the wound, seek medical advice without delay. Immunisation with anti-tetanus vaccine helps to protect a child against infection.

DANDRUFF

The common name for seborrhoea of the scalp, a disorder in which small flakes of dead skin form on the scalp. In babies the brownish flakes sometimes fall from the head and spread the condition to other parts of the body, such as the cheeks or the ears, where it can cause the skin behind the ears to crack. The flakes may even produce a rash in the groin

and on the genitals and buttocks.

The most effective treatment is to wash the baby's hair several times a week, with a medicated shampoo.

DIARRHOEA

Babies usually have a number of attacks of mild diarrhoea before they reach their second year. The fact that motions are looser than average, or that the stools stay green instead of turning to the more usual brown, does not in itself necessarily matter. As long as the child is eating and drinking normally and not vomiting, there is little need for concern. Even if the child has lost some appetite for solids, there is no cause for anxiety as long as he continues drinking normally.

If, however, the baby is vomiting or there is blood in the stool, call a doctor without delay. Babies cannot stand much loss of fluid, and the combination of diarrhoea and sickness can soon lead to dehydration, a drying-out of the body which leaves the eyes looking glazed and sunken, and the mouth dry. The lost fluid must be replaced at once with a correct solution.

Be sure to save the baby's stool for the doctor to see. This will help him with his diagnosis and to determine whether the diarrhoea is due to an infection in the bowel (caused, perhaps, by food poisoning or dysentery) or to an infection in some other part of the body.

E

EAR DISORDERS

Each ear consists of three parts: the outer ear and middle ear (concerned with hearing), and the inner ear (parts of which are also concerned with the sense of balance). The ear-drum is between the outer and middle ear. The middle ear is kept drained – and so free of infection – by the Eustachian tubes, which connect it with the back of the throat. The middle and inner ears are situated inside the skull.

Ear trouble in babies and children is normally confined to earache – caused by an infection, and resulting inflammation, of the middle ear. It is commonest in babies and in very young children.

Infection of the middle ear is common with enlarged ADENOIDS (which block the Eustachian tubes), and after TONSILLITIS, MEASLES, INFLUENZA and a COLD. In addition to pain there may be deafness, ringing in the ears and – if the ear-drum has been perforated – a blood-stained discharge from the ear.

If there are any of the above symptoms, the doctor should be consulted at once, for all middle-ear infections are serious. He will probably prescribe antibiotics to combat the infection, and other drugs to relieve the pain. Sometimes a doctor will prescribe nosedrops. These ensure proper drainage of the middle ear by keeping the Eustachian tubes open. Eardrops cannot reach the middle ear past an intact ear-drum. Most cases of earache recover completely, and even a perforated ear-drum usually heals quickly.

Not all earache is caused by a disorder of the ear. Swollen neck glands and even a bad tooth may cause earache. If a child complains that his ears ache when he has MUMPS or an infected throat, warmed cotton wool placed over the ear may relieve the pain.

If a child's ear is "runny", do not assume that the discharge is wax. It could be pus breaking through the ear-drum from a middle-ear infection. If this is not treated urgently, it can lead to deafness later in the child's life.

Inflammation of the outer ear is common in children, and is usually caused by poking objects into the ear, or by swimming, especially in chlorinated water. It can be extremely painful. If there is any discharge other than wax from the ear, see the doctor. Children with any sort of ear infection should not be allowed to go swimming.

A boil in the ear can also be very painful. It is not normally serious, but requires a doctor's advice.

ECZEMA

This complaint is characterised by a red, itchy rash and blisters, and the skin may crust and scale. Eczema does not normally affect a baby until he is two or three months old. It is caused by ALLERGIES, and is more common in boys than in girls. It often attacks a child with a family history of allergic conditions. Eczema usually starts as an irritating red patch on the forehead and cheeks, which may become inflamed and moist. It may be made worse by an emotional upset.

Eczema in very young infants is more common among those fed on cow's milk than among breast-fed babies. It may also occur if the child's skin is excessively oily or dry. It is sometimes caused by allergic reaction to substances such as rubber, metal and paints; or to drugs such as barbiturates and sulphonamides. In such cases, tests can be made on the skin to determine the exact cause or causes.

Eczema is particularly trying for babies, who become restless and irritable. Soap and water often only further irritate the skin, which should be cleaned with cotton wool soaked in olive oil. Avoid putting rough or fluffy materials next to the child's skin.

Allergic eczema may be prevented by avoiding contact with the cause, and some types of eczema clear up without treatment.

To reduce irritation, the doctor may prescribe sedatives and a skin cream. In most cases these will have a rapid effect. In the meantime it is advisable to keep the child's fingernails short to reduce the risk of infection from scratching. In severe cases of eczema, or where the rash spreads to a large part of the body, a baby may need hospital treatment.

EYE DISORDERS

The main eye troubles (apart from defective sight) that may affect babies and children are a sticky eye, a squint, conjunctivitis and styes.

A sticky eye is common in the first two days of a baby's life, and is nearly always caused by fluid and blood from the mother's womb getting into the eye during birth. Regular bathing with cotton wool dipped in a weak salt solution will soon clear the stickiness away. To reduce the risk of carrying any of the troublesome matter from one eye to the other, make sure that the eye is wiped from the inside towards the outside. It is also advisable when laying the baby down to place him with the affected eye nearest to the mattress. If the baby is lying the other way round, the matter can flow down into the good eye.

A repeated sticky eye, or an eye that keeps watering, could be the result of a blocked tear duct. Most blocked tear ducts clear up without treatment before the age of six

months. If the trouble persists after then, ask a doctor's advice.

A baby who squints, or looks cross-eyed, is usually suffering from an imbalance of the eye muscles. This need not cause concern unless the squint persists after the age of three months; then an eye specialist must be consulted. He will advise whether treatment is necessary, and whether it has to be immediate or can be deferred until the baby is older. Treatment is usually carried out by covering up the good eye with a pad. This forces the weak eye to be used, strengthening the eye muscles. An older child may also be given eye exercises.

Bloodshot eyes, or conjunctivitis, can be caused by an eye infection or simply by a foreign body entering the eye and causing irritation. Infectious conjunctivitis, or pink-eye as it is also called, is highly contagious, being easily transmitted by fingers or towels, and both eyes are invariably affected. The eyelids swell and tend to stick together, and there may be a discharge.

Most cases of conjunctivitis respond readily to home treatment. The eyes should be bathed several times a day in warm water that has been boiled. Cotton wool soaked in the water should be held against the eye with a wooden spoon. Dip this spoon in boiling water after each treatment. If there is no rapid improvement, consult the doctor, who may prescribe antibiotics.

A stye appears like a small boil on

the eyelid, and is caused by infection of one or more of the eyelash roots. First remove the eyelash or eyelashes causing the trouble, then apply warm, moist compresses for about 15 minutes every two hours. After one or two of these treatments, the stye usually opens and drains. Do not rub or touch the eyelid – this may spread the infection. If the stye does not open after several days, see the doctor, who may open the stye and remove the pus.

A child who suffers from styes or infectious conjunctivitis should always be given his own personal face flannel and towel, which should be kept separate from those of the remainder of the family. He may also need to see a doctor.

FEVER

An abnormal rise in body temperature is often caused by, and is a symptom of, an illness or a virus or bacterial infection.

Normal body temperature is said to be 37°C (98.6°F), but many children – and adults – have an average temperature that is half a degree above or below this "normal" figure. Body temperature also varies during the day, being generally at its lowest in the early morning and at its highest in the evening.

When a child's temperature rises to 37.8°C (100°F), he is said to have a slight fever. If the fever reaches 38.3°C (101°F), a doctor should be consulted. A high fever is marked by a body temperature of 40°C (104°F) or more.

But a child's temperature is not necessarily a certain indication of the severity of an illness. A child may have a normal temperature, yet be seriously ill. Diphtheria – a serious illness – generally produces only a slight rise in body temperature. On the other hand, a child may briefly run a high fever without being ill at all – for example, if he is over-excited, or has been crying excessively.

Fever due to illness usually occurs in combination with other symptoms. While the child's temperature is rising, he may feel a chill. He may also feel weak and light-headed, and often he will complain that his joints ache. His pulse rate increases, he loses his appetite and he may be constipated. However, when his skin becomes warm and he begins to sweat, it is a sign that his temperature is falling.

A fever accompanied by a sore throat may be a sign of a COLD, INFLUENZA, TONSILLITIS, glandular fever or MUMPS. In cases of CHICKEN POX, MEASLES and GERMAN MEASLES a fever is accompanied by a RASH. Only a doctor can make a firm diagnosis.

For a slight fever, a doctor may advise taking an aspirin tablet several times a day to help bring down the temperature. Drinking water or fruit juice will also help.

When a child has a high fever, and is very distressed and restless, his temperature may be reduced by sponging him all over with tepid water. Stop when the temperature has been reduced to 38.9°C (102°F).

G

GERMAN MEASLES

German measles (rubella) is less infectious and much milder than MEASLES. Symptoms are a pink rash on the face, neck and body, a mild FEVER, and SWOLLEN GLANDS, particularly at the back of the neck. The rash lasts not more than three days, and the child recovers completely without treatment.

German measles causes only mild discomfort, and many doctors consider it better to spread the infection rather than isolate it, except of course when isolation is necessary to avoid contact with a woman in early pregnancy.

In this case doctors recommend an isolation period of seven days after the rash has appeared. The glands at the back of the neck may remain swollen for several weeks after the rash has subsided.

H

HICCUP (HICCOUGH)

Hiccups are involuntary, spasmodic contractions of the diaphragm. The sound of the hiccup is caused by the sudden closure of the glottis (the upper opening of the larynx) at the moment of taking a breath. It can be brought on by eating too quickly, by disorders of the digestive tract, and by nervous tension. Ordinarily hiccups last only a few minutes and are no cause for concern. But if an attack is prolonged and severe, do not wait until it has exhausted the child. Consult a doctor, who may prescribe a sedative.

A new-born baby will frequently hiccup. The popular belief that this is caused by a feed that disagrees with the child is unfounded. This hiccupping can be ignored.

The number of "cures" for hiccups is legion. For older children, possible remedies include taking a series of deep breaths; pulling the tongue to induce swallowing; drinking a glass of water slowly; and breathing for a minute or two into a paper bag – *not* a polythene bag – held closely against the face.

IMMUNISATION

Immunisation is the process of artificially reproducing resistance to infectious diseases by introducing germs of the disease, in mild or harmless doses, into the body. It is generally done by injections; sometimes (as in the case of smallpox) the surface of the skin is scratched; or (with poliomyelitis) the vaccine is swallowed.

Infectious germs have certain protein substances called antigens. Each kind of germ has its own antigen. The body fights the infection in two ways. It produces substances called antibodies, which counteract the germs' antigens and thereby the germs themselves; or it produces antitoxins, which kill the poison produced by the germs. If the germs strike a second time, the body is prepared for the attack, having already produced the appropriate antibody or antitoxin.

Diseases that can be prevented in young children by immunisation include diphtheria, whooping cough, tetanus, poliomyelitis and measles, as well as a number of infectious tropical diseases such as typhoid, yellow fever and cholera.

It is essential to follow a strict immunisation programme, particularly during a child's first two years. The fact that some illnesses such as diphtheria have virtually disappeared from Western countries must not blind a parent to the necessity for immunisation. It is only by the immunisation of all children in a community that such dangerous illnesses as these can be kept in check.

There are two main types of immunisation – active and passive.

Active immunity is provided by introducing a weak form of the germ into the body so that the body produces antibodies without actually being attacked by the disease. Active immunity can protect for life, as in the case of diphtheria, or for only a year, as with INFLUENZA.

Passive immunity is given by introducing into the body serum – part of the blood – from an animal, or from another person who has had the disease. This serum already contains the relevant antibodies or antitoxins. Passive immunity is, however, usually only a temporary form of immunity and can sometimes cause a reaction in the body against

the serum. Some babies are born with their own built-in passive immunity, which is passed on to them from their mothers.

The inherited antibodies protect the baby during his first few weeks of life, but at the same time prevent him making the same antibody if he is immunised before they have disappeared. This is why most vaccinations – with the exception, in some instances, of whooping cough vaccine – are not given until the baby is about three months old.

The doctor will advise you when a child should be immunised, and when he should be given various boosters – extra doses to provide longer-term protection. But the following is a guide to the different types of immunisation:

Diphtheria, whooping cough, tetanus. This immunisation, known as triple immunisation, is given as three separate doses, usually in the course of the child's first year, unless there are medical reasons for delay, and a booster dose of diphtheria/tetanus vaccine is advised before school entry. (See pp. 138–148 for details of procedures in different countries.)

There has been some anxiety about the whooping cough inoculation, which was linked in the mid-1970s with cases of brain damage. Statistically, there is a far higher chance of a child suffering death or brain damage or other long-term effects from whooping cough

itself than from the immunisation, so having the immunisation is recommended. However, there are some circumstances in which children are more likely to have a serious reaction to being immunised, and it is wiser for these children not to have the whooping cough injection. If any of the following apply, tell your doctor:
– if your child has a temperature or is otherwise unwell;
– if your child has had a bad reaction to a previous whooping cough injection;
– if your child, or anyone in his immediate family (i.e. parents, brothers or sisters), is epileptic, has ever had fits or convulsions, or has any kind of brain damage.

Do talk to your doctor if you are at all worried about your child's reaction to the injection.

Measles. One injection of the live, weakened virus normally provides sufficient immunity. It is given in the baby's second year, when the passive immunity passed on from his mother has waned.

A baby may become tetchy after immunisation, but no more than that. If he shows any other symptoms, do not assume that these are due to immunisation. Consult your doctor because they may be signs of an illness.

Poliomyelitis. Immunity is given by a live, but weakened, virus which is taken either in a syrup, by babies, or on a lump of sugar, by the older child. This vaccination is given on the same days as the triple immunisation doses, with a booster dose when the child is five years old.

Smallpox. This highly contagious virus disease is now officially eradicated and vaccination is no longer necessary.

Typhoid, yellow fever, cholera. Immunisation against these is required only if the child is visiting certain tropical countries (see pp. 138–148 under Foreign Travel).

A parent should keep a record of a child's vaccination programme. This will be a reminder of when further immunisation is due, and will tell the doctor exactly what vaccination to give. Immunisation may be delayed: if, for instance, a baby has a bad cold, wait until he has recovered.

IMPETIGO

This skin infection, which attacks exposed parts of the body, such as the face, scalp and hands, may occur at any age, but is most common in babies and children. It may be a complication of ECZEMA, RINGWORM or COLD SORES. It is highly contagious, and is spread by discharged matter from the sores. These appear first as little red spots which get watery heads; these then break open to leave yellowish, crusty sores. Because impetigo spreads very quickly, a doctor should be consulted as soon as it appears. As it is so infectious the child must have his own flannel and towel, and his clothing must be washed separately from the family laundry. When handling it, rubber gloves should be worn to reduce the risk of the infection spreading.

Treatment consists of applying an antibiotic ointment prescribed by a doctor. Severe cases may require treatment with an antibiotic taken by mouth. To help restrict the infection, wash the skin around the sores frequently. Make sure that the child washes his hands often with medicated soap, and that he avoids touching or scratching the sores.

INFLUENZA

This illness is caused by a virus infection, and usually attacks children less severely than adults. The first symptoms are generally a COLD, and perhaps a sore throat. The child has a FEVER, and suffers from aches and pains, especially in the abdomen, legs and arms. His eyes may be inflamed, and his nose may bleed. He may lose his appetite. The attack should in most cases be over in three or four days.

If a child is suffering from other symptoms, or is obviously very ill, a doctor should be called. Antibiotics cannot help to speed up recovery, because they do not kill viruses, but

---

a doctor may prescribe them if he suspects that there may be another infection, involving bacteria. For normal influenza, the only treatment is to keep the child in bed for a day or two, and give him plenty to drink. A child may be protected against influenza for up to a year by means of IMMUNISATION.

ITCHING

The urge to scratch is instinctive in anyone who itches. It particularly tempts children, who do not realise that continuous scratching can injure the skin and admit infection.

Moderate itching may be due to dry skin, dirt on the skin or scalp, insect bites, or allergic reactions to certain foods, drugs or other substances. Alternatively, it may originate in some emotional upset. More severe and lasting itching occurs in conditions such as acne, ECZEMA and CHICKEN POX.

To help prevent damage to the skin, keep a child's fingernails cut short; and to discourage infection, make sure that the child's hands are washed regularly.

LARYNGITIS

This inflammation of the larynx – the voice box – has many possible causes, the most common being one of the infections leading to a sore throat. It can also be caused by straining of the vocal cords, by an allergy, or by the sufferer shouting for some time.

Laryngitis is accompanied by hoarseness. There may be coughing, and a tickling or soreness in the throat. If there is much swelling, breathing may be difficult and produce wheeziness. Steam inhalations may help relieve the breathing, but an adult should stay with the child to avoid any risk of scalding. If the child has difficulty in breathing, or if the condition persists longer than two or three days, see the doctor. A particular kind of acute laryngitis is called CROUP.

M-R

MEASLES

The most prominent symptom of this very contagious disease is a pink rash that starts behind the ears and across the forehead. Measles tends to occur in epidemics every two years – most often in the spring – and is usually caught by children between the ages of one and six.

The first signs of the disease often occur three to five days before the appearance of the rash. They resemble cold symptoms: sore eyes, sneezing, coughing and a running nose. The child may also vomit and have DIARRHOEA. His body temperature rises, occasionally reaching as much as 41°C (106°F) by the fourth day. The rash, which can spread over the entire body, consists of small red spots and will last for four to seven days. The fever begins to subside when the rash appears. Complete recovery from measles is usual in two to four weeks.

A child with measles is very vulnerable to other infections, from BRONCHITIS to pneumonia, so careful convalescence is important. The patient should be isolated in a well-ventilated room, not just to prevent others from catching the disease, but also to protect him from secondary infections. If the child's eyes are sensitive to bright light, it will help if the sick-room curtains are kept drawn. The child should be given a light diet while he has a fever, and kept in bed until his temperature returns to normal. He can be allowed to get up once he seems well enough to do so.

If the child does not get better once the rash fades, or complains of earache, the doctor should be called.

MENINGITIS

An infection of the meninges (the fine membranes surrounding the brain and spinal cord). The disease is picked up from close contact with a person who is carrying the organism without having the disease itself. The symptoms usually develop over a few hours.

There are various types: the symptoms are similar in all. They include headache, often very severe; vomiting, sometimes very severe; unnatural drowsiness or confusion; high temperature; intolerance to bright lights; convulsions; and painful and stiff neck or back. However, small children may have only fever and appear ill, while newborn babies may not even have a fever and diagnosis can be difficult. If you have any suspicion of meningitis you should call a doctor immediately.

The severity of the symptoms and seriousness of complications depend on the nature of the infecting organisms: these can be either bacteria or viruses (including the viruses responsible for mumps and gastroenteritis). Viral infections are not uncommon: they occur in little epidemics but do not usually cause complications. Bacterial infections are rarer but are more likely to affect children, who may be severely ill for several days. Complications can include brain damage and epilepsy. The commonest bacterial type is meningococcal meningitis, also known as cerebrospinal fever. However, all the bacterial infections respond to treatment with high doses of antibiotics, and most cases recover provided they are diagnosed early and treated promptly.

In some cases deafness may follow so a routine hearing test should be given.

MUMPS

A contagious disease, usually mild in children, that may attack them at any age, although it is more common from the age of five onwards. It is caused by a virus transmitted in the saliva of an affected person, and occurs mainly in the salivary glands, particularly the parotid gland in front of each ear.

The most typical symptom of mumps is a swelling of the face and neck, and tenderness of the parotid glands. It is usual for glands on both sides of the face to be affected, but often one side swells up a day or two before the other side, and sometimes only one side is affected. The child will find it difficult and painful to move his head and open his mouth. He will have a dry mouth and may have a slight FEVER.

Since eating is difficult, the child should be given nourishing drinks to make up for lack of solid food. Lack of saliva means discomfort and the possibility of infection, so the child should be given plenty to drink. His mouth should be kept clean by rinsing, and his teeth should be cleaned after meals. An aspirin tablet will help to ease the pain.

The child should be kept in isolation for seven days after the swelling has gone down. If there is a fever, he should stay in bed until it subsides.

Viral MENINGITIS is a complication which occasionally appears about ten days after the onset of the illness. Complete recovery is general.

RASHES

A rash is a temporary skin disorder consisting of a red area, or areas, sometimes with many small spots.

Rashes have many causes. They may be reactions to localised skin complaints, or they may be outward signs of abnormal conditions affecting the entire body, such as an ALLERGY or a reaction to a poison. Rashes also accompany infectious diseases such as CHICKEN POX, MEASLES, GERMAN MEASLES, SCARLET FEVER and shingles, and each disease has a characteristic rash. Emotional stress, too, can be a cause.

If a specific, avoidable cause such as an allergy is suspected, the rash should disappear when that cause is tracked down and avoided.

If ITCHING becomes particularly troublesome, a cup of baking-soda in the child's bath water, or antihistamine cream or calamine lotion on the affected area, may help. Consult a doctor if the rash persists, or if it is accompanied by other symptoms such as a fever or headache, or if the child complains of feeling unwell.

Nappy rash. Even the best-cared-for babies can get nappy rash – a reddening and soreness of the skin in and around the areas covered by the nappy. The rash is the result of the skin being in contact with a soiled nappy, and the soreness, which will often make the baby fretful and unhappy, can cause a skin infection.

However frequently nappies are changed, it is impossible to prevent the skin being in contact at some time or other with urine, or waste matter from the bowels. Certain precautions, however, can be taken. Apart from changing nappies frequently, make sure that they are perfectly clean and soft.

If nappy rash persists, consult a doctor. He may advise leaving the baby out of nappies for a few hours each day so that the rash is exposed to the air. Alternatively, he may prescribe a lotion or ointment which will form a barrier between the wet nappy and the baby's skin.

The most common form of nappy rash, ammonia dermatitis, is started by a chemical reaction between the urine and the stool. It can spread from the nappy area to the abdomen. The skin becomes spotty, red and moist, then wrinkled, and peels at the edges of the rash.

A parent can normally tell whether nappy rash is ammonia dermatitis by the strong smell of ammonia given off when a nappy is changed. A simple treatment is to give the nappies a final rinse in a weak vinegar solution. After the nappies have been washed, dip them into this solution, lightly wring them out, and dry them thoroughly.

Some nappy rashes are caused by infections far removed from the rash area. For example, THRUSH in the mouth can cause a rash in the region of the buttocks; and seborrhoea, a form of DANDRUFF on a baby's scalp, can spread to the buttocks and the groin. The doctor will advise the correct course of treatment.

Nettle rash. This allergic skin complaint (known in its most severe condition as hives) produces a rash that looks like nettle stings – itching and burning white weals, surrounded by reddened skin.

In a particularly severe attack, the small spots can join together forming a weal as large as a saucer. In some cases, the weals will disappear within an hour or two; in others they can last for several days, and even weeks.

Nettle rash is usually caused by a child's sensitivity – to foods such as shellfish or strawberries, to drugs such as aspirin, to emotional tension, or to a reaction to insect bites. It is not a serious complaint, and most people suffer only one or two attacks all their lives.

To relieve the symptoms, a luke-warm bath containing two cups of laundry starch may be helpful. For localised itching, a compress dipped in cold milk can bring relief. Calamine lotion, or a paste of bicarbonate of soda, applied to the skin may be soothing. In severe cases, the doctor may prescribe antihistamines, although these will only help a few children.

Prickly heat. Babies are especially susceptible to this uncomfortable, itchy rash. It appears as tiny red pimples and blisters, usually on the neck, face, chest, back and thighs, or in the armpits. The condition is also known as heat rash.

Chafing and perspiration when the child's body is overheated are the main causes of the condition. The rash usually disappears after the body has cooled.

Prickly heat is best cured, or prevented, by the regular changing of sweaty clothing, and by frequent baths (without soap, which can further irritate the skin), followed by a liberal dusting of baby talcum powder.

The alternative name of "heat rash" is misleading, for even in winter, if a baby gets too hot under his clothing or bedding, he can develop the rash. Avoid having wool next to the baby's skin, and in cold weather keep a cotton vest between the skin and his outer clothing. At night keep fluffy blankets away from his neck and face. If the rash persists, consult a doctor.

RINGWORM

A highly contagious infection that is known medically as *tinea*. The

CHILDREN'S HEALTH GUIDE

name is misleading as no worm is involved: the disease is caused by a fungus and may be acquired from other infected people or from animals. The symptoms usually include irritation or itching and patches of inflammation in the shape of a ring, often attacking the hair and scalp.

Inflamed areas may become infected with bacteria producing IMPETIGO. Consult the doctor if you suspect ringworm and if patches of baldness and scaling develop on a child's head. Treatment, usually with antibiotic tablets, will clear the condition in about 6–9 weeks, but be very careful to avoid reinfection. Keep all linen clean and if possible, give the child a clean pillowcase every night. Throw away old combs and hairbrushes as disinfectants and antiseptics do not kill all fungi.

RUNNING NOSE

Catarrh, or a persistently runny nose, may have several explanations. Snuffly babies have particularly small nasal passages, so they often sound as if they have permanent COLDS.

A young child's nose will run until he is taught how to blow it. This should be done one nostril at a time, closing the other with a finger. Other causes may be ALLERGIES, or enlarged ADENOIDS. If a child with catarrh seems unwell, or has earache, consult a doctor.

SCARLET FEVER

This illness is caused by a strain of streptococcus that produces a SORE THROAT, and a RASH. Scarlet fever may start suddenly, with loss of appetite, VOMITING and FEVER. There may also be a stomach ache. About the second day the rash appears, starting around the neck and chest and spreading over the whole body, except around the mouth. After about a week, the skin flakes off each spot.

A doctor should be called as soon as scarlet fever symptoms appear. He will treat it with antibiotics or sulphonamides.

SORE THROAT

A sore throat is usually part of the body's early-warning system – a symptom that the throat is being invaded by germs. The throat never becomes sore of its own accord – something makes it sore. That something can be dangerous if not treated, so seek the doctor's advice if the throat is still sore after two or three days.

Do not confuse a sore throat with TONSILLITIS, which is a specific illness.

SPEECH DISORDERS

There may be several reasons why a child cannot speak properly or clearly – and a wide variation in the length of time it takes a normal child to learn to talk properly. This period may depend on the child's particular physical make-up – there is no fixed age at which a child should be talking. Other children who are late in talking may be suffering from nothing more than a lack of stimulus – that is, their parents do not talk to them enough. This reduces the children's opportunity to learn by listening and by practising the sounds they hear.

Actual speech disorders can be caused by a physical abnormality (a cleft palate, for example), an emotional problem, or deafness; or by damage to the speech centre of the brain or to the nerves to the organs of speech; or by a mental handicap.

Physical abnormalities causing impaired speech can usually be corrected by dentistry or surgery.

Stuttering and stammering are two related forms of speech disorders which are often emotional in origin. They should not be confused with the normal hesitations, tripping over words and repetition common among children between the ages of two and a half and six. No attempt to cure a stutter or stammer should be made unless it becomes persistent, when the help of a speech therapist is needed.

Lisping is quite normal in young children learning to talk, and need not cause concern. But persistent lisping can be sign of partial deafness, or of faulty action of the tongue. Corrective treatment should be given before a child starts at school, where a speech defect could slow his progress and lead to teasing.

A deaf child is unable to hear either his own voice or that of another person. He will need special speech and language training in order to learn what sounds are like.

A child whose speech is affected by damage to the speech centre of the brain or to the speech nerves – leading to words being slurred, mispronounced or wrongly used – may require speech therapy to minimise the difficulties.

A child with a mental handicap finds speech difficult to understand as well as to use. Any mentally handicapped child will need extra patience from his parents if he is to make the greatest possible use of speech. Neither too much nor too little should be expected of such a child, for either expectation can slow down progress.

SPLINTERS

If a splinter embedded in the skin is not removed promptly, it can cause festering – pus forms beneath the skin, owing to infection by bacteria. First wash the skin around the splinter with soap and water. Sterilise a pair of square-ended tweezers by boiling them for five minutes; then pull out the splinter.

A splinter that is deeply embedded, or causes severe inflammation, pain and swelling, should be extracted by a doctor. IMMUNISATION with anti-tetanus vaccine helps to protect a child against infection.

SPRAINS

A sprain is a severe wrenching of a joint which may tear supporting ligaments. Children generally suffer sprains in the ankle and wrist. Knee and shoulder joints can also be sprained, but this is less usual.

Most sprains are caused by falls or by a simple twisting of the foot. The pain is usually intense, and the joint swells because of the damage to nearby tissues and blood vessels.

When an ankle is sprained, remove the shoe immediately. Laces should be cut, to save time during which the swelling could rise and make the shoe harder to remove, causing extra pain. Apply ice or a cold wet cloth to the joint, or immerse it in cold water.

Rest the sprained joint in a comfortable position for the child. In the case of an ankle, this may mean supporting the whole leg from heel to thigh. If necessary, put a long splint, such as a piece of wood, under the leg. Wind a thick layer of cotton wool around the joint, and gently bandage the leg to the splint. The leg, on its splint, can then be supported on a chair without causing additional pain. An aspirin tablet may be taken to relieve the pain.

STOMACH DISORDERS

Abdominal pains in children can be caused by any one of a number of disorders and diseases. These can range from emotional stress or a simple ache caused by eating too quickly, to food poisoning or a serious infection of the bowels, such as gastro-enteritis. It is therefore extremely difficult for a parent to tell whether the child is suffering from a minor stomach ailment or is showing signs of worse trouble.

The rule to follow is to note whether the baby or child shows any signs of illness – whether his pains are accompanied by a FEVER or VOMITING, or whether he looks ill, has DIARRHOEA or loss of appetite. If a baby who has been crying furiously, with his legs drawn up, stops crying when you pick him up, and takes his feed normally, there is no need to call a doctor. But a child who complains regularly of stomach aches should see a doctor. The problem could be emotional or it could be physical, and an early warning of a more serious disorder. If a child is in

165

obvious agony, call a doctor as a matter of urgency.

One common stomach disorder which must be attended to promptly is appendicitis. The word means inflammation of the appendix, which is a small, useless tube leading off the lower intestine. Because one end is closed, the appendix can only empty itself back into the intestine. It may therefore become infected, and so inflamed.

Appendicitis is invariably accompanied by severe pain around the navel. The child usually vomits. There is often CONSTIPATION, and sometimes a FEVER. A doctor should be called at once, for an inflamed appendix may burst within 24 hours of the onset of an attack, causing infection to spread dangerously throughout the abdomen (peritonitis). The doctor diagnoses appendicitis by examining the child's abdomen, and an operation is performed to remove the appendix.

There is no such thing as a "grumbling appendix" – an appendicitis pain does not come and go.

One of the more serious stomach conditions affecting babies, normally between 3 to 12 months, is known as acute intussusception – the telescoping of a section of the small intestine into the adjoining part, resulting in an obstruction. It is a fairly rare condition, and affects boys more than girls.

The first signs are a severe abdominal pain recurring every few minutes, sickness, DIARRHOEA and sometimes VOMITING. Blood may also be passed with the bowel movements. This condition must be diagnosed in its early stages and an operation performed to pull the intestine back into position. (See also COLIC, CONSTIPATION.)

STUFFY NOSE

Inhalants or pastilles may relieve a stuffy nose, if the cause is simply an accumulation of mucus. Some other causes need a doctor's attention.

In a child, swollen ADENOIDS are a common cause of nasal congestion, often leading to the child breathing only through his mouth. If the condition is persistent, the doctor will probably advise surgical removal of the adenoids. Jelly-like growths called polyps may also block the nose. These are easily removed by a simple operation.

SUNBURN

A certain amount of exposure to the sun is necessary for a child for the formation of Vitamin D, which plays an important part in bone growth, but over-exposure to the sun's radiation can easily cause a serious burn, the skin often becoming covered with large, watery blisters that are extremely painful. There is danger of infection of the blisters, and if the burn covers a large part of the body, a child may become feverish, have a severe headache, and even go into a state of shock. A baby's head should always be covered, even in weak sunshine.

The skin of fair or red-haired children is particularly vulnerable to the sun's radiation. While extra care must always be taken with such children, it is advisable to limit any child's first sunbathe of the season to about 15 to 20 minutes. Then increase the time of exposure each day by another 10 or 15 minutes. It is best not to allow the child to sunbathe during the middle of the day, and to remember that the effect of the ultraviolet rays in sunlight – which are mainly responsible for sunburn – is intensified by their reflection from sea, sand and snow.

Various tanning lotions and creams may help to prevent sunburn. Total sunblock cream, suitable for babies, is available. Calamine lotion may ease the soreness, and an aspirin tablet may relieve the pain.

SWOLLEN GLANDS

The glands of the body, which are most noticeable in a child's neck, form part of the body's defence against germs, filtering them out before they spread. Wherever there is an infection, the glands nearest to it swell as they deal with it. If a child has no other symptoms and seems well, there is no need for action.

T

THRUSH

An infection, caused by fungus, that produces patches on the inside of a baby's cheeks, and sometimes a thick white fur on the tongue. Thrush is caused by feeding-bottle teats that have not been properly sterilised, or it is passed on by a mother with vaginal thrush.

A baby with thrush will find feeding painful, and will sometimes vomit. Thrush is best treated by applying gentian violet to the patches, or by giving drops of an antibiotic obtained from a doctor.

TONSILLITIS

The tonsils, a pair of glands, are situated on each side of the back of the throat. Like the ADENOIDS, they help to protect the body against infection by filtering out germs before they spread. Enlarged tonsils are efficient tonsils that are doing their job.

Tonsillitis is an infection of the tonsils themselves, inflaming both throat and tonsils. But a child with tonsillitis seldom complains of a sore throat. This is why a doctor always examines a sick child's throat. For reasons not fully understood, the child may complain, instead, that he has an ache in the stomach. Other symptoms may be general aches and pains, a stiff neck, VOMITING and FEVER.

A doctor should be called when the symptoms appear. He may prescribe antibiotics to combat the infection, and an aspirin tablet to combat the pain or fever. Tonsillitis is infectious, so sufferers should be kept away from other children.

The decision whether or not to remove the tonsils rests with an ear, nose and throat specialist. Usually this is done only when repeated attacks of tonsillitis have stopped the tonsils from functioning properly, and they can no longer fight infection.

UV

URINARY PROBLEMS

Trouble can start anywhere in the urinary system – kidney, bladder or connecting tubes (ureters) – either because the system has become infected, or because an abnormality in the system has made it easier for an infection to be set up. In children, infection is more common in the kidneys than in the bladder.

If a child has pain or difficulty in passing urine, if he does so too frequently, or if the urine looks blood-stained, a doctor should be consulted immediately. Something eaten, such as beetroot or red sweets, may make urine red, but when in doubt, speak to a doctor. Urine becomes naturally lighter when a child has been drinking a lot, and darker (after sleep, for example) when he has not been drinking for some time.

Dark orange urine is normal when a child has a FEVER or has been sweating heavily. It is normal for urine that has been standing in a pot to go cloudy, but if it is cloudy when it is passed, take a sample of it to show to the doctor.

VOMITING

Being sick is common among newly born babies. In the first few days, a baby is probably bringing up mucus swallowed during birth; and later he may be sick because he gulps his food greedily, taking in too much air. Both these causes of sickness are perfectly natural and harmless, and need not cause concern.

If, however, a baby appears to be ill with the vomiting – if, for example, he whimpers continuously or goes off his feed – consult a doctor.

167

It is possible that the baby has an obstruction of the bowel, or an infection.

In older children, many other conditions may be responsible for vomiting. Emotional problems, eating contaminated food, or eating and drinking too much, are among the most common causes, as also are disorders of the digestive tract, such as gastro-enteritis. Travel sickness, too, brings vomiting.

If a child of any age is violently sick and does not soon feel better, if he vomits continuously, or if vomiting is associated with a fever or diarrhoea, a doctor should be consulted. Continuous vomiting and diarrhoea can result in dehydration (a drying-up of fluids in the body), which is dangerous and requires prompt treatment.

WARTS

Small, infectious growths, usually hard and benign (non-cancerous) that are formed on and rooted in the skin. Warts are caused by a virus, and appear mainly on the hands and feet.

Plantar warts – or verrucas, as they are commonly known – occur on the feet and are also infectious. Because these warts are pressed inwards during standing and walking, they are painful and become covered with a build-up of thickened skin. A child with a verruca should not walk about barefoot, and should not swim in public baths until the wart has cleared up.

Seek the advice of your doctor if your child has a sudden spread of warts, or a verruca. There are several methods of treatment. The doctor may advise regular applications of ointment, or may use minor surgery. Never attempt to remove a wart yourself. Those warts which are not too unsightly and give no trouble are usually best left alone – they often disappear without treatment. This probably accounts for stories of mysterious "cures" – these may coincide with the wart's spontaneous disappearance.

WHOOPING COUGH

Whooping cough is possibly the most serious of the infectious fevers, and is especially so in babies under one year old.

The usual incubation period is seven to ten days, and a child remains infectious for 28 days from the time the symptoms begin.

The first symptoms are similar to those of a cold – a cough often accompanied by a clear, watery discharge from the nose.

After a few days, bouts of coughing begin. The child coughs several times on the same breath. The cough catches the child by surprise before he has time to take in a breath, as happens normally with a cough. This makes him distressed because of the lack of air in his lungs.

Many babies do not get the "whoop" sound, and so a parent may not realise what is wrong. Any paroxysmal cough should, therefore, be considered as due to whooping cough. Consult your doctor.

The coughing can last three months, or even longer. Nothing has yet been discovered to suppress the cough effectively. Cough mixtures are of no help.

Your doctor may, however, show you how to tap your child's chest while he is lying head down. This helps him to shift phlegm, making it easier to cough up.

A young baby is vulnerable to whooping cough because he receives no immunity to it from his mother. It is therefore recommended that babies should be immunised as early as possible (see p. 159).

Immunisation may not prevent a child from getting whooping cough, but the attack will be milder. An immunised child is as infectious as an unimmunised child.

A very small proportion of children have suffered side effects from the whooping-cough vaccine, and if you have any misgivings, you should consult your doctor (see p. 159 for further details).

8
FIRST AID

First aid in an emergency

Very few people are adequately prepared for the consequences of an accident or emergency. It is not just a question of knowing where the sticking plasters are kept, but more a matter of deciding "Should I call the doctor or the hospital, telephone the emergency services, or cope at home?"; and, if going to the hospital, "What will they want to know? What will they do? Should I take anything with me?"

Parents do not like to think of their child being involved in any mishap, which is why the subject of first aid is often put off until tomorrow. This is a natural reaction, but avoiding the subject does not reduce the chances of having to cope with it. A few minutes devoted to reading this section now may help you to respond in a much more confident manner, and avoid panic, if an accident does occur.

Indirectly this will help your child too. A child is capable of detecting and responding to a parent's general attitude; confidence on the parent's part will be transmitted to the child, calming him and allowing the doctor to make an easier approach to his patient.

This chapter is intended as a guide to the general way in which to deal with an emergency. It cannot be fully comprehensive, and it should not be regarded as a first-aid manual to be consulted only after the event has occurred. A different approach is needed in different surroundings and circumstances – for example in town as opposed to country, or in isolated areas as opposed to places where medical services are nearer at hand. The subject can only be covered in general terms, leaving you to adapt the advice to the particular circumstances.

What to do in an emergency

How do you respond to a different sort of emergency – if, for instance, your automatic washing machine goes berserk? Do you panic, turn all the knobs, then rush off to find help? More likely you assess the situation quickly and react in a methodical manner. First you turn off the electricity and the water, then you take out the clothes, mop up the mess, take the clothes to the local launderette, and lastly telephone the service engineer.

Here is the clue to correct first aid. Assess what has happened, make the situation safe, prevent it becoming worse, deal with any complications as far as you can, and seek help from the appropriate service for problems needing specialised assistance.

A methodical approach to the problem is always likely to be more successful than a snap judgment that is made in haste.

The first step to be taken in any emergency is to make the situation safe. Failure to do this carries the possibility of exposing yourself to a similar risk, which is foolhardy rather than heroic. This applies in particular to electricity. If you see from your window that a child has fiddled with the electric lead to a garden hedgecutter, and is lying unconscious and in contact with the device, then remember to pull out the electric plug as you rush to the child's assistance. If the electric lead remains live, you will be exposing yourself, also, to the risk of electrocution; then the child will have no rescuer.

Having made the situation safe, try to stop it getting worse in any way you can – such as by removing or cooling anything hot in contact with the skin, or stopping a wound from bleeding. Next, try to find out what happened, as this can often help you to decide on the seriousness of the situation. How high was the wall that the child fell from, and was there a soft flowerbed or hard concrete at its foot?

Finally, give what treatment you can, and seek help if treatment is beyond you. Facilities additional to those of the usual doctor's surgery may be found at a health centre, or at a "neighbourhood" hospital (see also pp. 138–148). You may need to get help by bus, taxi or your own car, or call an ambulance to come to you.

If in doubt you can telephone for the advice of your doctor. If your three-year-old child has helped himself to three weeks' supply of contraceptive pills the doctor will be able to reassure you over the telephone that no treatment is needed. If, instead, the child swallowed sleeping tablets, you are likely to be directed straight to a hospital for emergency treatment.

You may decide that the best way to deal with the situation is to take the child to the Accident and Emergency Department of a large hospital. The purpose of these departments is to provide medical and nursing care for people involved in accidents or emergencies. They should not be used for the many minor and non-urgent complaints that a child may suffer. Such departments are always very busy, and have to give priority to critical or serious cases. This means that patients are not seen according to the order of their arrival. Minor cases may well be kept waiting for some while.

If the emergency is obvious, urgent and needs hospital attention, call the emergency services (see pp. 138–148). Tell them briefly what the emergency is, and where it has occurred. Give directions if the location is not easy to find. If possible, send someone to meet the ambulance at the nearest point on the main road.

When the ambulance arrives, describe what happened.

While the ambulance men prepare the child for the journey, make the house safe and, if necessary, get a neighbour to look after any other children left behind.

Take your purse, and lock the door on the way out.

Having called an ambulance, do not then change your mind and take the child to hospital by car. This will delay the ambulance men while they search for you, and also deprive the injured child of the opportunity of treatment during the journey.

A child needs the support of his parent, so where possible make sure that you go with him. Otherwise both child and parent will suffer from the distress of separation; in addition, there will be nobody to tell the doctor at the hospital exactly what has happened, and he will have to deal with a lonely, nervous and probably frightened child.

Taking teddy

If the need to get to hospital is not of the most urgent kind, try to remember to take something that your child can identify as a symbol of home and security. A teddy bear is a timeless favourite. A picture book may also help to while away the time during which a child may otherwise become restless.

The big advantage of a teddy bear or doll is that it acts as a "go-between", enabling the hospital doctor to introduce himself to the child as someone to trust rather than fear. With a few words from the doctor about the toy, the ice is broken and the child has established contact with a complete stranger.

Once in the ambulance, don't be alarmed by the flashing blue lights and emergency horns or sirens. They are occasionally essential to ensure that an urgent case is not delayed unnecessarily in a traffic jam. You are probably not used to riding in an ambulance, and you may feel travel sick. Try to avoid looking at the stretcher all the time and, instead, glance through the window at the scene outside; then you will find it easier to fend off that feeling of queasiness.

When you arrive at the hospital, remember that the building is nearly always kept warm. Don't wait until you get hot and flustered before removing your coat and thick jumper. You may well already be hot from exertion or apprehension, and to appear faint will undermine the child's confidence. Offer to keep your child company unless specifically asked not to by a doctor or nurse.

Before the doctor arrives, go over in your mind the details of what happened, and consider what the doctor is likely to want to know. Understanding what happened will help him to assess the seriousness or otherwise of the injury. At this stage every effort should be made to encourage the child himself to speak. Try to avoid talking over the child's head – it does nothing to encourage his confidence.

In particular, the doctor will want to know how long it is since the emergency developed, and what symptoms the child has shown. The doctor may also want to know about previous illnesses, home circumstances, allergies and tetanus vaccinations. Sometimes the questions may not seem directly related to the event that has occurred, but try to avoid becoming defensive in your replies.

If, for instance, the doctor asks if yours is a single-parent family, he may be only trying to judge whether to suggest admission to hospital or to offer home nursing help. He is not blaming you for leaving the child alone for the two minutes when the accident occurred, while you fetched shopping in from the car.

The doctor may then need to examine the child. If possible, stay in contact with the child, to help maintain his confidence. Holding hands, sitting the child on your knee or cuddling the child while the doctor examines him are all ways of demonstrating support for an apprehensive child. Above all, don't undermine his confidence by saying things that will alarm him, such as "Will it hurt?", or "He doesn't like needles". The doctor knows how to make his investigations with the minimum of discomfort to your child. He will not make the mistake of telling your child to "look the other way", which is frightening; or lie by saying that an injection will not hurt.

As far as possible, the doctor will arrange for any necessary tests to be done on the spot. An X-ray can often be brought in for the doctor to see, and he may explain this special sort of photograph to your child.

If surgery is needed

You may not like the idea of staying while a few stitches are put into a wound, but you do not have to see what is going on. Ask for a chair, and if possible avert your eyes from the actual surgery. You are far less likely to feel faint if you do this than if you try to put on a brave face and watch what is happening. Even if you think you do not mind the sight of blood, you may feel differently when your own child is involved.

Sit holding the child's hand, and talk quietly and confidently to him. If an operation like stitching needs to be carried out, the doctor will use some means of blunting the pain. Don't assume that continued protest from the child implies that an anaesthetic has failed, or is insufficient. Local anaesthetics sting when administered, and a child will often continue a rhythmic murmuring after the initial genuine tears. This is no more than a way of telling those near by that he fears the procedure is not over, and may hurt again.

No one likes hurting a child, and you may feel protective towards your child when a needle is produced. But don't let your tension and concern be turned against the doctor or nurse. They are trying to do their best for the child: help them, and the tension will be eased.

If a light anaesthetic is needed, for treatment such as setting a fracture or stitching a cut on the hand or face, your consent will be sought as the parent or guardian of the child. In your absence you may delegate this responsibility to a legal guardian, a neighbour or a school teacher. Even so, if time and circumstances permit, the hospital doctor may wish to discuss the details with you before an operation is undertaken, so leave a telephone number where both parents can be contacted by day or night. Then you can be confident that "no news is good news". In an emergency where life is threatened a doctor is permitted to go ahead with urgent treatment without consent, so you need not fear that your child's life will be endangered if for some reason you are not available to give consent.

Before an anaesthetic is given, you will be asked whether the child has had anything to eat or drink. Except in genuine emergencies, an anaesthetic is best delayed until the stomach is empty, to reduce the chance of vomiting. For this reason, don't give a child anything to eat or drink after an accident.

The consent form that you have to sign before an anaesthetic is given will usually include words to the effect that you will also consent to "such further alternative operative measures as may be found to be necessary during the course of the operation", and that you understand that "no assurance has been given that the operation will be performed by any particular surgeon".

These two points are not intended in any way to override your own wishes; they are there simply to ensure that you understand that there will be treatment for any unforeseen complications, and that the treatment will be provided by the doctor best suited to give it. In general, the more complex the procedure, the more senior will be the doctor undertaking the task. However, if a junior doctor performs the operation, this does not mean that your child is receiving second-best treatment. Certain common problems are more frequently dealt with by junior staff, who are therefore often just as skilled at these tasks as a consultant, a specialist or other senior staff.

While the operation is in progress, you may have a cup of tea or coffee inside the department. If you want a cigarette you will have to go outside; this is not just because tobacco smoke is undesirable in a hospital, but also because fire in proximity to oxygen cylinders is extremely dangerous.

You play your next part when the child regains consciousness. At first he will probably be sleepy and confused; then he may cry. This may just as easily be due to dreaming as to discomfort. The child commonly feels sick, with or without actually being sick; then he sits up and says he feels thirsty. Thirst is a side-effect of one of the drugs used in the anaesthetic, and care should be taken not to allow a child to gulp down a glassful of water. Small sips will avoid the distress of vomiting. Half an hour or so after the end of the operation the child asks, "Can we go home?", and the nursing staff usually agree.

Occasionally the treatment may prove more difficult or involved than expected, or the child's general condition may require observation for 24 hours, necessitating admission to a ward. Obviously you and your child would both prefer to go home. However, admission is advised only to safeguard the patient's health, so it is wise to agree.

To ease the wrench of parting, go with your child to the ward and offer to stay for a while to help him settle in. If you have brought it, offer him something of his own – pyjamas or a teddy bear, for instance – to help him feel secure.

Resist the temptation to give voice to your own concern by talking in front of your child about what you think he must be feeling. It does not help a child in accepting a strange experience to hear a parent say "He will create", or "He will scream the place down". If he hears this he may well do what is expected of him. If the hospital insists on a routine bath, ask if you can bath your child yourself. In any case, you should always undress him yourself.

You may like to inquire about the possibility of staying in the hospital overnight yourself. Many children's wards (or paediatric units) have a "parents' flat" for those in genuine need of such a facility. However, if you cannot stay, remember that most children do play quite happily when their parents have gone. You will see only the tears of parting or reunion, and not the smiles in between. When you have to go, be honest about it – never try to slip away unnoticed. This leaves a child feeling abandoned and betrayed.

If you do think of taking your child home against medical advice, remember to consider the child's interest first. Should you change your mind afterwards, or if the child gets worse, do not hesitate to go back. You may be asked to sign a form saying that it was your decision to remove the child. Even if you refuse to do this, the fact will be recorded in the case notes.

Rules for recovery

Now follows the period of recovery, which may involve looking after stitches, plaster or a burn, as well as administering medicine. The golden rules for recovery are:

● Don't disturb a dressing, except by medical advice.
● Keep dressings dry, or the skin will go white and soggy underneath and slow the healing process.
● Report any pain, swelling or redness that develops.
● Ask for advice if any general disturbance develops, such as vomiting, skin rashes or a high temperature.

You should seek medical advice immediately if a plaster becomes very tight, if it becomes very painful, or if the fingers or toes swell, become very blue or pale or lose their feeling.

After a plaster is applied, you should be told about the exercises which should be done. If you are not told, ask about them.

If medicine is to be taken, ensure that the child takes the doses correctly and at the right time. Don't exceed the dose; giving more does no good, and may do harm. Use the spoon provided for syrups, as an ordinary teaspoon may vary in size from under-dosage to over-dosage. Seek medical advice if vomiting follows, as the medicine then has no chance to do its job.

Do not stop giving medicine just because the child is getting better. Antibiotics such as penicillin often take up to five days to eradicate the bacteria causing the disease, even though the child may feel better at the end of the first or second day. To stop taking the medicine then could result in a flare-up of the complaint, and this might prove more difficult to treat than the original ailment.

The following pages offer some general advice on first aid when you are dealing with certain common childhood accidents or emergencies. A more thorough knowledge of the subject, together with practical acquaintance with first aid in the form of practice in applying dressings, slings and so on, may be obtained by attending the lectures and demonstrations given by the St John Ambulance or the Red Cross. If these organisations do not run classes in your area, they may be willing to send lecturers to address your local mothers' group, if you have one.

See International Facts and Figures, pp. 138–148, for addresses and telephone numbers.

DEEP CUTS AND GRAZES

To give effective first aid, you will need to know how the wound was caused; how extensive and how deep it is; whether any foreign body is left in it; how to control the bleeding; whether to seek medical help; and how to dress the wound, if you are looking after the child at home.

HOW WAS IT CAUSED?
Knowing how the wound was caused will give clues to its likely depth, and to the possibility of glass splinters or other foreign bodies remaining in it. You will also be able to judge if there is contamination with dirt that is likely to cause infection. In general, simple cuts are less painful and heal with less trouble than crushing or bursting wounds or grazes. These are more painful, because more skin – and therefore more nerve-endings – is damaged; and as dirt is often driven in, they are more likely to become infected.

HOW EXTENSIVE IS IT?
It is often necessary to clean a wound before being able to assess its extent. A teaspoon of blood can cover a child's hands and face and look horrifying, but when it is cleaned off the cut that is revealed does not look big enough to have been responsible. If the wound is extensive, however, medical help should be sought.

HOW DEEP IS IT?
If possible, the depth of a wound should be discovered. A deep wound may have affected important structures underneath the skin, and may need to be closed by a different method from that used for more superficial injuries. Knowing what caused the damage may help. A sharp penknife, a razor, a sliver of broken glass or the sharp edge of a food tin may cut deeply. If the wound edges are gaping, the depth is more obvious; if not, a small cut may be opened gently by carefully parting the edges with finger pressure.

If the wound is only a surface cut, you may be able to treat it at home. If it is deep or long, you should seek medical help.

IMMEDIATE ACTION

- Use a dressing to cover the wound completely.

- Apply gentle but firm pressure with your hand, or with a folded bandage.

- Relax the pressure when the bleeding has been checked.

- If blood soaks through the dressing, cover it with another, and maintain firm pressure for at least another five minutes. Use a sterilised pad-and-bandage dressing, or freshly laundered handkerchief.

- DO NOT apply a tourniquet – either by tying string around a finger or a tea towel around a leg. Even doctors rarely need to use tourniquets.

Sticking plaster – or a doctor?
Small, superficial cuts (which doctors call lacerations) or scratches and grazes (abrasions) may usually be cleaned and dressed at home.

To clean the wound use an antiseptic diluted in water to the correct strength as indicated on the bottle. Do not use a neat or extra-strong solution in the hope that it will kill off more germs; an over-strong chemical that can kill germs may also damage other living cells such as those exposed in the edge of the cut. The manufacturer of the antiseptic will have carefully worked out the best strength for the job in hand.

Do not use ordinary iodine solution for this application. It will sting, frighten your child and achieve little more than a less astringent alternative.

Cleaning
Use a non-fluffy lint, gauze or a soft paper tissue to clean the wound, wiping away from the wound edges and gently swabbing out any visible dirt.

Dressing
Apply a comfortable, practical dressing such as an adhesive plaster strip or patch. Wherever possible, it is better to use one of the types that will "breathe", or let out moisture. If a wound gets wet and stays wet it will often go white and soggy, then become infected and take a long time to heal. If sweat cannot dry, it will make the area as damp as if water has seeped in.

In general, a simple cut or graze should have healed in seven to ten days. If it gets swollen, red, hot or painful, or if there is a discharge, it is probably becoming infected and you should seek medical advice.

Tetanus
Any wound, however it is caused and however trivial it is, could let in the germs that cause tetanus. Most children will be protected against this by routine vaccination in the first year of life – the "triple", "three-in-one", or diphtheria, whooping cough and tetanus vaccine. If your child missed this, you should at least consider protection against tetanus. The disease is a distressing and dangerous one, which can be prevented by a vaccine which rarely has any side-effect other than tenderness in the area of the injection. If a child is already vaccinated, boosters –

additional vaccinations – are only necessary at five- to ten-year intervals, unless a wound is badly contaminated.

See your doctor or go to a hospital if an anti-tetanus vaccination is required, or if you cannot confidently treat the wound yourself. Ideally, the injection should be given within six hours of the injury.

Stitches
Stitching may be necessary if the wound is extensive, deep, gaping, on a moving area such as a joint, or in an exposed area such as the hand or face.

If foreign bodies such as grit, splinters or glass have remained in the wound, a doctor will have to clean the area carefully, perhaps with the use of a local anaesthetic to deaden pain.

In the case of a deep wound, the doctor will also check for any possible complication, such as damage to a tendon or nerve, that may need special attention.

If a graze is deep, with ingrained dirt that you cannot remove, do not leave it uncleaned, as the dirt may cause a permanent skin stain or tattoo. Seek medical aid for meticulous cleaning.

Scars
Remember that cuts will leave scars, especially if they are not treated properly or if they become infected. Medical treatment can help to reduce the amount of scarring and the chance of infection. A cut on a little child's face can be closed carefully, leaving a thin line that will scarcely show in later years. A lumpy scar from an infected wound may not be disguised so easily, even by plastic surgery, so make sure that prompt treatment is given.

If a child falls over and cuts his face, he will cry from fright and pain and come to you for help and security. Crying will make him red in the face and cause the wound to bleed more. The blood will run down his face and frighten him still more. He will rub the area, spreading the blood and disturbing the clot. This will make the injury look worse than ever, to the point of frightening you – a fear which the child will sense.

So remember that things often look worse than they really are. Do not panic; the child wants reassurance. Talk confidently and soothingly; cover the wound; calm and comfort the child; clean up the mess; find out what happened and decide what treatment is required.

BURNS AND SCALDS

A child's skin is easily damaged by heat, and every home contains a number of potential hazards – including matches, boiling kettles and saucepans, teapots, coffee jugs, hot fat, fires, stoves, hot taps and electrical appliances.

SIZE AND DEPTH

Burns and scalds may damage only the upper layers of the skin, in which case – provided it does not become infected – the area should heal in seven to ten days without scarring. If the damage goes deeper, healing may be delayed and require special treatment. If the damage is more extensive than the area of a whole arm or its equivalent, the amount of blistering and "weeping" of the injury may require special measures in hospital for the purpose of replacing lost body fluids.

In general, if a burn is deep, or more than 25 mm (1 in) across, medical help should be sought. A deep burn very often looks white and waxy, compared with the invariably red or raw appearance of a superficial burn.

The longer a hot substance is in contact with the skin, the greater the damage. Boiling water on thick clothes, or hot sticky jam or fat from a chip pan allows the transfer of more heat, resulting in more damage. So that he can assess the damage, a doctor will want to know how hot the substance was that caused the burn; what clothing the child had on; and what action you have taken.

Treatment includes rapid, careful removal of clothing – do not touch the injured area but cool it by pouring water over it – and covering with a non-fluffy dressing. A pad and bandage or a clean pillowcase may be the most suitable materials easily to hand. Give an aspirin to relieve pain.

Molten plastics
Burning synthetic fibre materials may melt and stick to the skin. If they will not come off easily, do not risk more damage or waste time by trying to peel the clothing off. Instead, cool the area with running water, and leave the removal of clothing to medical and nursing experts.

IMMEDIATE ACTION

- Remove the child from the source of danger.

- Remove or cool the source of heat.

- If clothing on the burned area will come off easily, remove it quickly and carefully.

- Cool the burn by pouring cold water over it, and cover it with a sterile (or at least clean) dressing.

- Decide whether home or medical treatment is indicated.

- If medical aid is sought, remember cause of burn and degree of heat.

Chemicals

Acids, caustic substances and other chemicals can burn the skin. As a general rule, the immediate treatment is to wash the area thoroughly by pouring generous quantities of water over it; then seek medical advice as soon as possible, preferably at a hospital.

Eyes

If a child's eye is burned by heat or chemicals, immediately wash the eye with water from a tap or container, and if necessary hold the eye open to ensure that the irrigation is thorough. Continue washing with copious amounts of water for about five minutes, making sure that the eye is cleansed of any chemicals. Cover the eye with a clean pad, and then seek medical attention.

Electrical burns

The burned area resulting from an electric shock may look small, but is almost always deep. It will look more serious after a day or two, and it may be slow to heal. After covering the burn with a dry, sterile dressing, seek medical advice.

FOREIGN BODIES

By accident, foreign bodies can easily get into a child's eyes, ears, nose or stomach. Growing children explore objects with their fingers and mouths, and prod their own ears and noses while holding objects in their hands. Occasionally these objects slip out of their grasp and cannot easily be retrieved. The bead stuck in the ear, the button lodged up the nose or the coin that is swallowed alarm both parent and child.

EAR AND NOSE

The first point to remember is that the object itself is unlikely to do any harm if left alone for a short while – so there is usually no need to act in haste. The second point to remember is that the deeper structures in the ear and nose are very sensitive and delicate, so attempts to remove any foreign object with an implement or finger should be avoided.

Look first, if necessary with a torch, to see what the object is and, in particular, whether it has caused any bleeding. If it has, you must visit the doctor or the hospital. In the case of the nose, if there is no bleeding, and if the object is easily visible and seems loose, it may be possible to dislodge it.

Ear

If a foreign body becomes lodged in the ear, seek medical advice straight away. A matchstick or other probe may well push the object further in, while using tweezers will probably have the same effect. This is because the foreign body is often smooth, and by now wet or waxy. Tweezers grasp the surface, but as pressure is applied the object shoots forward, like an orange pip squeezed between thumb and finger.

A doctor will generally use a slender wire-like probe with a loop at one end and a curved "beak" at the other. The beak is used to hook the offending object out. Only rarely is it necessary to give the child an anaesthetic to enable the object to be removed.

177

Nose

Try to persuade the child to "blow" the object out. Many children will sniff instead, and worsen the situation. It is no good telling the child not to sniff – he is probably scared, feeling uncomfortable, and not listening properly. It is much better to begin without telling him to blow; instead, give him a handkerchief and tell him to open his mouth and take a deep breath. At this point, after you have set the stage for a blow rather than a sniff, the command "now blow" is more likely to be met with success.

If a few nose-blows do not succeed in expelling the foreign body, do not keep on trying; instead, you should seek the help of a doctor.

THROAT

Objects that are swallowed usually pass through the system without much difficulty. Should the child choke or have a coughing fit, a small object such as a peanut may have "gone down the wrong way" into the windpipe. Medical help must be sought to remove it. (See also Choking on p. 186.)

It is far more usual for the object to pass down the gullet into the stomach. The size of the object in relation to the size of the child will usually determine whether the foreign body will pass down or not. If it sticks in the gullet, the child will usually complain of a pain somewhere between the throat and the pit of the stomach. X-rays will be required to locate the object. It may then be necessary to remove the object under anaesthetic, with the use of a "flexible telescope" instrument. For this reason, it is sensible to take a child with a gullet obstruction straight to hospital.

If the object swallowed has passed down into the stomach, it will in most cases pass on through the system without hindrance. If the object is of a material which will show up on an X-ray film – unlike, for instance, plastic – an X-ray may be taken to ensure that it has reached the stomach. The doctor is likely to advise keeping the child on a normal diet, with no laxatives. Search the faeces by getting the child to use a potty, and expect the object to appear in two to four days. If it does not, or if the child vomits, passes blood, or complains of stomach pains, do not hesitate but seek further medical advice without delay.

Fish bones If a fish bone is stuck in a child's throat, it may cause distress. If it is still present after an hour, seek medical advice. The fish bone may be lodged in the back of the throat around the tonsils, or it may have passed on down, leaving an uncomfortable scratch. A doctor's experienced eye, backed up by a lamp and a mirror, may be necessary to decide which is the case.

EYES

When a foreign body gets on to the eyeball or under the eyelid, the eye's normal reaction is to water and so flood out the intruder. But this may not be sufficient to dislodge it. Irritation in the eye may be caused by an eyelash, a piece of grit, or a scratch resulting from something having been poked into the eye. Ask the child what happened, then look carefully on the surface of the eye and under the lids. Try washing out the foreign body, or, so long as it is not on the cornea (the clear part of the eyeball), try to remove it very gently with the corner of a handkerchief.

If the object will not move, or if the irritation remains, blank off the eye gently with a headscarf, a handkerchief or similar piece of material, and seek medical assistance. A scratch on the eye can be painful, and will only show up with staining drops. It will, however, heal quickly with eye ointment.

Be particularly cautious if a child complains of pain or irritation in the eye after watching someone hammering or using a power tool. A fragment of masonry or a flake of metal may have pierced the eye, demanding specialist attention. In general, it is best to travel the extra distance to an eye hospital if there is one within reasonable distance.

POISONS

The risk of a child accidentally swallowing a poisonous substance is very high, even in the apparent security of home. Among the many hazards are disinfectant in the bathroom, tablets in the bedroom, bleach and detergents in the kitchen, turpentine substitute in the garage, weedkiller in the garden shed, and fungus – or poisonous seeds of plants such as laburnum – in the garden.

MAKING A CHILD SICK
Vomiting should never be induced when a child is unconscious, or when the poisonous substance swallowed is either oily or corrosive.

A child can be made to vomit by putting a finger or the smooth handle of a dessert spoon down his throat. Do not use salty water. Too much salt in association with some substances can upset the chemical balance of the blood and do more harm than good.

TABLETS
If the child is conscious, make him vomit. Depending on the time of day and the distance involved, either telephone or go to your doctor or to the nearest hospital with an Accident and Emergency Department. Take the bottle and any remaining tablets. In most instances the bottle will be labelled with the name of the drug; if it is not, the doctor will be able to identify the tablets by their shape, colour, markings and codings.

OILY SUBSTANCES
Never make a child sick if he has swallowed oily, petroleum-based substances such as turpentine substitute, petrol, and car and furniture polish, as these can find their way into the lungs during vomiting and cause a "chemical pneumonia". Get the child into the care of a doctor or hospital as quickly as possible.

IMMEDIATE ACTION

● Identify the poisonous substance, if possible. Look around for pills, bottles or berries; sniff for the smell of paraffin, petrol or cleaning fluid.

● If the child is conscious, *and if you are certain that the poisonous substance is neither oily nor corrosive,* make him vomit.

● If the child is conscious, give him milk or water to drink. Do not give him anything else, and do not give him anything at all to drink if he has lost consciousness.

● Wash any chemicals off the skin with water.

● Take off any contaminated clothing.

● If you cannot immediately contact a doctor, get the child to hospital.

● Take the container and a sample of the substance to help the doctor to identify the danger.

CORROSIVE SUBSTANCES

These often leave a tell-tale white film on the lining of the mouth and throat, indicating damage to the delicate membranes. Vomiting will result in more damage as the corrosive is regurgitated. Instead, give a drink of milk or water and seek medical help immediately.

OTHER SUBSTANCES

If medical aid or advice is not readily to hand, give the child milk or water to drink to dilute the poison, and then make him vomit.

HOSPITAL TREATMENT

At the hospital, the doctor will want to know what has been swallowed, how much, and when; what the symptoms are; and the age of the child. Poison manuals, and a Poisons Information service available on 24-hour telephone contact to doctors, will enable the right treatment to be given.

Hospital treatment will probably include an emetic to make the child vomit (if appropriate), a stomach tube (the "stomach pump") to empty the stomach, drugs or injections, and admission for observation for 24–48 hours.

BROKEN BONES AND SPRAINS

The untrained person is often confused over the distinction between fractures, dislocations, sprains and strains. A fracture is the medical term for a broken bone, and includes all breaks from a major injury to a hairline crack. Any bone can be broken, but the common fractures occurring in children are those of the wrist, forearm, elbow and lower leg.

A dislocation involves displacement of the bone at a joint. Dislocating a shoulder is commonly described as "putting your shoulder out" – that is, out of its socket.

Sprains and strains both involve a stretching or tearing, but the term "sprain" is used for damage to ligaments, and "strain" for muscle damage.

IS IT BROKEN?

The signs of a fracture include pain, swelling, bruising, restriction of movement, and deformity caused by the broken lengths of bone being out of line. All these features will be present in a severe fracture. Often, however, in a child a seemingly trivial fall or blow may be followed by only moderate pain, swelling and restriction of movement, and no bruising or deformity. Do not be misled into believing that the bone cannot be broken, but only sprained. The signs of a dislocation include some of those of a fracture – pain, deformity, and loss of movement in the joints.

As a rough guide to how serious an injury is, consider how and where the accident happened; ask the child to try to move the area in question; and feel gently for any local areas of tenderness. A limb is unlikely to be fractured if the child can soon move it freely, if there is only a diffuse tenderness, and if after half an hour there is no pain or swelling. Keep watching the child, however. If later you see that he is not using an arm, or if he complains of pain at the elbow, or is unable to bear weight on a leg, medical advice should be sought. It is a good general rule to consult a doctor whenever in doubt.

A FRACTURED ARM

If you suspect a fractured arm, what should you do? In many cases the answer is as little as possible. For almost all injuries to the arm, except the elbow, it is

BROKEN ARM *The arm of the child on the left has been temporarily immobilised by pinning his sleeve to his overalls. A permanent sling (right) consists of a large triangular bandage folded to give broad support for the arm, and to immobilise it against the body.*

enough to make a triangular sling, or tuck the arm in the jacket, or pin the sleeve to the jumper.

Children with injuries to the elbow, common in falls from playground swings and roundabouts, must not be moved by the untrained. You may stretch or pinch a vital nerve or blood vessel, and make things much worse.

It is often safer and kinder to leave the child to support the damaged arm with the undamaged one. Alternatively you can use triangular bandages to immobilise the arm against the body in the same position, or do the same with a headscarf, a belt from a coat, or a tie.

A FRACTURED LEG

A leg fracture should be splinted by tying the two legs together at ankles and feet. Tie a second broad bandage just above or below the knees, avoiding any areas of local pain or swelling. Dislocated or severely broken limbs are best dealt with by leaving the child alone and calling for an ambulance or other professional help.

PULLED ELBOW

This is a condition that characteristically affects a two- to four-year-old who has been pulled, lifted or swung by the arm. The symptoms are pain, tears and refusal to use the arm. What has happened is that the end of one of the forearm bones has slipped partly out of a ligament at the elbow. No one without medical training should try to rectify this condition – it calls for manipulation by a doctor. He will turn the child's hand palm upwards; this action is painful, but it clicks the bone back into place, and within minutes the arm is back in use.

GOING TO HOSPITAL

If you are taking your child to hospital yourself, sit him comfortably – preferably where he can see out of a window, to avoid car sickness. Across the back seat is the safest and most comfortable place. Drive smoothly and carefully; don't rush. On arrival, ask for someone to help you lift the injured child; remember that children are very patient and long-suffering, but they don't understand what is going on, they are naturally frightened, and they can only stand so much.

In a young child, X-ray examination may reveal a "green-stick" fracture. The bones of young children are softer than those of adults or older children, causing them to break only on one side, like a green twig. Because the bone is not broken in two, the limb need not be set so that the bones join straight.

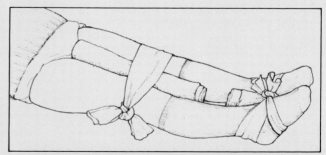

SPLINTING A BROKEN LEG *Place padding between knees and ankles to prevent chafing. Tie the legs together at ankles and feet, then above or below the knees.*

HEAD INJURIES

Children bump their heads many times as part of the rough and tumble of growing up. When should you take the matter seriously? In general the answer is: when the child does so himself. If he forgets the accident quickly, resumes play **and remains alert**, you can be fairly sure that the injury was trivial. If he does none of these things, he may need a doctor.

Concussion – loss of consciousness at the time of the blow – indicates a physical jarring of the brain. It is always serious, and an unconscious child should always have immediate medical attention, in case he is developing a complication that only a doctor can assess and deal with.

WHAT YOU CAN DO
An unconscious child may choke if placed in the wrong position.

The worst position is on the back, with a pillow or rolled-up jacket behind the head.

The best position is lying on one side, as shown in the illustration, with the chin up and mouth open. Anything in the mouth should be removed. In this, the correct recovery position, breathing is safeguarded and choking is prevented.

RECOVERY POSITION *Remove anything in the mouth. Turn the child gently on one side, chin up and mouth open, with one leg and arm bent for support.*

Once the child is at the hospital, tell the doctor there exactly what happened. The child may be put under observation, or treated with drugs or surgery.

Cuts on the scalp look alarming because they always bleed profusely; but the wound is often very small and superficial. Stitching may be needed, however, as these wounds are difficult to close with dressings alone.

DANGER SIGNS

DROWSINESS AND PALENESS These are warning signs of possible complications. Seek medical advice at once, even though most children will recover without complications.

VOMITING This is another danger sign, which may follow drowsiness and paleness.

LOSS OF CONSCIOUSNESS This may be immediate, or follow later. In either case, urgent medical attention is needed, in case complications make their appearance.

FALLS, ACCIDENTS, SHOCK

There are circumstances in which a child should not be moved. They include:

● A fall from a height, followed by complaints of pain in the neck or back. The child may have injured his spine.

● A fall from a bicycle, with pain concentrated in the hip or groin.

● Injury resulting from a road accident.

In each case movement may worsen the injury, so leave the child where he is unless this exposes him to even greater danger. For instance, if flames are spreading fast in the direction of a child, he must of course be moved. Again, although a child's spinal injury may be made worse by movement, if he is choking his life is in danger, so turn him very carefully and gently into the recovery position.

But as a general rule, the child should be moved only by a trained person who has assessed the injuries.

If a child is lying injured in the road, thrown out of a car in an accident, do not attempt to move him. Instead, stop the traffic, or direct it round the scene of the accident; or enlist help to do so.

SHOCK

A child who has suffered a major injury is often in a state of shock. He may show some or all of a number of symptoms. His colour may be pale or greyish; he may break out in a cold sweat; his breathing may be quick and shallow. Usually, his pulse is rapid. He may be listless, restless or frightened; thirsty, giddy or sick.

Severe shock needs immediate treatment. If the physical injury allows it, lay the child on his back. Reassure him, and loosen his clothing. Even if his skin is cold, do not warm him. It does nothing to stimulate his circulation, and may make his state of shock worse. His skin is cold because, in shock, the amount of blood going to the skin is reduced to make extra available for more vital organs. Warming the skin dilates the blood vessels, thereby counteracting this safety measure. It also causes sweating, which makes the shocked child colder as moisture evaporates from the skin.

A child suffering from severe shock must be taken to hospital as quickly as possible so that expert treatment can be given.

IMMEDIATE ACTION

● Do not move the child, unless he is lying in a dangerous position. If he is choking, turn him very gently on to one side, chin up and mouth open. Remove anything in the mouth.

● Call an ambulance.

● Cover the child to prevent chilling.

● Do not give the child anything to drink.

● Stay with the child, and watch for bleeding or difficulty in breathing.

● If you did not call the ambulance yourself, double check that someone did so, and wait patiently.

IF BREATHING STOPS

Drowning, severe electric shock or suffocation from fumes can all cause a child's breathing to stop. Four minutes without breathing means a dead child, so you must act swiftly and decisively.

IMMEDIATE ACTION

- **Put your ear or cheek against the child's mouth and nose, to detect any breathing.**

- **If the child is not breathing, or is dusky-blue in the face, tilt the head back by lifting the chin and pressing the forehead down.**

- **If breathing does not then start immediately, clear the mouth and start mouth-to-mouth artificial respiration – the kiss of life.**

GIVING THE KISS OF LIFE

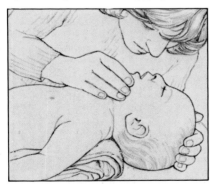

Tilt back the child's head, by pressing the forehead down and lifting the chin. Take a deep breath.

In the case of a small child, cover the mouth and nose with your mouth. In the case of a larger child, where your mouth will not cover his nose as well as his mouth, pinch his nose closed, unless your cheek blocks it.
Blow gently.
Look for rising of the chest.

Remove your mouth and take a breath while the child's chest deflates.
  Blow four times quickly, then repeat blowing at the rate of 20 *shallow* puffs a minute until recovery starts or medical help arrives. Over-inflation of a child's lungs is dangerous.

IF THE HEART STOPS

Drowning, severe electric shock and suffocation can cause the heart to stop beating.

Signs of a stopped heart are stopped breathing, a dusky-blue complexion, dilated pupils, and the absence of a pulse.

Check the pulse either at the wrist, or in the neck to one side of the Adam's apple.

If you have help, one person should give mouth-to-mouth artificial respiration and the other the heart massage, at the rate of one puff to five compressions. If you are on your own, do not give alternate puffs and compressions; give two puffs and then 15 compressions. In this way you lose less precious time in changing over.

IMMEDIATE ACTION

● Try to get the child breathing by means of mouth-to-mouth artificial respiration (the kiss of life) – see opposite page.

● If you fail, continue trying to revive breathing, and at the same time begin to give heart massage.

HOW TO GIVE HEART MASSAGE

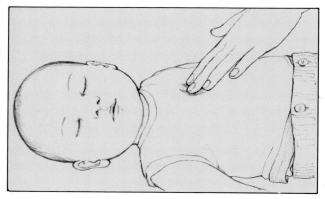

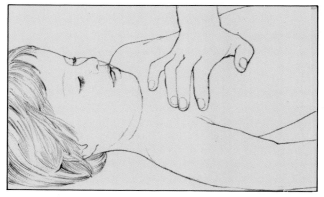

In the case of a baby, press the tips of two fingers just below the centre point of the breastbone. Press rapidly, at the rate of 80 to 100 compressions per minute (between one and two compressions per second).

In the case of a child, press with the heel of one hand, at the rate of 80 compressions per minute.

OTHER EMERGENCIES

BITES AND STINGS
Animal Wash the wound immediately with clean water to flush out the animal's saliva. Cover with a dressing or a clean cloth.

Take the child to a doctor or hospital at once. There the wound will be treated more effectively, and measures will be taken to prevent tetanus (lockjaw) and other infections.

Insect Particularly if they bring on an allergic condition, *stings* can be painful and distressing to a child. A solution of bicarbonate of soda can give relief from the pain of bee stings, and vinegar or a weak solution of ammonia does the same for wasp stings. Removal of the sting may be necessary if a bee has stung the child; wasps and hornets do not leave their stings behind. Wipe off the sting with a pin or needle held flat to the skin. Do not try to pick it up with tweezers or more poison will be squeezed into the skin.

Tick bites should be promptly treated. Do not try to pull the tick off but apply the glowing end of a cigarette to the tick to encourage it to fall off. Clean with soap and warm water; rinse and dry well.

Snake If bitten by an *adder*, do not panic. Do not suck the wound. Do not cut the wound. Do not apply a tourniquet. None of these measures will help the patient. Instead, lay the child down. Keep the bitten area immobilised and, if possible, below the level of the heart. Gently wipe the poison away and cover the wound with a dressing. Seek medical help immediately. This applies also to *coral snakes*, *cobras* and other snakes found in North America, Australia and South Africa. For treatment for bites from North American *pit vipers* (including rattle-snakes) see p. 148.

Spider Bites from, for example, the Australian *funnel-web spider* or the North American *tarantula* or *black widow* can be dangerous. Do not cut or try to cauterise the affected part. Keep it as still as possible and get the child to hospital at once.

Jellyfish Treat simple jellyfish stings with cala-mine lotion or vinegar. If the child becomes short of breath or faints, get him to hospital at once.
See p. 139 for information on Australian venomous marine animals.

CHOKING
In the case of a baby, hold him upside-down and deliver a few firm smacks between the shoulder blades. If the obstruction is not removed, apply mouth-to-mouth artificial respiration: see p. 184.

In the case of a child, lay him across your knee and deliver a few firm blows between the shoulder blades. If the obstruction is not removed, apply mouth-to-mouth artificial respiration: see p. 184.

DROWNING
Do not waste time tipping a child upside-down to drain water out – if any does come out, it will probably be from the stomach, rather than from the lungs.

Clear any obstruction from the mouth.

Give mouth-to-mouth artificial respiration: see p. 184. Apply this as soon as you reach the victim – do not waste precious time getting the child out of the water first. Give five or ten puffs, then make for dry land, continuing artificial respiration all the time, or at least intermittently.

When ashore, check the pulse: see IF THE HEART STOPS, p. 185.

Give heart massage, p. 185.

ELECTROCUTION

Cut off the electricity before touching the child, or you may be electrocuted too. Do this by turning off the switch, removing the plug, or using something dry and non-conducting (such as a wooden chair) to push the source of current away from the child.

Give mouth-to-mouth artificial respiration: see p. 185.

Check the pulse: see IF THE HEART STOPS, p. 185. If no pulse, give heart massage, p. 185.

Call medical aid.

FISH HOOKS

Hooks have a barb on the point, so don't pull them out, as the end may break off or tear the skin. Go to your doctor or local hospital. The doctor will freeze the surrounding skin to anaesthetise it, then push the point out through the skin, nip off the barb or the eye, and remove the hook, leaving only two small punctures in the skin.

FEBRILE FITS (CONVULSIONS)

Babies or young children may occasionally have a febrile fit or convulsion when they are ill. This happens in response to a very high temperature. It is obviously distressing, but rarely dangerous. The tendency to febrile fits runs in families.

The characteristic signs of a fit are as follows: loss of consciousness, twitching, rolled-up eyes, heavy breathing, clenched teeth and possibly a slight frothing at the mouth.

Turn the child into the recovery position (p. 182), remove any very warm clothing, wipe the mouth clear of any secretions, and seek medical help without delay.

Usually the fit passes in minutes. It has no permanent effect. Although resembling an epileptic attack, in some respects this sort of fit is not the same. Either the child will never have another fit, or he will eventually grow out of them.

NOSEBLEED

Sit the child up leaning forward, and pinch the soft part of the nose between thumb and forefinger. Maintain a gentle pressure of five to ten minutes, or until the bleeding stops. Reassure the child that the bleeding is not as serious as it looks.

Before you let go, tell the child that he must not sniff or blow, or the bleeding will start again. Since a young child may ignore the exhortation, it is a good idea to put something firm but comfortable, and too large to be easily swallowed, between his teeth. Traditionally, a cork is used. It is difficult to sniff or blow with an open mouth.

Repeated or severe nosebleeds should be referred to a doctor.

A HOME FIRST-AID KIT

BASIC ITEMS
3 large sterilised wound dressings
3 medium-sized sterilised wound dressings
3 triangular bandages
1 10 cm (4 in) crepe bandage
1 7.5 cm (3 in) crepe bandage
1 packet assorted safety-pins
1 pair of small scissors
1 bottle of antiseptic solution
1 packet of gauze swabs
1 packet of adhesive plasters (assorted sizes)

ADDITIONAL USEFUL ITEMS
1 roll 2.5 cm (1 in) adhesive plaster
1 eyebath
1 pair tweezers
1 chamois leather finger stall
1 tube of aspirin or paracetamol
1 bottle of calamine lotion
1 aerosol container or tube of an antihistamine preparation
1 thermometer

INDEX

Page numbers in **bold type** indicate the main treatment of a subject. Page numbers in *italic type* indicate diagrams or photographs.

The Publishers wish to express their gratitude for contributions by the following:

Judi Meredith BA for editorial help; Miriam Polunin and Nora Shariff for recipes; Fred and Kathie Gill for proof reading; Vicki Robinson for indexing; the NSPCC for editorial advice; Kenneth Jameson for the use of drawings and paintings on p. 120; Fanny Rush, stylist; Barbara James, hairdresser.

Additional photography by:
Geoffrey Chamberlain (p. 8 left); Daily Telegraph Colour Library/S.J. Allen (p. 8 middle right); John Larsson, St. George's Medical School (pp. 42–43); Susan Griggs Agency: Alain Evrard (p. 71 top right), Victor Englebert (p. 71 top left), Horst Munzig (p. 71 bottom right); Daily Telegraph Colour Library: Charles B. Knight (p. 113); Anthony Horth (p. 116 top right & bottom right, p. 117 top right); Kenneth Jameson (p. 118).

The Reader's Digest Mother and Baby Book is based on *The Reader's Digest Mothercare Book*, to which the following made major contributions as Consultant Editors:
Hugh Jolly MA, MD, FRCP, DCH
Geoffrey Chamberlain MD, FRCS, FRCOG
David Morris FRCP, MRCS, DCH

16-019